"With extensive experience in military, mental health, academic, and international crisis environments, Dr. Glenn Schiraldi is uniquely prepared to offer excellent and expert guidance in developing and maintaining resilience. In *The Complete Guide to Resilience* he covers the essentials of developing and maintaining health and resilience in any demanding situation, or in life itself. We are guided to the best principles and practices for optimizing our physical, mental, emotional, and spiritual health and fitness, for managing new crises or post-traumatic stress disorder from the past, and for achieving great creativity and well-being under challenging circumstances. As in his previous books, Dr. Schiraldi again offers wise, caring, comprehensive, and accessible guidance. We can rely on him with trust and confidence for negotiating life's challenges."

—Edward Tick, Ph.D., author, *War and the Soul*; Director, Soldier's Heart for successful warriors return; clinical psychotherapist focusing on veterans issues

"This is a great book! Comprehensive, authoritative, understandable, practical. Dr. Schiraldi has pulled together the current research for mind and body, and produced a 'How-To' guide to inoculate you and those you care about against the inevitable trials of life. Even better, it is a guide to healthy, happy, fulfilling living in general. I'm getting a copy for every member of my family."

—Thomas W. Garrett, Major General (ret), U.S. Army

"A remarkably comprehensive, yet accessible and practical, treatise on resilience. I really believe that everyone will benefit from reading and using it. While this book will certainly benefit high-risk groups, it is also a great how-to and must read for business professionals, entrepreneurs, students, parents, and anyone else who experiences stress and adversity."

—Alan D. Boss, Ph.D., Assistant Professor of Business, University of Washington Bothell

"Dr. Schiraldi's *The Complete Guide to Resilience* is clearly the authoritative work in the field. Dr. Schiraldi methodically takes the reader through the three critical steps of resilience training: gaining a basic understanding of the critical issues of resilience, helping the reader determine his/her own level of resilience, then guiding the reader through step-by-step exercises to build and maintain a resilient mind. This guide is clearly a seminal work in the field of warrior and first responder resilience."

—Steve O. Steff, Ph.D., President-CEO, Crisis Care International

"In twenty-one years as a cop my assignments have ranged from undercover narcotics and crisis negotiation to current head of the Peer Support Team. Dr. Schiraldi has in this book answered every question I've ever had about resilience. His articulate and well-defined techniques are the most applicable to the real world we live in.

"This is the real deal—you won't see this on afternoon television. If you've ever wondered how two people can go to the same nightmare call, but one comes out unscathed and the other is significantly scarred, then this is a must read.

"To all my brother and sister police officers, if you want to mentally protect yourselves and your families, get a copy of this book and read it front to back."

—Sergeant Sergio Falzi, Calgary Police Service, Alberta, Canada

D1599726

"The importance of resilience in sports, the workplace, and life is far from a new concept. However, Dr. Schiraldi has provided one of the first truly comprehensive overviews of this critical human strength. Filled with practical advice, drills, skills, exercises, and real-life anecdotes, *The Complete Guide To Resilience* offers us mental armor to fight the simple life challenges and daily frustrations that confront us all, in addition to the more serious and sobering anxiety, stress-provoking, and life-threatening challenges. The take home message underscores the importance of building a mental and emotional structure that can weather a storm, and this book provides a well-researched and highly practical blueprint."

> —Spencer Wood, Ph.D.
> Member, Association for Applied Sports Psychology
> President, Icebox Athlete Mental Skills & Toughness Training

"As a former special operations soldier, having served as a Green Beret in combat and deployed various times around the world, I thoroughly appreciate this material. The organized and straightforward manner in which Dr. Schiraldi presents the information is very user friendly and easy to quickly grasp and understand. His ability to present concepts, followed by practical applications, easy to follow steps, and examples, enables comprehensive learning and results. I would highly recommend *The Complete Guide to Resilience* to really everyone, as we all have some type or form of stress or difficulty to deal with in life."

> —Colby Jenkins, U.S. Army Special Forces and Army Ranger

"Fantastic! Dr. Schiraldi has taken the complex concept of resilience and provided us with skills for life in a beautifully written, user-friendly book. The language is down-to-earth. The flow is easy to read and also allows the reader the option to skip around. Whether you have a psychology degree or not, this is a must read to help others and, more importantly, to help yourself. This book will help a lot of people."

> —Peter Volkmann, Chief, Stockport, NY, Police Department, MSW, EMT-B

"Resilience is the final frontier in human psychology. Dr. Schiraldi has created a wonderful resource and valuable compendium of academic science and practical behavioral suggestions...a powerful foundation for the acquisition of resilience skills."

> —George S. Everly, Jr., Ph.D., Johns Hopkins University School of Medicine; Executive Director, Resiliency Science Institutes, International; author, *The Secrets of Resilient Leadership*

"This book is a breath of fresh air for practitioners who treat combat related stress or injuries every day. I have seen so many books designed to assist this population but this is the most comprehensive and the most positive. Thank you, Dr. Schiraldi, for not over-pathologizing our warriors and other high-risk occupations. Thank you for showing how it can be done without pharmaceuticals. This book will become a staple in my practice."

> —Mary Neal Vieten, Ph.D., ABPP, Commander U.S. Navy (RC), Operational Psychology Solutions

"Life's trials are inevitable. How we respond to them is a product of the resilience we consciously develop, and Dr. Schiraldi shows us how."

—Greg Baer, MD, author, *Real Love and Post-Childhood Stress Disorder*

"Impressed with Dr. Schiraldi's previous work, I have adopted *The Complete Guide to Resilience* as required reading for my Disaster Resilience Leadership course (DRLS 6010), to benefit future leaders who care about the resilience of themselves and those they lead."

—Charles R. Figley, Ph.D., founding president, International Society for Traumatic Stress Studies; Kurzweg Distinguished Chair in Disaster Mental Health and co-director of the Disaster Resilience Leadership Academy, Tulane University; author, *Combat Stress Injury;* Vietnam veteran

"The stated purpose of providing useful information regarding resilience is well and truly met in this volume. The book moves logically and smoothly from definitions and rationale to methodology—simply describing a wide range of practical activities, including self-assessment techniques, the difficult task of changing attitudes and beliefs, and developing critical personal strengths. Viktor Frankl, after his survival of the horrors of the Holocaust, explained that the "why" precedes the "how" of survival. This book essentially enhances our quest for each.

"In our time-poor existence, this book is a valuable asset both for the practitioner and their clientele. It is exactly the kind of reference I would not hesitate to recommend to any of my own patients as well as seeing it as an extremely applicable and useful training aid in my work with emergency services and military personnel.

"I really hope it gains the widest circulation as it is an excellent aid to everyone with an investment in enhancing performance and strengthening the naturally occurring, but often impaired, resistance of the individual to psychological injury."

—Monica Kleinman, Captain, Psychologist, Headquarters, Forces Command, Australian Army
Clinical Director, New South Wales State Emergency Service's Critical Incident Support Team
(These personal views do not imply endorsement by either organization)

"The way this book presents resilience is a milestone for everyone in the crises business...an interaction between scientific findings, real life experiences, and exercises that will involve the reader from the first page. It is easy to understand and apply to real life situations. Whether readers want to learn or not, in the end they will have gained a massive knowledge of the secrets in resilient crises leadership management."

—Peter Jonsson, Former Director of Training for Swedish National Police; Founder, Mental Preparedness and Conduct Training, Swedish National Police; Advisor to FBI

"Dr. Schiraldi goes beyond preparing or finding a way back. This resilience guide leads us to higher ground. It is the very best I have seen for both pre-occurrence preparedness and post-exposure recovery—providing greatly encouraging, comprehensive growth and integration, especially in the core values of spirituality, meditation, religion, ethics, and morality."

　　　　—Glenn Calkins, MDIV, LCSW, BCC
　　　　Firefighter, EMT, fire chaplain
　　　　Certified Supervisor, Association for Clinical Pastoral Education

"This book is written for any person at any level of emotional health. The true beauty is that individuals—be they professionals looking to enhance their skills or people struggling with their own tragedies—can implement the strategies in their own life and then use them to strengthen and help others. This guide will be a boon to every parent and homemaker. Nearly every chapter has something I'll use on a daily basis. As a mother and a counselor, I deeply appreciate Dr. Schiraldi's expertise and insight. An amazing book."

　　　　—Janet Harkness, homemaker, mother

"This marvelous, thought-provoking resource will help a great number of people, even those who don't feel they have mental health issues. In trying to be our best, we all face a great deal of stress, maybe self-imposed. Often we're not even aware that stress exists until a problem surfaces. This book can not only make one aware that there may be a problem, but more importantly gives exercises and guidelines to alleviate stress issues before they become a problem.

　　"As a career firefighter, I never really thought about the lack of education in the area of mental health. In the academy, all recruits were trained well in the technical aspects of the job, but received very little training in the ability to confront or cope with the tragic events that commonly occur. The mechanism for dealing with a traumatic incident was usually comedic relief or quiet silence—expressing one's feelings was just not something that was done. This seemed to work well until you were alone after the event and then it was difficult to get it out of your mind. So it was especially enlightening to read about verbalizing and writing about difficult incidents.

　　"I also particularly subscribe to the principles of socially intelligent leadership. If used in the Standard Operating Guidelines of the Fire Service, officers would be much better communicators and leaders of their personnel."

　　　　—William Joseph Donaldson, Captain (Retired), Ft. Pierce, FL, Fire
　　　　Department

"As a former emergency responder in both the fire service and law enforcement, I found *The Complete Guide to Resilience* to be very informative and helpful. It is well written and documented, but not cluttered with the abstract opinions of mental health professionals who have never 'walked the walk.' Had the book been available during my career, I am certain that I would have benefited even more so than now after having read and applied the skills that I have learned."

　　　　—Robert B. Dwyer, former firefighter, deputy sheriff, detective,
　　　　Tucson, AZ

THE COMPLETE GUIDE TO
RESILIENCE

WHY IT MATTERS
HOW TO BUILD AND MAINTAIN IT

ALSO BY GLENN R. SCHIRALDI

The Resilient Warrior Before, During, and After War
World War II Survivors: Lessons in Resilience
The Post-Traumatic Stress Disorder Sourcebook
The Self-Esteem Workbook
Ten Simple Solutions for Building Self-Esteem
The Anger Management Sourcebook
Conquer Anxiety, Worry and Nervous Fatigue: A Guide to Greater Peace
Facts to Relax By: A Guide to Relaxation and Stress Reduction
Hope and Help for Depression: A Practical Guide

THE COMPLETE GUIDE TO
RESILIENCE

WHY IT MATTERS

HOW TO BUILD AND MAINTAIN IT

GLENN R. SCHIRALDI, Ph.D.

RTI

Resilience Training International℠

Ashburn, Virginia

This information in this book is intended to provide useful and educational information regarding resilience. It is not intended to replace needed medical or psychological care. If expert assistance is needed, the services of a competent professional should be sought.

Library of Congress Control Number: 2011931911
ISBN 978-0-9834755-1-4

Printed in the United States of America

Resilience Training International
20322 Bowfonds Street
Ashburn, VA 20147
www.resiliencefirst.com

Cover Design by Steve Palmer

This book is available through www.Amazon.com.
For special quantity discounts, contact Resilience Training International. Visit the "Contact Us" page at www.resiliencefirst.com.

Contents

UNIVERSAL RESILIENCE TRAINING

PART VII   SUCCEEDING: PEAK PERFORMANCE AND ADAPTIVE COPING

SPECIFIC RESILIENCE TRAINING FOR HIGH-RISK POPULATIONS

PART VIII   CRISIS PREPARATION

Acknowledgments

Completing this guide to resilience training has been my most challenging, but also the most satisfying, writing endeavor—challenging because resilience is such a broad and deep topic, and satisfying because the gains of resilience training are so enormous. I realize that this undertaking would still be a dream without the aid of so many important people.

I first wish to thank the students at the University of Maryland who, through their patience and determination in the resilience courses I developed and facilitated, have helped me to better understand how resilience is actually cultivated. Similarly, I thank the many emergency responders, peer counselors, and mental health professionals who have taken my resilience training workshops through the International Critical Incident Stress Foundation. You have all taught me more than you know, and have greatly deepened my appreciation for the courage and resilience of the human spirit.

I express sincere appreciation to the tireless researchers who have clarified the complexities of resilience. The pioneers in resilience research include Drs. Emmy E. Werner, Emory L. Cowen, George E. Vaillant, Norman Garmezy, Michael Rutter, William R. Beardslee, and Ann S. Masten. Others whose research I have especially appreciated include positive psychology researchers Drs. Martin Seligman, Christopher Petersen, Ed Diener, Sonja Lyuobomirsky, and Barbara L. Fredrickson.

I am most grateful to the many people who gave so generously of their time to review this book, provide feedback, and suggest helpful improvements: Drs. Greg Baer, Alan D. Boss, George S. Everly, Jr., Charles R. Figley, Edward Tick, Mary Neal Vieten, Spencer Wood; Chaplain Glenn Calkins, Captain William J. Donaldson, Detective Robert B. Dwyer, Sergeant Sergio Falzi, Major General Thomas W. Garrett, Mrs. Janet Harkness, Major Colby Jenkins, Director Peter Jonsson, Captain Monica Kleinman, Chief of Police Peter Volkmann, and all of the dear members of my family.

Finally, I acknowledge the many resilient people who show us by their examples that it is possible to face adversity with determination and a triumphant will. Some are famous people like Mother Teresa, Arthur Ashe, Christopher Reeve, and Viktor Frankl. Most are ordinary people—family members, neighbors, and friends. I dedicate this work to all who have weathered and bounced back from the storms of life with honor and courage, and in so doing inspire us all. Thank you one and all.

Portions of this book are adapted from my previous works, including: *World War II Survivors: Lessons in Resilience; The Post-Traumatic Stress Disorder Sourcebook; The Self-Esteem Workbook; Ten Simple Solutions for Building Self-Esteem; The Resilient Warrior Before, During, and After War;* and *The Anger Management Sourcebook.*

PART I

ABOUT RESILIENCE

Chapter 1

Introduction

You know how well the roof has been built only when the rains come.
African saying

Why do some people sail through life's storms well, while others are knocked down and out, never to fully recover? For example, after Allie[1] lost her husband, she was understandably sad and lonely. After a mourning period, she became an even more effective family leader and a valued, competent colleague at her new job. Suffering a similar loss, her friend Marta became depressed, anxious, and dispirited. Ty, a U.S. Navy SEAL, performed steadily throughout his extremely violent tour in Afghanistan. According to his wife, he returned the same loving, communicative, upbeat man that he was before he left. Since returning, his SEAL teammate Cliff has become reclusive, cynical, and a heavy drinker. What makes the difference? Resilience!

Resilient individuals have the knack for surviving *and* thriving. They discover creative ways to solve their problems. Some resilient people never seem to stumble too badly. Others fall and later recover. As they persevere, resilient people figure out better ways to cope with and overcome adversity, discovering ways to make life more meaningful and satisfying. Such people show us much about resilience.

This is a book on optimizing mental health and performance. Nearly everyone wants to be more resilient. Resilience keeps us going despite our bruises. Many think resilience is something we are born with—we either have it or we don't. However, we are learning that:

- *Resilience is standard issue.* Everyone has it to one degree or another or else we wouldn't still be here.
- *Resilience can be increased.* Strengths can be discovered and built upon. Nearly everyone can learn to master resilience skills, which, more than most of us realize, will improve our chances of overcoming adversities ranging from everyday stressors to disasters.
- *Those who are psychologically prepared for adversity are less vulnerable to mental disorders, and perform better under duress.*
- *Prevention of stress-related disorders is far more effective than treatment.* However, resilience helps us bounce back better from the stress symptoms that inevitably arise.

This book will show you how to increase resilience. It is highly experiential. Your success in developing resilience will be determined by how much you practice and apply these principles and skills. With practice, new neural pathways in the brain will form to increase brain efficiency and resilience.

Why Is Resilience Training Needed?

First, resilience training brings out our best. For many people, this is all the motivation that is needed to begin. People start life with an "upward reach"—the inner desire and intent to be, do, and feel their best. It is innately satisfying to be moving in this direction. However, stress that we are unprepared for derails us all to one degree or another. Overwhelming stress might discourage us from trying again. Lesser stressors might distract us from our usually successful methods. Resilience training can put us back on course and help us to progress in the most effective and satisfying ways.

Second, we desperately need to prevent mental illness. The prevalence rates for stress-related mental disorders are increasing globally, and prevalence rates in the United States are especially high. For example, nearly one of every two American adults will experience a mental disorder—principally stress-related disorders such as anxiety (including post-traumatic stress disorder, or PTSD), depression, substance use disorders (such as alcoholism), or impulse disorders (such as conduct disorder and ADHD).[2] In high-risk groups, including the military, police, firefighters, and other emergency responders, we see higher than expected rates of post-traumatic stress disorder, anxiety, depression, problem anger, substance use disorders, suicide, domestic violence, divorce, sleep disorders, and leaving one's chosen profession prematurely. While the emotional toll of mental illness is bad enough, excessive stress levels also make us more vulnerable to a variety of medical diseases, earlier death, and impaired functioning.

For stress-related mental illnesses, prevention, not treatment, is the ultimate answer. While competent treatment is extraordinarily helpful, there will never be enough mental health professionals to sufficiently treat all mental disorders. Even if there were, many people would not seek professional help for fear of losing face (or a job), ignorance of treatment options, or inability to pay. Just as infectious diseases have been largely controlled through inoculation, so might mental illness be more effectively managed through prevention. Resilience training offers the promise of prevention for stress-related mental illnesses. This includes helping people to recover from stress before stress turns into psychological disorders. Resilience training can be very inexpensive and effective, especially when weighed against the costs of waiting passively for serious psychological damage to occur.[3]

From the study of disease, first we learn how to treat it, then to prevent it, and ultimately to optimize health and performance. This is true both in medicine and psychology. Unfortunately, in both these fields, preventive and optimization efforts typically lag behind treatment efforts by years and even decades. Given the distressing challenges of modern living, relying on treatment alone is no longer feasible. We need to equip soldiers, firefighters, and cops with tough mental armor, not just physical protection. We need to prepare them not only to fight the enemy, criminals, and fires, but to cope with the emotional strains of living in stressful environments. And because life has become more stressful generally, we really all need to learn how to better care for ourselves and our families emotionally.

We are gradually awakening to the idea that preventive skills learned pro-actively—before crises strike, even very early in our lives—can prevent so much needless suffering and immensely enhance the quality of our lives. Thus, the armed forces of the U.S. and Australia have initiated resilience training, as have some government agencies, schools, and workplaces. While these initial efforts are encouraging, they are often quite limited in scope. We can do much more. Fortunately, the skills that prevent disease, promote recovery from stress, and optimize health and performance overlap and blend together beautifully. In this program we will bring them together in a comprehensive way.

How This Book Evolved

In the early 1980s, I received a career-changing invitation. Decision makers at the Pentagon were concerned about the number of people dying of heart attacks in what should have been their most productive years. Back then we understood that anger and hostility were risk factors for heart disease. The decision was made to have all Department of the Army workers, civilian and military, attend training to manage stress, especially stress related to anger and hostility. Because of my association with the military, and because I was serving on the stress management faculty at the University of Maryland, I was invited to join the faculty there. Although I was very busy at the time, I agreed to teach the training two afternoons each week. I learned that these capable and earnest people were very willing to grow, to become better individuals, leaders, and family members. Although we explained the risk factors for heart disease, we never stigmatized the participants. We simply said that we all have strengths to build upon, and participants in the classes would work together to become even more effective in the various areas of their lives. It was there that I caught the vision of how small groups of people—working together in a safe setting to strengthen each other, using common sense and common language—could effect measurable change. I began to wonder if we could implement a similar skills-based course in the university setting.

Shortly afterwards, research showed that not only anger, but also depression and anxiety, in practically any combination, lead to diseases ranging from headaches to heart disease. I reasoned: Why not use the approach we refined at the Pentagon to reduce, and hopefully prevent, depression, anxiety, and problem anger? Rather than simply memorizing information, students would be taught each day new principles and skills, and would practice these skills to gain mastery. Again working with functioning adults, ranging in age from 18-68, we found that coping skills that were preventive in nature could be effectively taught in an educational setting. The course, which I called "Stress and the Healthy Mind," resulted in reductions in depression, anxiety, and anger/hostility, and improvements in self-esteem—changes that persisted at one-month follow-up (Schiraldi & Brown, 2001).

Then 9/11 hit. Exactly two weeks later a tornado ripped through campus, killing several people. The students looked shell-shocked. I decided that stiffer medicine was needed. So I mixed the best from my "Healthy Mind" course with more intensive resilience-building skills in a course called "Beyond 9/11: Stress, Survival, and Coping." I wasn't sure what the effects would be. However, the course resulted in significant gains in resilience, optimism, happiness, self-esteem, and curiosity (which relates to enjoyment, undistracted focus, engaged persistence, creativity, and resilience in general), while significantly reducing depression, anxiety, and anger.

Meanwhile, I had been teaching resilience training courses to emergency responders, mental health professionals who serve them, and peer counselors—preparing them to train others to care for themselves emotionally. I have also formally interviewed many combat veterans, including members of elite special operations

5

units. These experiences have provided additional, invaluable insights from a very different population.

Altogether I have been teaching coping skills in diverse settings for more than thirty years. This experience has taught me that people are very capable of learning the skills that strengthen and protect them against extreme forms of stress. This book will show you how these skills are learned.

Who Is This Book For?

Resilience training benefits a wide range of people. This book is for those who:
- Already are mentally strong, and who wish to become stronger and more effective in any challenging domain of life—such as job, family, or athletic competition
- Are trainers, practitioners, parents, educators, coaches, or individuals who want to optimize health and performance in self and others
- Have known risk factors in their family—either genetic or learned dispositions—for depression, anxiety, or other stress-related mental disorders
- Have survived or are likely to face combat, rape, abuse, terrorism, or other forms of potentially overwhelming distress
- Are in a high-risk profession, and thus likely to encounter great adversity and traumatic stress. Such professions include:
  - Emergency responders (military service members, police, firefighters, search and rescue teams, emergency medical personnel, public safety and construction workers, sanitation and communication experts and engineers, and other disaster workers) and those who support them (mental health professionals, pastoral counselors/chaplains, peer counselors, leaders, trainers, and family members)
  - Others who work in combat zones, including contractors and Department of State employees

In short, this book is for everyone. It is difficult to imagine a parent, teacher, coach, manager, leader, employee, or any other individual who would not benefit from developing more resilience.

The Goal And Objectives of Resilience Training

The aim is that you realize that you, and each individual, already have resilience and are capable of building even greater resilience. By the end of the program you will:
- Know what resilience is
- Have the tools needed to increase resilience levels in self and others

What Can I Expect?

It is reasonable to expect that resilience training will help you to:
- *Prevent or lessen the severity of stress-related mental disorders such as PTSD, anxiety, depression, substance abuse, and problem anger.* While the original

purpose of the course was to prevent PTSD, the most complex of the stress-related disorders, research indicates that resilience protects against a range of psychiatric symptoms amidst adversity.

- *Optimize mental health and the ability to bounce back from mental and physiological distress.* In other words, to thrive and be stronger.
- *Attain peak performance and coping under pressure* (e.g., improved occupational and social functioning). Whether your pressure comes from overwhelming crisis or "less stressful" financial reversals, rejection, natural death of loved ones, or overload of everyday stressors, the needed skills have much in common.
- *Enjoy greater satisfaction with life, job, and relationships.*
- *Increase career retention in self and others.* Satisfied soldiers and first responders, for example, stay on the job longer.
- *Improve physical health, and reduce medical disease and absenteeism.*
- *Become a resource for others to help them become more resilient.*

About The Skills You'll Learn

We'll explore many tools to keep you and those you care about strong. These tools are drawn from the best of traditional and positive psychology.

Traditional psychology fixes problems. It generally takes us from negative to neutral in terms of mood and performance. We'll take tools taught in the clinic and use them to promote prevention, recovery, and effective coping. The ideal is to learn these skills before you are exposed to severe stress. However, sometimes we learn to cope by learning to manage and recover from distressing emotions that we are presently experiencing. *Whenever we learn a skill that asks you to remember a distressing event, be sure to pick one that is not so distressing that it overwhelms your ability to learn.*

Positive psychology focuses especially on strengths and growth. This focus moves us closer to peak health and performance, and appears to effectively aid treatment and prevention efforts.[4]

As much as possible, we'll stick to coping skills that are evidence-based (i.e., supported by research), only filling in the gaps when necessary based on our best judgments, experience, and/or theory. The skills that you'll learn are for everyone. Nearly everyone can master them with practice. You don't need to be a trained mental health professional to become very skilled. These skills will help you as an individual. Once you master them, you can be a useful resource for those you associate with. In fact, the best way to teach these skills is to first learn them through your own experience and practice. Then you can teach them with confidence.

The skills are presented in a logical sequence. Thus, most will find it most useful to work through the workbook in the order presented. Most will find value in all of the skills; however, you might find that some are not for you. Use your judgment. Feel free to experiment with, or bypass, such skills. Often initial success will indicate whether a skill will be a useful addition to your coping tool bag. Sometimes, however, a skill only "clicks" after repeated practice.

To repeat, the benefits of resilience training are a function of practice. You'll get out what you put in. Brief exposure to a skill is not the same as skill mastery. Think of golf or playing the piano. You'll be asked to practice, then go back to determine which are the most promising skills and principles, and finally make a plan to master them through additional practice.

As you begin, your attitude is important. Try to keep an open mind. Don't expect that resilience skills will perfectly solve all your problems. Such an attitude can lead to disappointment. On the other hand, try to avoid cynicism, which might prevent you from giving a skill a fair trial. Start with the assumption that a new skill *might* work, and then see what happens. A Navy SEAL once told me that it's the more seasoned SEALs who are more open to learning new coping skills. Perhaps when we are younger we are too confident, insecure, or proud to acknowledge the need for help. Try to have a beginner's mind. The beginner's mind keeps us open to growth, whereas the expert's mind learns nothing new.

How Resilience Skills Are Taught

Fortunately, a very effective approach to teaching coping skills has been used for years. The approach is called Stress Inoculation Training (SIT), which was developed by the influential psychologist Donald Meichenbaum (1985). In this approach, only about 15% of the time is devoted to discussing principles and vocabulary. The rest of the time is spent learning and practicing skills, first in safe settings such as a classroom and then in real life. In this approach, the teacher is more like a coach—explaining, demonstrating, and then trusting individuals to learn through their own practice. In my experience, this approach is much more effective than the lecture-oriented classes that are typically used in academic settings.

You might wish to learn resilience skills by working through this workbook independently at your own pace. This can be very effective. However, if you can I recommend joining with others in a small group. Something synergistic happens when people come together to learn and support each other in the learning process. A small group might be a military squad, a family, a class, or a workplace team. The ideal group size is eight to fourteen. This is small enough to allow everyone to participate, and big enough to provide a breadth of experience and support. However, group size is flexible. One student was unable to attend my resilience training class because of a scheduling conflict. So I equipped her with the course materials. She successfully organized her own small group, consisting of herself, her roommate, and her sister. They rotated teaching responsibilities, a great idea since teaching others helps to reinforce resilience in oneself. With SIT, each day a new principle and skill is discussed, practiced in the group, and then assigned for home practice. During the next session, the individuals in the group discuss their experience with practicing the skill. It is here that the brilliance of group work shines. Sharing successes motivates other group members. On the other hand, sharing concerns often prompts group members to problem solve and/or share tips on making skills work, tips gained from their own experience. Bonds form as participants learn that group members respect and support one another, and that no one need worry about being imperfect. I am remembering the first night of a group I was facilitating. We were discussing the freedoms to experiment and be imperfect. One participant asked, "What if we say something that is embarrassing?" Another quickly responded, "Well, we'll help each other." Such is the attitude that high-functioning groups foster. Generally, participants will learn much more from each other and their own practice than they will from the group leader.

It usually takes about three sessions before participants begin to fully relax and trust each other. It helps to go over small group norms and freedoms on your first meeting (see Appendix 1). These norms emphasize things like respect, confidentiality, avoidance of disruptive behaviors, and the freedoms to experiment and to be wrong.

Meeting once or twice a week permits enough time between sessions for participants to practice skills. Ninety minutes or more per session is generally long enough to process home practice experiences (assignments) from the previous session and to practice new skills.

Group members sit in a circle to facilitate discussion. Each member has an assigned buddy. Buddies can update each other should one miss a session. To put people at ease, I like to have a get-acquainted exercise on the first session. Here each member turns to the person seated next to him. For a few minutes one member of the pair will interview the other, asking questions like, "What makes you happy/annoyed?"; "How many kids were in your family?" and recording the responses. After a few minutes the process switches, such that the interviewed member now becomes the interviewer. After a few minutes, group members in turn introduce the person they interviewed to the group and share any information that is respectful. Then I will ask the pairs to swap contact information; buddies have now been assigned.

Whether you work individually or in a group, organize a loose-leaf notebook in which to keep your notes and skills records. These records will help you remember successes and lessons, and decide which skills are most promising for future practice.

How Long Does Resilience Training Take?

Completing the program will involve about thirty minutes of practice a day (in addition to time spent exercising), over a course of about 150 days. It is good to work through the skills steadily. However, depending on time constraints, you might wish to break up the material into smaller units and spread sessions out. Skills can be taught at in-service or booster sessions by the facilitator or those who have completed the training.

The Sequence of Teaching Resilience

Ideally, resilience training follows this sequence:
- *Screen for and treat mental disorders.* It is very difficult to function well when one has unresolved issues. For example, people with unresolved traumas are more likely to develop PTSD when exposed to subsequent traumas. We've seen this in soldiers. If individuals cannot be thoroughly screened by mental health professions, then it is wise to educate them about the symptoms of mental disorders and direct them to available treatment resources. Once mental disorders are treated, individuals can more readily learn resilience skills.
- *Encourage independence from family dysfunction* (Wolin & Wolin, 1993). Resilient survivors acknowledge and accept family dysfunction. They learn to leave abusive homes figuratively and/or literally. They might move far enough away to avoid too frequent contact with negative family dynamics, perhaps staying close enough to visit occasionally. They challenge the irrationally

negative family messages, and determine to create a better life for themselves. Perhaps the resilient survivor thinks: "Mom struggled with depression"; "I'm different from Dad, and I don't accept his negative view of me"; "I realize that I can't fix my parents"; "It's a relief to have some distance from them"; "I've accepted that I won't gain their approval"; "I'll improve upon my past."

- *Teach universal resilience skills.* These are skills that help people generally improve mental health, coping, and performance; they are helpful to virtually everyone.
- *Teach specific crisis preparation skills for high-risk groups.* These skills prepare people for the unique demands of traumatic environments. This includes preparing people both physically and emotionally. Thus, in addition to physical training, a firefighter might prepare emotionally to encounter death and gruesome sights.
- *Make a plan to regularly practice the most effective resilience skills over your lifetime.* Otherwise your skill levels may wane.

Each Person Makes A Difference

Resilient people are everywhere. They are sometimes famous, like Christopher Reeve, Mother Teresa, or Arthur Ashe. Sometimes they are ordinary people living nearby. I think of my childhood friend Tim. Tim is among the most kind and athletically gifted people I've ever known. In his twenties, he contracted multiple sclerosis (MS). Some years later, his children nominated him for MS Father of the Year. They noted that he wasn't like most fathers who curse; rather he spent time with them even though he is in a wheel chair. He received the award from the President at the White House. Today Tim remains cheerful, donating time to mentor prison youth. Here is the story of another resilient person who made a difference.

Most people are not familiar with the name Rick Rescorla. If you saw the movie "We Were Soldiers," you might remember him. The movie chronicled the true story of Hal Moore, who commanded the first major military engagement in the Vietnam conflict. Moore was an excellent leader who truly cared about his troops. His undermanned air cavalry battalion was dropped into an area surrounded by a vastly superior number of North Vietnamese regulars. Under his leadership the battalion survived, despite nearly being overrun. Next to Hal Moore, the person who most impressed me in that movie was Rick Rescorla, a platoon leader in Moore's battalion.

As a boy in England during World War II, Rescorla fell in love with the Yanks. He later volunteered to serve with American troops in Vietnam. There he not only demonstrated unusual tactical competence, but also great social intelligence. Rescorla had a knack for knowing how to buoy his troops, whether with song, banter, or words of encouragement.

Fast forward to 9/11. Rescorla was then the head of security for Morgan Stanley Dean Witter at the World Trade Center. He had predicted the 1988 bombing of Pan Am Flight 103 over Lockerbie, Scotland, and the bombing of the World Trade Center in 1993. Finally officials began to listen to him and backed his recommendations. Rescorla believed it unwise to wait passively for rescue from a likely terrorist attack. Instead he created an action plan, assuming that average people, when properly lead, would capably care for one another and execute the plan well. Pushing through the resistance of workers who didn't want to be interrupted during the workday, Rescorla did the unpopular thing. He over-trained the entire company, drilling them in his escape plan frequently and without warning, until they could carry it out efficiently. After the first tower was hit, Rescorla was seen with his bullhorn, walkie-talkie, and cell phone implementing the evacuation plan, this time for real. After his tower was hit, he instructed, "Be still. Be silent. Be calm." He sang into his bullhorn the same Cornish songs he'd sung to his soldiers in Vietnam: "Men of Cornwall stand ye steady. It cannot be ever said ye for the battle were not ready. Stand and never yield." Of nearly 2700 employees working for his company, all but seven made it out safely from the tower that day. He was among the fallen, remaining to the last to ensure the safety of his charges, just as he had remained in the World Trade tower in 1993. In his last communication, he phoned his wife, saying, "If something should happen to me, I want you to know I've never been happier. You've made my life."[5]

Cost/Benefits Analysis

Mastery of resilience skills doesn't happen overnight. It takes effort. Before you commit the time and effort required to complete the program, it might be helpful to do a cost benefits analysis, just as a manager might do before implementing a new plan. List below the disadvantages and advantages of embarking on resilience training.

Cons. The bad thing about resilience training is......

Pros. The good thing about resilience training is.....

Cons that you might list include: I'll have to commit the time for regular practice. People might look more to me for leadership. I'll have to be responsible; No more helplessness or excuses for passivity.

Pros could include:

- I'll perform closer to my peak under pressure: better concentration, calmer, more creative problem solving, more productive
- I'll handle strong emotions better (and not beat myself up when I don't)
- Each day will be more enjoyable
- I'll be less reactive to stress, less troubled by worry and negative emotions

- I'll recover more quickly from daily strains and major disasters
- I'll be more flexible
- I'll experience more positive emotions, and be more productive and satisfied with my life (job, relationships, leisure)
- I'll experience enhanced emotional well-being (self-esteem, happiness, optimism, sense of purpose, confidence, mental health, etc.)
- I'll encounter fewer symptoms of depression, anxiety, stress
- I'll be able to teach these things to people I care about
- I'll grow more from adversity (A chance to practice my new skills!)
- I'll probably live longer and happier
- I'll have more energy (e.g., depression saps energy)
- I'll be better prepared to face the inevitable hardships before me
- I'll be less likely to engage in self-destructive behaviors (such as addictions, giving up, or avoiding problems)

Another effective strategy is to complete the following sentence stem in as many ways as you can:

The positive consequences of my becoming more resilient are...[6]

Chapter 2

Key Concepts and Background

I have lots of courage, I always feel so strong and as if I can bear a great deal, I feel so free and so young! I was glad when I first realized it, because I don't think I shall easily bow down before the blows that inevitably come to everyone.
Anne Frank, summer of 1944[1]

Resilience is a bit like the elephant and the blind men.[2] Each blind man touched one part of the elephant in an attempt to discover its nature. One, feeling the tusk, concluded that the elephant is like a spear. One touched the leg and decided that the elephant is like a tree. Another, touching the trunk, determined that the elephant is like a snake, and so on. All were partly right, but none saw the whole picture. The elephant contains all those features. Like the elephant, resilience is the sum of its parts. This chapter will briefly clarify the sometimes-confusing nature of resilience, and describe how our understanding of resilience has developed. The definition of resilience is central to our journey, so let's begin by understanding what it is.

What Is Resilience?

Look up the word *resilience* in the dictionary and you will find definitions such as the tendency to bounce back or recover from setbacks; buoyancy; elasticity. Resilience researchers have added such strengths as the ability to adapt well to stressful circumstances, coping and functioning well in the various areas of life, maintaining internal equilibrium, overcoming adversity, preventing illness amidst hardship, flexibility, and growing. Combining these, we will define resilience as the strengths of an individual,[3] both innate and developed, that enable one to adapt well to adversity, including the capacities to:
- Maintain and improve mental health
- Function optimally—calmly, competently, flexibly
- Prevent the development of stress-related psychological disorders, such as post-traumatic stress disorder, depression, anxiety, substance use disorders, and domestic violence or other forms of problem anger
- Overcome the damaging effects of adversity, should they occur, by minimizing the number and severity of symptoms, speeding recovery, and protecting against relapse

In short, resilience is the ability to bounce back and thrive.

Adversity refers to extremely difficult life stressors, such as trauma (e.g., rape, combat, abuse, terrorism), health problems and hospitalization, death and dying, divorce (one's own or that of family members), unemployment, and financial setbacks. Happily, resilience training also helps us cope with less profound sources of stress, including arguments, job pressures, overload, and other everyday challenges.

Notice that our definition embodies the 3 R's of resilience: resistance, recovery, and resourceful responding:

- *Resistance* refers to the preventive dimension of resilience as regards mental illness and impaired performance. One form of resilience is shown by people who remain steady as a mountain, despite being pounded by life's storms. They don't give in to self-destructive habits, like drugs, which degrade health and functioning.
- *Recovery* refers to the ability to rebound from setbacks to previous levels of health and functioning, should we temporarily stumble. Some people might bend but not break under pressure, rolling with the punches and bouncing back— "bloodied, but unbowed," perhaps, as the poet says. Other resilient people will mend *after* breaking under the weight of overwhelming stress. Resilient people do not remain stuck in despair.
- *Resourceful Responding* means we adapt as the situation requires. To *adapt* to adversity is to change oneself to new or changed circumstances through skills and judgment. Adapting is being flexible. *Resourceful* means able to deal with difficulties promptly and effectively. A resource is a strength that can be drawn upon, as in emergencies. So resourceful people draw upon available strengths, be they mental, spiritual, emotional, physical, financial, social (e.g., older mentors, supportive spouses, friends), and environmental (e.g., psychotherapy has been found to help foster children adapt). Resilient people make sense of their surroundings, and figure out what to do—remembering and utilizing their experience, sometimes coming up with new coping strategies. They don't merely survive, but flourish and thrive. We survive when we simply acknowledge that we made it, and accept our scars. We flourish when we persevere, often growing stronger along the way as a result of adversity and learning how to lead more satisfying lives.

Notice also that resilience is a flexible, relative concept. It does not occur in an all-or-none fashion, but exists on a continuum:

Complete helplessness & vulnerability	Surviving	Resilience (optimal coping)	Perfection, invulnerability

- While everyone is resilient to some degree, no one is perfectly resilient, or resilient in all circumstances. Resilience does not mean invulnerability, because anyone can be overwhelmed when circumstances are severe enough. Rather, resilience means generally working, playing, loving, and expecting well (Werner, 1992), functioning at our best possible level in any given situation. As legendary coach John Wooden taught his highly successful basketball players: success is doing *your* personal best; sometimes the other team will simply be better on a given day.
- Resilience can vary even within an individual depending on many internal and external factors, such as how rested and nourished one is, one's training and

experience, or the nature of the situation. As we train, our aim is to grow our resilience to a level that is greater than the challenges we will encounter.

- Resilience can be learned across the lifespan, not just in times of stress, by nearly anyone. Some develop resilience in anticipation of adversity. Some rediscover strengths or become resilient through crises. Some might "get it together" later in life.

How Has Our Understanding of Resilience Developed?

As was mentioned in chapter 1, disease usually captures our attention first. This makes sense. Disease is a clear and present danger that moves us to decisive treatment efforts. Eventually, the study of disease and its treatment usually aids our efforts to prevent disease[4] and optimize health and performance. This has been the case with resilience. The study of stress-related problems, especially post-traumatic stress disorder, has greatly aided our understanding of resilience. So let's start there.

PTSD and Risk Factors

When you understand post-traumatic stress disorder you will also understand much about resilience and the stress-related mental disorders. PTSD has a special relationship with resilience. In fact, PTSD is sometimes defined as the exhaustion of resilience. Conversely, resilience helps to prevent PTSD,[5] while the treatment of PTSD increases resilience (Connor & Davidson, 2003). Indeed, much of resilience training started as an attempt to prevent PTSD. PTSD is undoubtedly the most complex of the stress-related mental disorders. Its treatment incorporates the learning of principles and skills that are typically used in the treatment of depression, anxiety, and the other stress-related disorders. It is likely that teaching these principles and skills could help to prevent a wide range of mental disorders.

PTSD results when exposure to an extremely distressing event or events, such as rape, abuse, combat, or terrorism, overwhelms our ability to cope. Symptoms include arousal (difficulty sleeping or concentrating, being easily startled, anger), haunting memories (intrusions, flashbacks), emotional numbing, and attempts to avoid remembering the trauma.

PTSD rarely occurs alone. Typically, a person with PTSD will also experience depression, anxiety, and/or substance use disorder. In addition, people with PTSD are more likely to develop a medical disorder, such as: irritable bowel syndrome, fibromyalgia, chronic fatigue, headaches, chronic pain, gynecological complaints, psoriasis, rheumatoid arthritis, metabolic syndrome, ulcers, eating disorders, obesity, and thyroid diseases. Unresolved trauma has even been found to predict coronary heart disease, high blood pressure, and cancer within a one- to two-year period (Prigerson et al., 1997). In war veterans, PTSD is associated with worse family relationships, less sexual satisfaction, more smoking, less happiness, greater use of mental health services, and more non-specific health complaints (Koenen et al., 2008). Even among those whose traumatic symptoms are not severe enough to warrant a PTSD diagnosis, we still see many indications of emotional suffering, such as depression, anxiety, nightmares, and suicidal thoughts. It appears that PTSD and its co-morbid disorders share many common mechanisms that could theoretically be altered through treatment and/or resilience training.

In 1980, the American Psychiatric Association formally recognized PTSD as a mental disorder. This recognition triggered a spate of studies that tried to identify the risk factors that make us vulnerable to developing PTSD. We now have a solid understanding of these risk factors. It is extremely helpful simply to know what these are, to know what we are up against. One risk factor is the severity of the stressful event. Thus, knowing that one is facing or will face combat, abuse, rape, or similar adversity alerts us to the need to strengthen ourselves psychologically. Existing mental illness and unresolved trauma also heighten the risk for developing PTSD. Thus, soldiers who have suffered childhood physical or sexual abuse are more likely to develop PTSD when they go to combat,[6] as they are when traumatic symptoms from previous combat have not been resolved. Knowing this can motivate us to find proper treatment and to build resilience so that we can function at our best.

It will be helpful to glance at the full range of risk factors at Appendix 3. Notice that risk factors are not only what happens to people. They also include internal psychological processes, such as how we think about and emotionally react to adversity. Even our physical health and health habits affect our vulnerability. Notice particularly the following risk factors:

- Difficulty experiencing positive emotions
- Difficulty remaining calm under stress
- Negative attitudes about expressing emotions; difficulty expressing feelings
- Aroused nervous system
- Inability to manage strong negative emotional reactions to stress, including intense anger, anxiety, depression, and shame
- Extreme discomfort with, inability to deal with, and avoidance of troubling emotions

These risk factors—which describe a relative lack of emotional intelligence skills—are largely modifiable. This book will help you deal with the risk factors you can control.

Strengths and Protective Factors

It was assumed that the factors that protect against PTSD (and mental disorders in general) would be the opposite of the risk factors. Key research began to confirm this assumption and broaden our understanding of what keeps people strong amidst adversity. We'll highlight key findings from three of the most influential studies.

1. **Children of Kauai Longitudinal Study.** Much resilience research traces back to the landmark work of "Mother Resilience," Emmy E. Werner, professor emeritus at University of California, Davis. A resilient survivor herself, she lived through saturation bombing and starvation in WWII Germany. Werner tracked several hundred children in the Hawaiian island of Kauai for decades. She started out trying to understand why children become casualties to mental illness, serious learning and behavioral problems, delinquency, and teen pregnancy. Predictably, she found that children born into difficult circumstances are more likely to experience these problems. Risk factors for these problems include being born into homes marked by

parental mental illness, alcoholism, abuse, discord and instability, divorce, and poverty.

Soon, however, Werner's focus shifted to studying the majority of the children who were resilient despite their adverse circumstances. There were two kinds of resilient individuals. She found that one third of the children born into these difficult circumstances never succumbed to the problems mentioned above. They did well in school and in their families, turning into competent, confident, and caring adults. These were the stable resilient group. Of the remainder who did succumb to these problems, most demonstrated a "self-righting capacity," becoming emotionally stable and competent adults by the time they were forty years of age. These were the resilient individuals who bounced back. In studying these two resilient groups, Werner found that inner strengths and protective factors offset the difficult external circumstances.[7] These strengths and protective factors included the following:

Internal strengths. Resilient children:
- *Were active and resourceful.* They were involved in diverse activities to gain solace, satisfaction, and support (e.g., extracurricular activities, hobbies, church, YMCA); used their strengths and skills effectively to solve problems (which built confidence), worked hard.
- *Possessed a sense of independence/self-reliance*
- *Believed that their life had meaning and purpose*
- *Had a positive self-concept*
- *Were optimistic*
- *Had an intrinsic religious orientation; prayed*
- *Were compassionate, caring, got along with others*
- *Had a sense of humor*

Other Protective Factors
- *Social ties.* Every resilient child bonded to at least one unconditionally accepting, caring adult. Often this was a non-parent adult, such as a teacher, coach, or pastor. Social skills facilitated this bonding and connecting with others. In addition, the strength of parental bonds in the first three years of life set the tone for the rest of the individual's life.
- *Family stability.* Children were required to be helpful in the family; they had structured rules and chores

2. **Rochester Child Resilience Project**. Like Emmy Werner, Emory Cowen started out studying disease in children living in difficult environments, but ended up studying protective factors and advocating that these be taught preventively in early, school-based interventions. In studying highly stressed inner-city children, he found that five strengths could predict with 84% accuracy whether those children would be resilient or seriously affected by adversity. These strengths are:
- Global self-worth
- Confidence gained from successes
- Empathy (knowing what it feels like to walk in another's shoes)
- Realistic control attributions (knowing what you can and can't control; accepting that there will be ups and downs)

- Social problem-solving skills (knowing how to solve social problems; knowing how to seek support when needed)

He found that a twelve-session school-based intervention for inner-city children that taught these strengths along with understanding their feelings resulted in improvements in learning problems, anxiety, and other variables related to resilience.

3. **Harvard Study of Adult Development.** The psychiatrist George Vaillant has followed Harvard men from the classes of 1939-1944, including those who fought in WWII, for decades. He found that mental health in college was the best predictor of health and functioning decades later, suggesting the importance of optimizing mental health as early as possible. Those men who showed five mature coping styles in college fared better decades later in all areas studied: *occupationally* (earned more, more promotions), *medically* (less chronic illness and death), *psychologically* (less anxiety, less use of sleeping pills and mind-altering drugs), and *socially* (stable marriages, better friendships, more pleasure in relationships). They were also more likely to be happy with their life, job, leisure time, and health. These five mature coping styles were (see if you can notice a common thread):

    - *Sublimation.* Feelings are acknowledged, and channeled in a disciplined way. Thus, grief might be expressed in poetry, aggression might be vented in sports, and anger might be directed to social change.
    - *Suppression.* Emotions could be consciously postponed until an appropriate time. Thus, an angry reaction might be delayed until it could be discussed calmly, or until such time that the listener is receptive. Those who suppress could delay their own grief in order to comfort others, and *then* they grieved. They could also override the desire for immediate gratification in order to accomplish a desired goal.
    - *Anticipation.* Emotional awareness of future discomfort leads one to prepare and take action. Thus, one studies for a test rather than procrastinating. Fearing job loss in uncertain economic times, one takes additional training to broaden her occupational skills.
    - *Altruism.* This is finding pleasure in helping, loving, giving another a "leg up."
    - *Humor* is acknowledging pain, but emphasizing the ironic or amusing. Mature humor includes and soothes others, without sarcasm, and is kind with people's imperfections.

    The thread uniting these coping styles is that the mature copers comfortably acknowledged feelings and responded to them constructively. In contrast, immature copers tended to run from uncomfortable emotions in various ways. They might forget what they couldn't bear or refuse to acknowledge distressing feelings ("I'm not angry"; "Dad [who is abusive] is really a perfect father"). Unable to face uncomfortable feelings, immature copers were unlikely to respond constructively, resulting in greater distress. Other protective factors found in those who were successful later in life included: no smoking or alcohol abuse, maintaining a healthy weight, regular exercise, and a stable marriage. Note that those who demonstrated mature coping styles tended to come from secure, loving families. If this was not your experience, it might take more persistence and patience to build resilience. Remember, though, that everyone can climb the resilience staircase, regardless of the starting point.

Conclusions

From these and many other studies of those who didn't permanently fall to stress, we can draw certain conclusions:

- Individual protective factors (i.e., internal strengths or coping mechanisms) compensate for and are more important than external hazards. The strengths of resilience protect against psychological disturbance, even among those who have suffered difficult circumstances.
- Protective factors not only prevent disease, but also optimize health and performance.
- Delayed recovery can occur later in life.
- The most effective resilience training modifies as many risk factors and builds as many strengths as possible—ideally before disease strikes.

Drawing from the many resilience studies, we can summarize the following as the individual strengths of resilience:

- *Sense of Autonomy* (appropriate separation from family dysfunction; being self-sufficient; being determined to be different—perhaps leaving an abusive home, being self-protecting, having goals to build a better life)
- *Calm Under Pressure* (equanimity)
- *Rational Thought Process*
- *Self-Esteem*
- *Optimism*
- *Happiness & Emotional Intelligence*
- *Meaning and Purpose* ("My contribution to life matters")
- *Humor*
- *Altruism* (learned helpfulness)/*Love/Compassion*
- *Character/Integrity*
- *Curiosity* (which is related to commitment and interested engagement)
- *Balance* (engagement in a wide range of activities, such as hobbies, education, jobs, social and cultural activities)
- *Sociability/Social Competence* (getting along, using bonding skills, being willing to seek out and commit to relationships, interdepending)
- *Adaptability* (persistence and hard work, confidence, flexibility, accepting what can't be controlled, creative problem solving, active coping strategies)
- *Intrinsic Religious Faith*
- *A Long View of Suffering*
- *Good Health Habits* (sufficient sleep, nutrition, and exercise; no immoderate alcohol use; no tobacco; good personal appearance; physical arousal levels that are low and return to baseline quickly)

These are the strengths that you will solidify and expand in this book. Please glance at the Resilience Training Model at Appendix 4, which incorporates these strengths and summarizes emotional intelligence, an important aspect of resilience. You might also find it interesting to see how the creed of the elite U.S. Navy SEALS, a highly resilient group, embodies these strengths of resilience (See Appendix 5).

See Where You Are Now

Resilient people are aware of, and use, their strengths. The following Resilience Checkup will assess your strengths, providing you with a starting point from which to measure your progress as you work through this book. Taking the checkup will also begin to reinforce some of the goals of this book. It is reassuring to know that you already possess some measure of resilience to build upon. There is nothing tricky about this assessment, nor does it matter how your scores compare to others. So relax and be as honest as you can.

The Resilience Checkup

First, rate from 0 to 10 how much you believe each of the following statements. 0 means you completely disbelieve it. 10 means you think it is completely true.

Statement	Rating
1. I generally feel strong and capable of overcoming my problems.	_____
2. When I get stressed, I usually bounce back fairly quickly.	_____
3. I generally function well in the various areas of life: job, relationships, school, and play.	_____
4. I generally stay calm and steady when the going gets tough.	_____
5 I am generally flexible, meaning if my usual way of doing things isn't working I readily try something else.	_____
6. I am in a good mood most of the time.	_____
7. I think well of myself and like who I am inside.	_____
8. Difficult times don't change the way I feel about myself.	_____
9. I believe that if I try my best things will usually turn out well.	_____
10. I am good at reaching out and connecting with people.	_____
11. I usually try to solve my problems, but I know when to bend if something is beyond my control.	_____
12. I anticipate difficult situations, make a plan, and carry out my plan.	_____
13. I enjoy life and am satisfied with what I am contributing to the world.	_____
14. I am good at coping with strong negative emotions.	_____
15. I am good at separating myself from people who get me down or upset me.	_____
16. I have goals and am optimistic about my future.	_____
17. I'm involved in a variety of activities that I enjoy.	_____
18. I don't have self-destructive habits.	_____
19. I feel at peace with myself and my past. I've grown stronger from what I've experienced.	_____
20. I don't beat myself up when my best efforts don't succeed.	_____
21. I know when to seek help, and where to find it.	_____
22. I stay focused and think clearly under pressure. I am persistent, determined, and resolved.	_____

Total Score _____

Next, rate your resilience on the following scales:

0   100

Total lack of   Total fullness
resilience   of resilience

Your Response _____

How often do you feel restricted in your daily activities because of difficulties with resilience?

1   2   3   4   5

Always   Often   Sometimes   Rarely   Never

Your Response _____

Activities

- Over a two-day period, notice resilience traits in others.
- Over another two-day period, notice resilience strengths in yourself.

Where We Are Going?

You are now ready to begin building the strengths of resilience. As we mentioned in chapter 1, we'll start with universally useful resilience skills. These include optimizing brain function (both "hardware" and "software"), calming the nervous system, and learning to cope adaptively. Then we'll explore skills that prepare us for specific crises. While crisis skills are especially useful to high-risk groups, understanding them can benefit everyone.

UNIVERSAL RESILIENCE TRAINING

PART II

WHERE IT ALL STARTS

Chapter 3

The Resilient Brain: New Findings on Exercise, Nutrition, and Sleep

Take as good care of [yourself] as [you] do of your equipment.
Ellen Kirschman, Ph.D.

Resilience starts with the brain. The resilient brain functions at optimal efficiency. It learns, remembers, and retrieves information. It flexibly adapts to challenges—coming up with new ideas, making and executing decisions. It regulates moods. And it does all this relatively quickly, even under duress. The resilient brain also resists and reverses cognitive decline and brain cell death. To better understand how we can optimize brain functioning, let's first take a brief tour of this amazing structure.

Brain Overview

The brain consists of 100 billion neurons, or nerve cells. Each gets input from thousands of others before it fires. The brain is the consistency of Jello, tofu, or butter at room temperature, suggesting the need to protect it from physical trauma. Let's explore some of the key regions related to resilience (refer to Figure 3.1)

Figure 3.1
THE RESILIENT BRAIN

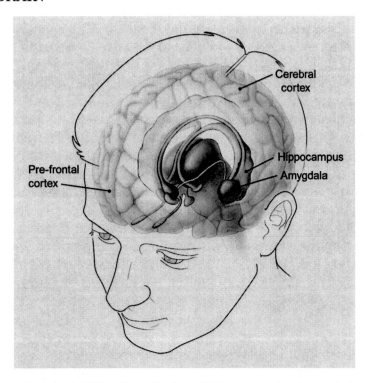

©2004 Haderer & Müller Biomedical Art, LLC. Reprinted with permission.

Cerebral Cortex

Comprising the outer shell, the *cerebral cortex* is the seat of conscious thought, logic, and reason. Memories, which are stored as networks spreading throughout the brain, primarily reside here.

The CEO of the brain is the *pre-frontal cortex* (PFC), the portion of the cortex sitting just behind the forehead. The PFC organizes all mental and physical activity, and enacts all executive functions. Weaving together facts, memories, and what is happening in the environment, the PFC judges, predicts, plans, organizes, solves problems, initiates action, and regulates impulses and emotions.[1] In its working or short-term memory, the PFC holds onto relevant facts and blocks out irrelevant information. In brain scans, the PFC lights up when learning something new, then fairly quickly goes dead as it delegates tasks to other areas. As "Spock-like" as all this sounds, the PFC considers emotions until the decision feels right. So let's take a look at the parts of the brain associated with feelings.

Limbic System

The limbic system is the emotional center of the brain. Forming a ring around the inner portions of the brain that regulate automatic biological functions, the limbic system includes two key structures that play complementary roles—the *amygdala* and the *hippocampus*.

Amygdala

The almond-shaped amygdala takes its name from the Greek word for almond. Like an emotional early warning center, it attunes to novel or important stimuli, picking up emotions from non-verbal cues, and tripping immediate emotional reactions. For example, we see a baby smile and immediately smile without conscious thought. However, the amygdala preferentially attends to frightening and negative stimuli. We might sense another's posture, facial expression, or tone of voice, or our own inner thoughts, memories and sensations—including sensations from strong stimulants like caffeine. Such stimuli set off the alarm. The amygdala signals the hypothalamus in the inner brain to initiate all the physical changes of the stress response. We feel strong emotions like fear, anger, or disgust—and the associated bodily sensations. We might jump or run in fright, only to think about it later.

The amygdala informs the PFC of the feelings and body sensations, without which the PFC can't make a decision. It also picks up memories with similar emotional content and sends these to the PFC to further inform decision-making. These feelings in turn get woven into new memories and help the memories be retained.

Hippocampus

Sitting beside the amygdala is the hippocampus, which plays a key role in learning and memory. Bigger hippocampi are associated with resilience. This is easy to appreciate when we consider its roles. The hippocampus complements and balances the amygdala.

Whereas the amygdala deals in strong emotions and promotes quick and unthinking reactions, the hippocampus deals in cold facts and promotes cool, rational thought.

The hippocampus links the PFC with long-term memory networks. Say you are walking down a path and see a large snake. The amygdala would automatically hit the panic button and send you running. However, the hippocampus calmly pulls up your memories of snakes, which allows the PFC to realize that this snake is different from the rattlers you've encountered in the past. In fact, it looks more like a harmless garden snake. It's as though the hippocampus were saying, "Let's see the whole picture before jumping." Once the situation is deemed safe, the hippocampus dampens the amygdala and the stress response that the amygdala initiated.

Should you learn a way to cope with a problem, the hippocampus sends this learning to be stored in long-term memory, and connects this new memory to related memories and beliefs that are already stored. Thus, with practice, you might learn to move deliberately and calmly to a certain exit during a terrorist attack. Practicing with concentration and some emotion (in other words, moderate activation of the amygdala, but not too much) helps you store and retrieve this memory optimally.

The hippocampus gives context and reality to learning. This enables us to know what happened, where, how, and when. This is very important for the proper storage of traumatic memories. When the hippocampus is properly functioning, the fragments of a memory hang together in a way that makes sense. Thus, a rape survivor knows that a rape happened ten years ago. It had a beginning and an end. Although the rape can be remembered, the memory does not intrude with undue emotion as if the rape were happening now. The perpetrator was a man named Joe, not all men named Joe—so not all men are untrustworthy. In other words, the hippocampus allows us to store, think about, and talk about memories in a rather cool and rational way.

Finally, the hippocampus helps us orient in space. Thus, rats with larger hippocampi can better remember the location of an unseen rest platform just below the surface of water. Taxi drivers who have driven city streets for a long time have larger hippocampi than rookie drivers.

When Things Go Wrong

The amygdala can get us moving quickly and automatically, which can be lifesaving at times. Usually, however, resilience is better served when strong emotions are regulated. The hippocampus and PFC temper the strong emotions of the amygdala through thoughtful, rational decision-making. These three structures must work together. However, when this delicate balance is upset, the brain becomes less resilient.

Excessive stress is one factor that can upset this balance. One of the hormones secreted under stress is cortisol. Moderate amounts of cortisol sharpen thinking. However, excessive amounts[2] disrupt brain function in several important ways. Excessive cortisol:

- *Over-activates the amygdala.* This can lead to excessive anxiety that hinders learning and makes thinking more emotional and negative. The hyperactive amygdala also imprints memories with excessive, intense emotion, rather than details. Thus, one might overreact with excessive fear or freezing to a threat that triggers a distressing memory. The amygdala is hyperactive in people with PTSD. This gives traumatic memories their strong emotional charge.

27

- *Shrinks and/or impairs the functioning of the hippocampus.* Recall that the hippocampus down-tunes the amygdala, recalls existing memories when needed (Where was that emergency exit?), and stores traumatic memories in a cool, integrated way.
- *Disrupts PFC function*, probably degrading creative thought, problem solving, emotional regulation, concentration, and the ability to shift attention quickly and effectively.

The following story demonstrates how excessive stress can disrupt normal memory storage (Rothschild, 2000, p.72):

> Roger was in his early twenties when as a rookie policeman he shot and killed a suspect for the first time. He froze as he watched blood flow from the man's chest. He kept yelling, "I'm sorry. Why'd you make me do that?" He seemed to recover and handle the situation well until two years later when he was the first officer on the scene where a man had been shot during a brawl. The next officer to arrive found Roger yelling those same words, apparently confusing the two situations.

Here an overactive amygdala caused the first extremely emotional memory to intrude inappropriately. An unimpaired hippocampus would have enabled Roger to think, "This second shooting is a totally different time, place, and event."

Aging is a second factor that interferes with optimal brain functioning. With aging, we typically see a shrinkage that begins with the hippocampus, and spreads to the PFC. We have learned much about brain function from the study of Alzheimer's disease, which is characterized by declines in mental functioning. Those with Alzheimer's have hippocampi that are below average in size, and the pathways from it to the PFC deteriorate. The brain starts to decline by age thirty, but this can be slowed and possibly reversed. We assume that much of what prevents Alzheimer's disease optimizes brain function in healthy people.

Two Important Findings

Two intriguing recent findings about the brain give us great hope for improving resilience.
1. *The brain is plastic.* This means that it changes structure and function in response to new experiences throughout the lifespan in ways that can improve resilience. We now know that new neurons can grow in the hippocampus, replacing old ones or those damaged by stress. This growth rate, as well as the size and health of neurons, can be affected by factors including exercise, nutrition, and rest. We also know that neurons can link together, forging new neural pathways as we learn adaptive coping skills. The more we practice these skills, the stronger and more efficient these neural connections become.[3] Conversely, neural connections can deteriorate through disuse, while practicing poor coping skills reinforces maladaptive pathways.
2. *Brain health equals heart health.* What kills the body kills the brain. What keeps the heart healthy keeps the brain healthy. The metabolic syndrome is a risk factor for

coronary heart disease, as well as stroke and diabetes. This syndrome also negatively affects the brain. It includes at least three of the following:

- *Large waist circumference* (abdominal obesity). Being overweight doubles the risk of dementia. This risk is six times higher when high blood pressure and high cholesterol also exist.
- *High blood pressure*
- *High blood sugar*
- *Elevated triglycerides*, a type of blood fat
- *Low HDL, or good, cholesterol*

Cognitive impairment and heart disease also share these risk factors:

- *High total cholesterol*, which increases the risk of dementia and depression
- *Type 2 diabetes*, which accelerates cognitive decline and increases the risk of dementia. Executive functioning and mental processing speed are particularly affected by diabetes.

We might compare the brain to a computer. A computer's hardware is like the capacity and health of the brain. The software is like the programming or learning that forms new neural pathways. In this chapter and the next we will primarily explore ways to optimize brain *hardware*, beginning with exercise, nutrition, and sleep. Subsequent chapters will explore ways to etch adaptive ways of coping into the brain—the *software*, if you will.

Aerobic Exercise

From the studies of animals and humans we have learned that regular aerobic exercise does more than burn stress and lower cholesterol. It is good brain medicine that directly enhances cognitive function, prevents cognitive decline, and may even reverse cognitive decline. Cognitive function includes many things, such as concentration, the ability to learn and remember, reasoning ability, productivity, creativity, and the speed of thinking and switching focus from one situation to another. It turns out that exercisers have sharper brains at all ages.

Aerobic exercise tunes up the brain hardware, priming it for learning, by producing four factors, or master molecules, which normally decrease with age and stress.

- Brain-derived neurotrophic factor (BDNF) causes a number of changes that improve neuron function and growth, protects against neuron death, and improves memory:
  - BDNF causes neurogenesis, or the growth of new neurons in the hippocampus. These new cells help to dampen the amygdala and improve learning and memory. BDNF also steps up the production of antioxidants in neurons, protecting them from deterioration.
  - Within and between neurons, BDNF causes changes that promote the transmission of signals. First, BDNF causes the neurons to form new dendritic branches, the means by which neurons will "reach out and touch" their neighbors when learning causes neurons along new neural pathways to connect. Second, BDNF causes changes that enhance the reception of signals

at receptor sites on neurons. These two changes prime the neurons to make a new memory, such as learning a new coping skill or a more adaptive thought to combat a traumatic memory. Third, BDNF stimulates the growth of the thin fatty coat around neurons that speeds impulses. This tends to quicken cognitive functions.

- Three other factors produced in the body and brain by exercise promote brain resilience. Vascular endothelial growth factor increases the flow of blood (and therefore oxygen) to the brain by growing capillaries. Fibroblast growth factor promotes the growth of supporting tissue, and insulin-like growth factor improves brain plasticity and learning.

How effective is regular exercise? Research has found that:
- Exercise increases brain volume overall, and in the PFC and hippocampus in particular—probably through neurogenesis, increased vasculature, decreased cortisol secretion, and/or increases in dendrites and other tissue. Brain shrinkage appears to be associated with dementia, including Alzheimer's disease.
- Fitness is associated with better academic performance[4] and executive function. Fitness also generally reduces metabolic syndrome symptoms.
- Exercise improves psychological health, mood, happiness, confidence, and self-esteem. It reduces tension, anxiety, and depression. In fact, aerobic exercise works as well as the antidepressant Zoloft in reducing depression, with less relapse. Preliminary studies indicate that PTSD symptoms are reduced by moderate aerobic exercise, suggesting its use as a possible adjunct to treatment—particularly for children or others who find it difficult to talk about their traumatic experiences.
- Employees who exercise are more productive and less stressed.
- Exercise results in greater adaptation to stress.

In addition to the above changes, which directly influence brain function, regular exercise also:
- Reduces fatigue, increases energy, and improves sleep
- Reduces the risks of cardiovascular diseases and diabetes, which is linked to the reduction of metabolic syndrome symptoms
- Reduces risks for certain, and perhaps all, cancers
- Lowers heart rate before, during, and after a psychological stressor (reduced physiologic reactivity helps us remain calmer during stressful times)
- Increases longevity
- Reduces problems in the joints, including the knees

Exercise Guidelines to Maximize Resilience and Brain Plasticity

1. *Gradually build an aerobic base.* A reasonable goal is 2.5 hours of moderate aerobic exercise a week. This might mean 30 minutes of brisk walking, slow jogging, cycling, or swimming five days a week. Moderate intensity means you can just carry on a conversation. If you can't you might be overdoing it. Start by doing less than you think you can do, increasing exercise time by 10% per week until you reach your goal.

Don't push. If you are unfit and struggle with fatigue and low energy levels, it will likely help to aim for thirty minutes of walking at a leisurely pace, rather than twenty minutes of walking at a moderate intensity. The intensity can increase later. Warm up and cool down for five minutes with slower walking. If you can't get in thirty minutes per day, don't be discouraged. Three ten-minute exercise bouts seem to confer benefits that equal (or perhaps even exceed) those of continuous thirty-minute bouts.

2. *To your aerobic base, add*:
   - *Complex motor movements*, which further increase BDNF and greatly sharpen brain function. This is done by engaging in: ballroom, aerobic, or other types of dance; martial arts; tennis; ping pong; juggling; rock climbing; yoga; tai chi; or playing a musical instrument.
   - *Lifelong learning.* Work out *and* go to the library! Learning creates neural pathways that can later help in the learning of resilience skills. Pick something enjoyable and novel: socialize, volunteer, take classes, play word or board games, join a book club, cook, travel, debate, get politically active, find a hobby or musical instrument to learn. Challenging work also lowers the risk of dementia.
   - *Strength and flexibility exercises.* Strength or resistance training could involve light weights, elastic bands, pushups, curl-ups, or the like—ten repetitions of each exercise, done 2-3 days a week. Flexibility and stretching exercises can be done most days to keep us limber. Don't overlook yoga, which has been found to improve post-traumatic symptoms and mood in many studies, or tai chi, which effectively reduces stress.

3. *Try morning workouts*, which seem to help people better stick to their exercise programs.

4. *Exercise before you need to learn or solve something difficult.* Students who take their most difficult class right after morning aerobic exercise get better grades than those who take it later in the day.

5. *Get a medical exam if you are starting an exercise program and are forty years old for a man and fifty for a woman.* Also get an exam if you have a chronic disease or risk factors for a chronic disease.

6. *Try outdoor exercise.* Ten to fifteen minutes of sunlight a few times a week raises levels of vitamin D, which improves brain function.

See the resource section, Appendix 9, to find information about finding a certified fitness instructor or to read more about exercise guidelines.

Brain-Healthy Nutrition

With our national obsession with weight and calories, we often forget that nutritious food is critical to optimal brain health and functioning. As with exercise, if it is good for the heart it is good for the brain. Substances typically found in the so-called power, or functional, foods—plants (vegetables, fruits, cooked dry beans/peas, nuts, and whole grains) and fish—greatly benefit the brain. It is also wise to limit red meat and high-fat dairy sources. As much as possible, follow these principles for brain-healthy nutrition:

Choose Good Carbohydrates

The brain functions best with a steady supply of blood sugar (glucose), which is its preferred fuel source. Low carbohydrate diets, such as the Atkins diet, are not good for the brain as they quickly deplete stores of glucose and impair brain function.[5] On the other hand, diets that lead to spikes in blood sugar are also not brain friendly.

Glycemic load (GL) describes how much and how fast carbohydrates in food are absorbed into the blood stream. High GL diets are associated with more heart disease and Type 2 diabetes. High GL foods include processed foods made with refined flour and sugar (which reduces BDNF), such as sugary sodas, candy, cake, many cereals, white rice, and pasta. High fructose corn syrup, found in sweetened sodas and many processed foods, accounts for 10% of our caloric consumption. It may especially jeopardize heart and brain health. Reducing sugary drinks to less than one per month is associated with significant reductions in weight and diabetes risk. In one animal study, the equivalent of five sodas per day instead of water was associated with poorer memory, greater weight, and greater changes in the brain related to Alzheimer's disease.

Excellent sources of glucose are vegetables, fruits, whole grains, and cooked dry beans/peas. In scores of studies, diets rich in these are associated with less dementia, mental aging, cardiovascular diseases, and metabolic syndrome. For example, in separate studies, eating at least three daily servings of whole grains or an apple a day is associated with significantly fewer metabolic syndrome symptoms. Diets high in carbohydrates and low in protein also increase serotonin, which helps to regulate moods.

Fiber, acid, and small amounts of protein and fat tend to beneficially slow the absorption of sugars in food. Thus, preceding a meal with a salad with olive oil and lemon dressing and beans makes sense from the perspective of brain health.

Choose Foods Rich in Antioxidants

Like tiny furnaces, the mitochondria within the cells of the body convert fuel to energy. With age and stress, this process becomes less efficient as the mitochondria spew free radicals of oxygen. These free radicals damage cells, including neurons in the brain. Antioxidants neutralize these free radicals and prevent cell damage from oxidative stress. Antioxidants keep the brain sharp as we age. They appear to:
- Slow aging and neuronal degeneration, including that seen in Alzheimer's disease
- Reduce inflammation, which is associated with brain aging and many chronic diseases
- Activate cellular repair
- Stimulate growth of new neurons
- Combat, and perhaps even reverse, loss of memory and cognitive function
- Boost heart health, raising HDL levels, lowering blood pressure, and lowering the risk of cardiovascular diseases

Many antioxidants are found in colorful plant foods, such as red grapes, cherries, dark berries (blueberries, blackberries, strawberries, cranberries, raspberries), dark beans (red, black, kidney), tomatoes, pomegranates, dark green vegetables (e.g., broccoli, spinach), apples, chocolate, green and black tea, and orange, red, and yellow fruits and vegetables, including onions. Other antioxidants are found in pale plant foods, including pears, white beans, green grapes, cauliflower, and soybeans.

Spices are a particularly rich source of antioxidants. These include cinnamon, cloves, oregano, allspice, marjoram, rosemary, sage, tarragon, thyme, cumin, saffron, fennel, garlic, basil, ginger, red and black pepper, and turmeric (a component of curry; people in India have low rates of Alzheimer's disease). Store spices in a cool, dark place and use them within two years, before they loose their potency. Antioxidants are also found in the germ and bran of whole grain products and in nuts (e.g., pecans, walnuts, hazelnuts).

Getting antioxidants from foods is a better choice than supplements, since the components of foods seem to work in combination. Select from a rainbow of colors. Emphasize orange, red, green, and yellow fruits and vegetables. The darker and richer the colors, the better. Look for fresh or frozen produce. Don't peel skins, which have the most antioxidants (think of how the apple's red skin protects the inner fruit from oxidative damage and you get an idea of how antioxidants protect cells). Generally choose foods rather than juices, although even a glass of vegetable or fruit juice a day has been found to reduce the risk of Alzheimer's disease.[6]

Restrict Calories

A growing number of studies, ranging from small animals to humans, suggest that restricting caloric intake by 30% might improve memory and longevity, while reducing insulin resistance, inflammation,[7] and brain changes related to Alzheimer's disease.[8] For example, people in Okinawa are among the longest living humans on earth. They follow the principle of hara hachi bu, whereby they stop eating when 80% full. They consume about 30% fewer calories than the average American (1800 calories vs. 2500 for Americans). Suggestive studies indicate that an occasional 24-hour fast might improve heart health. You might try this if you are healthy and not pregnant.

The challenge in practicing this principle is to balance caloric restriction with obtaining needed nutrients. This can be achieved by carefully following the U.S. dietary guidelines found at www.ChooseMyPlate.gov.

Benefit From Fish

The label of *brain food* for fish is richly deserved. Fish contains the omega-3 fatty acids called DHA and EPA. These fats are critical components of the brain's neurons that are involved in memory, language, and thinking. In fact, the brain is mostly fat, and DHA is the most abundant fatty acid in the brain's gray matter. Omega-3s are only obtained or derived from what we eat. Among the benefits of omega-3s are that they:
- Increase BDNF
- Improve normal day-to-day cognitive function
- Protect against cognitive decline, inflammation, and dementia (including Alzheimer's disease)
- Improve mood, reduce depression, and improve depressed people's response to antidepressant medication
- Improve heart health (by lowering blood pressure, the risk of heart attack, and triglycerides, while aiding in the operation of arteries)

33

- Might help to reduce stress in traumatized people, according to preliminary studies

Aim to eat at least 2-3 servings of fish per week, totaling at least eight ounces. The benefits of eating seafood outweigh the risks of mercury and PCB for most people. The best choices are fish that are high in omega-3s and low in mercury, such as salmon, herring, Atlantic mackerel, sardines, anchovies, trout, tuna (not albacore), bluefish, and shellfish. For mercury, avoid large predatory fish, such as king mackerel, shark, and swordfish—especially if you are pregnant or may become pregnant, are breast-feeding, or are under twelve years of age. Limit albacore tuna. Fried fish is often prepared with unhealthy fats, which cancel omega-3s' benefits. To reduce PCBs, eat wild fish rather than farmed fish as often as possible. Remove the skin, which is where PCBs accumulate, and don't fry, since frying doesn't permit PCBs to drain. Eating a variety of fish also helps reduce the risk of contaminants.

If you don't like fish, or wish to augment your omega-3s from fish, you might consider fish oil supplements. Generally, look for supplements totaling at least 500-1000 milligrams of DHA and EPA (*not* total fish oil).[9] Supplements do not contain significant amounts of mercury or other toxins, because mercury accumulates in the flesh, not fat, and because smaller fish are typically used to produce supplements. While supplements raise blood omega-3s as well as fish, we are not sure if other nutrients in fish confer additional benefits. Some plants contain alpha-linolenic acid (ALA), which is converted in the body to DHA and EPA better than previously thought, although it does not appear to raise levels of DHA and EPA as well as fish. Good ALA sources include green leafy vegetables, walnuts, pecans, flaxseed, tofu, and canola, olive, and soybean oils.

Be Selective About Other Fats

Saturated fat is found primarily in animal products, such as meats and full-fat dairy products. While omega-3s in fish increase BDNF, saturated fats and sugar appear to decrease it. The combination of saturated fat and sugar also increases inflammatory and oxidative stress. In addition, saturated fat also raises LDL more than anything else in the diet, and increases the risk of Alzheimer's disease. So if you want to be brain- and heart-healthy, a cheeseburger, French fries, apple pie, and a super-sized soda would not be wise choices. Neither would typical fast-food breakfasts. The following guidelines apply:
- *Minimize trans-fat, which appears to be unhealthier than even saturated fat.* Most trans-fat comes from hydrogenating vegetable oil to make it solid. It is found in cakes, cookies, crackers, fried foods, other processed and frozen foods, and fast food and restaurant foods.
- *Replace sources of animal and trans-fat with fats from plants* (e.g., nuts, avocados, olive oil, canola oil, peanuts). Such diets help to reduce cognitive decline and diabetes risk.
- *Strive for low-fat meals,* which result in lower blood pressure and heart rate in response to stress two hours later. Practically, this means filling up mainly on plant and low- or no-fat dairy products. Don't avoid low- or no-fat dairy products. They seem to promote cardiovascular health and reduce diabetes risk.

- In moderation, eggs don't appear to increase the risk of cardiovascular diseases. One or two a day, a few times a week, is probably fine. But spare the fatty meats, biscuits, gravy, and cheese.

Go With Whole Grains

Consuming sufficient whole grains has been linked to reduced metabolic syndrome symptoms (including reductions in abdominal obesity), cardiovascular diseases, and diabetes. Whole grains also may reduce C-reactive protein (a marker for inflammation), while refined grains may increase C-reactive protein levels.

Whole grains contain the entire kernel, consisting of bran, germ, and endosperm. Refining removes most of the bran and some of the germ, resulting in the loss of fiber, vitamins, minerals, healthy fat, protein, and many nutrients that are unique to grains. Whole grains can have as many beneficial nutrients and antioxidants as fruits and vegetables.

Whole grains include whole wheat, oats, whole-grain corn, popcorn, brown rice, whole rye, wild rice, bulgur (cracked wheat), millet, quinoa, sorghum, spelt, triticale, and wheat berries. Two whole grains are especially noteworthy: 1) Oats regulate cholesterol, blood sugar, and insulin sensitivity, and protect against hypertension. Antioxidants in oats relax blood vessels and help to prevent heart disease. All forms (rolled oats, quick oats, steel-cut, etc.) are similarly nutritious since the bran and germ remain. Rolled oats are usually heated and pressed flat to cook faster. 2) The sugar in barley is absorbed quite slowly. In addition to the health benefits of other whole grains, barley aids memory and concentration better than other grains even ten hours after eating it for breakfast. Barley also effectively lowers levels of unhealthy cholesterol.

So try to replace products made from refined white flour or refined grains with whole grain products (e.g., whole grain couscous or pasta, brown or wild rice). Look for *whole grain* listed as the first ingredient in breads, pastas, cereals, etc. *Multi*-grain does not necessarily mean *whole* grain. The dark color of such breads might be artificial. Refrigerate corn meal, whole grain flour, and wheat germ.

Check for Fiber

Fiber is found mainly in the "good" carbohydrates: vegetables, fruits, whole grains, and cooked dry beans/peas/lentils. The many benefits of fiber include protection against the metabolic syndrome and its related diseases. Of course fiber comes packaged with antioxidants and many beneficial plant nutrients, and foods with fiber generally are low in fat and calories.

Try for at least fourteen grams of fiber for every 1000 calories consumed. You will probably be getting sufficient fiber if you follow the guidelines at ChooseMyPlate.gov and page 40. Try the rough calculation on the next page to see if you are getting enough fiber. Fiber intake can be increased by adding wheat germ, wheat bran, oat bran, nuts, and seeds to yogurt, baked goods, and other foods. Replace juices with fruits and vegetables as much as possible.

Food	# Servings		Grams (g) of fiber/serving		Total grams of fiber
Beans, lentils		X	6 g	=	
Vegetables, fruits, whole grains, nuts, or brown rice		X	2.5 g	=	
Refined grains (e.g., white bread, white rice, pasta		X	1 g	=	
Breakfast cereals (These vary, so check label for fiber content. Look for cereals that have at least 3 grams per serving. Refined cereals have less.)		X	_____ g	=	
DAILY TOTAL GRAMS OF FIBER					

Source: *University of California Berkeley Wellness Letter*, April 2007

Got Vitamins?

Vitamin D has been getting quite a look-over by researchers. Vitamin D in the blood is associated with better mental function (including executive function) in older people—it probably plays a role in the formation of new memories, planning, and the processing of information. Vitamin D is also linked to the prevention of stroke, heart attack, hypertension, diabetes, and obesity. The current guidelines recommend 400-600 IU daily from sun, food, and supplements. Some researchers are recommending 1000 IU or more to optimize health. Get vitamin D from a little unprotected midday sun—10-15 minutes between 11:00 a.m. and 3:00 p.m. several days a week (think outdoor exercise). Get it also from fatty fish and fortified foods (milk and some brands of cereal, orange juice, and yogurt). Since many Americans are deficient in this vitamin, you might also look for supplements providing 400-1000 IU of D3, the most potent and readily absorbed form (people who supplement with vitamin D live longer). People who are over fifty years old, have dark skin, do not get sufficient sunlight exposure, or are obese are most likely to need supplements.

B vitamins enhance nervous system function and energy use. Although the research is not always consistent, there is some evidence that B vitamin supplementation to an otherwise sound diet (especially folate or folic acid, B6, and B12) might enhance cognitive function and mood, slow cognitive decline and dementia, and protect against brain volume loss. Most people get sufficient B vitamins, especially if following MyPlate. Supplements might be considered for people over fifty (who might have trouble absorbing these vitamins), vegetarians (B12 is not found in plant products), dieters, pregnant women, or those who expend high amounts of energy.

As a general rule, rely primarily on a sound nutrition plan for the nutrients you need to feel and function at your best. The limited nutrients in supplements are not usually as effective as the nutrients in foods, which probably work together synergistically. So we would not expect supplements in the absence of sound nutrition to benefit us. If you take supplements for extra insurance, look for a brand that provides 100% of the recommended amounts of vitamins and minerals.[10]

Eat Some Dark Chocolate

In moderation, chocolate, especially dark chocolate, is heart healthy, reduces levels of cortisol, and might improve brain function. Components of chocolate, either eaten or drank, help blood vessels relax. This improves blood flow to the brain and lowers blood pressure, perhaps helping to prevent stroke or dementia. Chocolate is very high in antioxidants (although the milk in milk chocolate or chocolate milk diminishes antioxidant effects). And chocolate raises healthy HDL cholesterol levels, without raising overall cholesterol (most of the fats in chocolate are heart healthy). Of course, chocolate is high in calories, so aim for about an ounce a day. Look for dark chocolate high in cacao.

Go Nuts

Nuts are high in calories. Otherwise their nutritional benefits are extremely impressive. All nuts are probably heart healthy. They contain healthy fats, antioxidants, vitamins and minerals, fiber, arginine (an amino acid that that relaxes blood vessels), and many beneficial phytochemicals. Regular, moderate nut consumption is associated with improvements in blood cholesterol and triglycerides, reduced risk for Type 2 diabetes, improved cognitive and motor function in animals, improved blood vessel health, and weight loss and weight maintenance when nuts are part of a sensible eating plan. Try for about an ounce of unsalted nuts per day. This amounts to a small handful (e.g., about 7 walnuts), and furnishes about 160-200 calories.

Hydrate

The brain is 80% water. Even minor dehydration can impair mental and physical performance and leave us feeling tired, confused, moody, and perhaps hungry when we are actually just thirsty. As WWII U.S. Army researcher S.L.A. Marshall said, "No one ever told me that dehydration causes cowardice in its most abject form."

Assuming normal eating, which provides about 20% of needed liquids, adults typically need to drink around 9 to 13 cups of liquid per day—more if you are large in size or active, even in cooler climates. Football players, for example, might need four times as much fluid.[11]

Drink often and steadily throughout the day. Listen to your thirst, which is an early indicator of the need for fluids. However, thirst is not always an accurate indicator of need. If you are older, you might not as readily sense thirst, and busily engaged athletes might not notice thirst. Drink mostly water, which is calorie free, other beverages that are unsweetened or sweetened with calorie-free sweeteners, and low- or no-fat milk. Drink no more than a glass of fruit juice daily (instead eat whole fruit). Limit sugary soft drinks to one (or preferably none) per day. Watch the added calories from sports drinks. You probably don't need them unless you are training for endurance, in which case a little is okay.

Go Lean

Leanness, especially in the abdominal area, is associated with better cognitive function, greater brain volume,[12] less dementia, less secretion of stress hormones, and quicker recovery from stress. Conversely, obesity is linked to depression, impaired ability to feel satisfied after eating, fatigue, and a wide range of diseases. Being lean in our culture of overeating and inactivity is challenging, but achievable. The following guidelines can help:

1. *Focus on eating good food, not avoiding calories.* If you fill up on good food, you will feel satisfied and be less likely to overeat or fill up on empty calories.
2. *Keep goals realistic to stay motivated.* If you are overweight, even losing 5-10 pounds benefits health and performance in substantial ways. This can be done with small lifestyle changes.
3. *Eat a good breakfast.* Studies consistently show that breakfast eaters are leaner and perform better cognitively. A good breakfast includes:
    *   Protein, which prolongs fullness throughout the day. Good protein sources include low- or no-fat milk or yogurt,[13] egg whites, poultry, seafood, tofu, beans, nuts, peanut butter, and protein powder.
    *   Slowly digested carbohydrates, which maintain steady blood sugar levels. Instead of bagels, white bread, pastries, processed cereals (e.g. Cream of Wheat), English muffins, pancakes, or waffles, try oatmeal, barley, and other whole-grain cereals, whole wheat toast/pita, and whole fruits, especially berries. People who eat more refined grains and processed foods tend to have larger waists.
4. *Drink two glasses of water thirty minutes before eating.* This might promote fullness and result in fewer calories consumed.
5. *Avoid beverages sweetened with sugar or high fructose corn syrup.* Liquid calories don't fill as much as calories from solid food. Replacing a single 12-ounce serving of sweetened soda or fruit drink per day with water could result in the loss of over ten pounds per year.
6. *Savor food.* Eat very slowly, concentrating on flavors. Chewing and the passage of about twenty minutes send satiety signals to the brain. Enjoying food more prevents the tendency to eat more to gain satisfaction (see mindfulness in chapter 26).
7. *Begin meals with soup, salad, or fruit, which has been found to reduce caloric intake.* These are filling foods that are high in water weight (and usually fiber) relative to calories. Look for broth-based soups, such as vegetable soups, rather than creamy soups. On salads, avoid high-fat dressings, and limit fatty cheese, dried fruits, and croutons. Throughout the day, restrict foods low in water or high in fat, sugar, or refined flour. These include dried fruits, cheese, butter, crackers, pretzels, French fries, soda, jams, ice cream, cake, cookies, butter, fried chips, cookies, bacon, and other fatty meats. Favor foods such as vegetables, applesauce, legumes (including tofu and other soy products), no-fat dairy products, and cooked whole grains. Choose whole fruit over fruit juice.

8. *Remember the Okinawan principle of hara hachi bu.* Stop eating when you are 80% full.

9. *Keep a food diary.* This resulted in dramatic weight loss in 1685 overweight or obese patients at several clinical-research centers in the United States. Diary keeping was more effective at weight-loss than caloric restriction, group sessions, or exercise. Writing down what we eat helps us to be mindful of those extra calories. You might try keeping a diary on a notepad or note card that you carry with you, on your laptop, or on email or text messages to yourself.

10. *Graze.* Eating five or more smaller meals rather than two or three larger meals promotes weight loss. "Meals" can be snacks of fruits, vegetables with hummus, yogurt, or peanut butter on whole wheat bread. Stop eating several hours before bed. Consuming multiple smaller meals also tends to promote efficient brain function.

11. *Avoid starvation diets.* These adversely affect thinking and mood.

12. *Increase fitness with added exercise.* To lose weight or maintain weight loss, increase total exercise time to 60-90 minutes daily. Even housework or gardening contributes to exercise time and relieves mental stress.

13. *Replace saturated and trans fats with heart-healthy fats.* The fats in nuts, peanut butter, olive oil, and avocados can promote weight loss. Recall that the fiber, fat, and protein in nuts tend to satiate the appetite longer. Use moderation, though, since calories from fat can add up quickly.

14. *Eat out infrequently.* Fast or restaurant foods tend to be high in calories, salt, and unhealthy fats.

15. *Control stress.* The stress hormone cortisol increases the desire for sweet and high-fat foods. It also promotes the storage of abdominal fat. Belly fat, in turn, stimulates cortisol secretion—setting up a vicious cycle. The stress of extreme diets raises cortisol levels, as does rushed eating. So don't loose weight too quickly. Losing about a pound a week or less is a reasonable goal. Subsequent chapters will help you manage stress effectively.

Keep It Simple

Dietary recommendations converge on a few simple principles. The average person would greatly benefit by: 1) eating more plant foods (vegetables, fruits, whole grains, cooked dry beans/peas, and nuts), fish, and no- or low-fat dairy, 2) eating less unhealthy fat, sugar, and salt, and 3) restricting fatty meats, whole-fat dairy products, and processed foods. Table 3.2 on the next page explains what you need to eat for optimal health and performance, according to the U.S. dietary guidelines. Most people can use the second column for planning purposes. Make a week's menu that conforms to these guidelines. You might be surprised at how far your normal eating differs from them. If you wish to get more precise, go to www.ChooseMyPlate.gov to tailor an eating program that more closely meets your needs.

These guidelines are similar to the Mediterranean diet, which is linked to reduced cognitive impairment, Alzheimer's disease, and metabolic syndrome.[14] These guidelines also parallel the heart-healthy Okinawan and Dash diets. Okinawans also keep physically and mentally active.

Table 3.2   NUTRITIONAL NEEDS FOR PEOPLE 14 YEARS AND OLDER*

Food Group	How Much Is Needed Each Day	What Counts As….	Comments/ Provides
Fruits	1½ -2 Cups	**1 Cup** • In general, 1 C of fruit or 100% fruit juice • 1 large banana/orange/peach, 1 medium pear, or 1 small apple • ½ C dried fruit	• Provide fiber, energy, many vitamins, minerals, & phytochemicals that reduce risk of various diseases (e.g., potassium lowers risk of high blood pressure).
Vegetables	2-3 Cups	**1 Cup** • In general, 1 C of raw or cooked vegetables or vegetable juice, or 2 C of raw leafy greens • 1 C dry beans and peas (black, garbanzo, soybean/tofu, split peas, lentils, etc.). Count these here or in protein group, but not both.	• Seek a rainbow of colorful fruits & vegetables — green/red/ orange/yellow. • Several times a week include cruciferous vegetables, such as broccoli, cauliflower, cabbage, Brussels sprouts, kale, etc.
Grains	5-8 ounce-equivalents	**1 ounce–equivalent** • 1 slice bread or "mini" bagel • 1 C ready-to-eat cereal (check label) • ½ C cooked rice, pasta, cereal • 3 C popcorn, popped • 1 pancake (4½") or 1 small tortilla (6") • ½ English muffin	• At least half of servings should be *whole grains*, which reduce risk of heart and other diseases. Whole grains contain fiber, B vitamins, antioxidants, minerals, and various plant chemicals. Whole grains include oatmeal, whole wheat, bulgur, whole barley, popcorn, & brown or wild rice.
Protein	5-6½ ounce-equivalents	**1 ounce-equivalent** • 1 ounce of cooked fish, poultry, lean meats • 1 egg • 1/4 C cooked dry beans/peas or soy/tofu • 1 Tbsp peanut butter • ½ oz nuts or seeds	• Most or all days should include nuts, seeds, and/or cooked dry beans/peas (e.g., pinto beans, kidney beans, lentils, tofu or other soybean products). • ½ oz nuts = 12 almonds, 24 pistachios, or 7 walnut halves
Dairy	3 Cups	**1 Cup** • 1 C low-fat or fat-free milk, yogurt, or calcium-fortified soymilk • 1½ oz of low-fat or fat-free natural cheese, such as Swiss or cheddar • 2 oz of low-fat or fat-free processed cheese (American)	• Major source of calcium, potassium, protein, B vitamins, and other vitamins and minerals.
Oils	5-7 tsp equivalents allowance (not a food group)	**1 tsp** • 1 tsp vegetable oil • 1 tsp soft margarine • 1 tsp mayonnaise • 1 Tbsp salad dressing • ½ Tbsp peanut butter	• Provide needed unsaturated fatty acids and vitamin E. • Olive & canola oils are particularly beneficial. • Avoid trans/hydrogenated fats found in commercially made snacks, baked goods, stick margarine, & fried fast foods.
Empty Calories (mostly solid/satur-ated fats and/or added sugars)	Not needed or recommended. Try to limit to 10% of you total caloric intake or less. Many prefer to "spend" these calories on other food groups.	Calories in typical serving sizes: • 12 oz can of sweetened soft drink or fruit punch = 150 cal. • 1 slice cheesecake (1/8 of 9" cake)= 620 cal. • 1 Tbsp jelly/jam = 50 cal. • 12 oz light beer = 110 cal. • 2 oz. candy bar = 250 cal. • 1 C ice cream = 400 cal. • 1 oz corn chips = 152 cal. • Jelly donut = 290 cal.	

*Adapted from *USDA Dietary Guidelines for Americans 2010*. See www.ChooseMyPlate.gov. Except for dairy, amounts depend on age, sex, and level of physical activity. These figures assume you get less than 30 min./day of moderate activity beyond normal activity. For example, a younger male's needs would tend toward the higher figures.

Sleep

"Corn," as Henry David Thoreau observed, "grows in the night." So apparently does the brain. We are beginning to understand how sleep affects people. Most people need between 7 and 8 ¼ hours of sleep per night to feel and function at their best. Sleep refreshes and energizes the mind, and maintains brain function and metabolism. Sufficient sleep has been linked to resilience: greater creativity in problem solving, better performance on complex tasks, more enjoyment of the day's activities, and many other benefits. However, Americans are sleeping less than ever. In 1900, the average American logged over 9 hours of sleep per night. Today, that figure has shrunk to less than seven. What happens when people get too little sleep?

1. REM sleep is shortened. Normally, we cycle between Rapid Eye Movement (REM or dreaming) sleep and deep sleep four or five times each night. The duration of REM sleep periods increase as the night goes on. Short sleep, then, disproportionately shortchanges REM.[15] Why is this a problem? REM sleep:[16]
   - Helps the hippocampus consolidate newly acquired information, thus affecting our ability to remember and problem solve.
   - Seems to help to process and settle traumatic memories.[17]
   - Might help us remember and call up survival behaviors. For example, REM-deprived rats wander around recklessly, failing to protect themselves from threats, as they would normally do instinctively.
2. Sleep shortage is linked to weight gain—probably because it raises cortisol, alters two hunger hormones, and can make us too tired to exercise as much. Sleep shortage is also linked to early death, heart attacks, hypertension, diabetes, gum disease, and colds.
3. Sleep restriction is linked to decreased blood flow to the brain, depression, anxiety, suicide, poorer executive function and work performance (including accidents and mistakes), and, in animals, slower hippocampal neurogenesis and changes related to Alzheimer's disease.

In most studies, the harmful effects of sleep deprivation are pronounced for people getting six or fewer hours of sleep. However, one study found that cognitive performance for those who sleep less than eight hours was poorer compared to those getting more than eight hours.

The Army has, understandably, been interested in sleep's relationship to performance. As Patton noted, "Fatigue makes cowards of us all." Fatigue also impairs judgment and ethical self-restraint. Colonel Gregory Belenky, a researcher at Walter Reed Army Institute of Research, said, "There's nothing heroic about staying awake for long periods of time." In fact, sleep deprivation can cause missions to fail. Army research has found:
- Staff/planners are frequently the most sleep deprived. This is unfortunate because executive function is especially affected by sleep shortage.
- Sleep deprived soldiers might still perform simple motor tasks like shooting a stationary target acceptably. But they react slowly to pop-up targets, and fail to distinguish friend from foe in combat incidents.

- Artillery troops can indefinitely maintain high-level performance on 7-8 or more hours of sleep (see table below). However, performance falls steeply with increasing levels of sleep deprivation. For example, after twenty days of getting six hours of sleep per night, performance was only 50% of peak efficiency.

Hours Sleep Per Day	% of Peak Efficiency
7	87
6	50
5	28
4	15
0 (24 hours without sleep)	Legally drunk (.10)

- Troops in Iraq averaged 5.6 hours of sleep per night, sometimes staying up late to check email and play computer games to unwind. Among soldiers in Iraq and Afghanistan there was shown a direct relationship between sleep loss and mental health problems, including PTSD. Sleep deprived soldiers put their buddies at risk, so wise leaders will enforce a lights out policy.
- Naps of at least thirty minutes duration, provided there is quiet and darkness, partially offset the effects of sleep deprivation. (Longer naps work better than caffeine to boost physical and mental performance, even though those who take caffeine say they feel less sleepy than nappers). In terms of performance, we don't get used to sleep shortage.
- Nicotine does not offset sleep deprivation. Neither does caffeine, once tolerance is developed. Caffeine might be useful in the short term if it is used infrequently.

Tips for Good Sleep

1. *Get enough sleep.* If you need an alarm, wake up feeling tired, or need caffeine to wake up you probably need more sleep. Aim for eight hours a night. The extra sleep usually results in getting *more* accomplished the next day because it results in greater efficiency.
2. *Keep a regular sleep schedule.* Vary your go-to-bed and wake-up times by no more than an hour from night to night, even on weekends. A regular sleep schedule solidifies sleep rhythms and helps to prevent insomnia. If you have to stay up late, wake up at the usual time the next day to preserve sleep rhythms.
3. *Create a sleep-friendly environment.* Light, noise, and movement degrade sleep more than we realize. Try using eyeshades, dark window shades that keep out morning light, earplugs, or white noise. Block light from clocks or other light sources. Keep room temperature comfortably cool. Have pets sleep away from the bedroom. Use the bed only for sleep and intimacy. If possible, remove TV, computers, and anything else not associated with sleep from the bedroom. Use a comfortable mattress and pillow.
4. *Develop a relaxing routine.* Wind down with relaxing reading, music, prayer, writing in your journal, or structured relaxation (see chapters 5 and 6). Turn off the TV or computer, stop work and chores, and turn down the lights at least an

hour before going to bed. Even light from a computer screen can signal the brain to stay awake. A warm bath an hour or two before bed also aids sleep.

5. *Exercise.* Thirty minutes of daily aerobic exercise helps adults fall asleep sooner, sleep longer, and enjoy better quality sleep. Tai chi has been shown to improve sleep and daytime functioning. As a rule, avoid exercise within two hours of bedtime to reduce arousal. Early morning exercise in the sunlight can help regulate sleep rhythms.

6. *Avoid heavy meals and excessive liquid intake before bedtime.* Instead, try a light snack before bed, such as warm low- or no-fat milk with honey. Milk's tryptophan promotes sleep. The carbohydrate in honey helps the tryptophan enter the brain. Also, the protein in milk might help prevent awakening from low blood sugar, while calcium might reduce muscle cramps.[18] Other possible snacks include sweetened yogurt, a banana, walnuts, almonds, an egg, avocado, tuna, turkey, oats, or a cup of healthy cereal and milk.

7. *Challenge distressing thoughts that heighten arousal.* Such thoughts might include, "It's awful if I don't get a good night's sleep. I've got to get some sleep!" Sleep disruption is inconvenient, but we can live with it. And sleep typically improves when such distressing thoughts are eliminated. If you don't fall asleep within twenty minutes, simply get up and do something relaxing so that you don't pair the bedroom with wakefulness. Go back to bed when you feel sleepy.

8. *Limit or avoid:*
   • *Alcohol,* which makes you feel sleepy, but disrupts sleep quality and reduces REM sleep. Alcohol also worsens snoring and increases drowsiness the next day. Avoid it for at least two hours before bedtime.
   • *Caffeine* (found in coffee, tea, colas and other sodas, chocolate, and certain medications). A single cup of coffee can disturb sleep in those who are sensitive to caffeine. Try gradually cutting back to 1-2 cups of coffee or less, taken before midday.
   • *Nicotine.* The nicotine in smoking or chewing tobacco is a stimulant, which degrades sleep, while giving a sense of relaxation. Avoid it altogether, or for several hours before bedtime.

9. *Reduce.* Even losing five to ten pounds through exercise and healthy eating can reduce snoring and improve sleep quality.

10. *Consider regular naps.* About 60% of adults can successfully nap, meaning they feel and function better without interference with nighttime sleeping. Try it shortly after lunchtime in a cool, dark, quiet place. Most sleep experts suggest naps ranging from 20-120 minutes. There is no amount that works best for all, so experiment. If napping interferes with nighttime sleep, avoid it to consolidate sleep at night.

11. *Get off shift work.* On average, shift workers sleep less, have more sleep disturbances, and suffer more from a variety of mental and physical disorders. If you must work in shifts, shift forward—from morning, to evening, to night shifts. Stay on each shift for as many weeks as possible to help the brain regulate sleep rhythms. Also, use eyeshades and practice the other steps above to promote sufficient and good quality sleep.

12. *Seek professional help for conditions that interfere with sleep.* These include sleep apnea and other sleep disorders, mental disorders (such as depression,

anxiety, PTSD, and substance use disorders, which cause about half of all insomnia cases), thyroid conditions, heartburn, arthritis, diabetes, cardiovascular disease, hypertension, respiratory conditions, pain, and urinary problems (see chapter 4).

13. *Ask your doctor about side effects of drugs and medications.* These include cold and allergy medications, anti-diuretics, anti-depressants, anxiety medications (especially benzodiazepines[19]), anti-arrhythmia drugs, appetite suppressants and pain medications (these often contain caffeine), steroids, and stimulants.

14. *Try other steps before using sleeping pills.* Sleeping pills can be unpredictable, and sometimes risky. They can lead to tolerance and rebound insomnia when they are stopped. Cognitive-behavioral therapy, which involves the management of thoughts and sleep behaviors, is more effective than sleeping pills in the long (and sometimes short) run. If you and your doctor decide to try sleep medications, use the smallest effective dose and don't drink alcohol. If you feel groggy in the morning don't drive or use machinery. Set a goal to stop using sleep medication by addressing the underlying causes of troubled sleep.

Activity: Make a Plan

With a written plan you'll more likely stick to a regimen that optimizes brain health and performance. Try to make a plan that you can keep for life. Keep your goals realistic.

1. **Exercise.** Aim for at least thirty minutes of aerobic exercise all or nearly all days. You can also add strength and flexibility exercises. Work up to these goals gradually. Describe your plan below:

2. **Sleep.** I will commit to getting _____ hours of sleep per night (Aim for more than you think you need to get by. Can you set a goal of eight hours?), retiring at _____ p.m. each night and awakening at _____ a.m. throughout the week.

3. **Eating.** Ensure that you eat at least three meals daily (e.g., grazing on five smaller meals helps to regulate blood sugar and fat). Make a week's written menu that follows the guidelines previously discussed (i.e., mostly plant foods; good carbohydrates/fats; reduced sugar, salt, caffeine, processed foods; low- or no-fat dairy). Include everything you plan to eat and drink, including snacks. Check calories with an online calorie counter.

Forms at Appendix 6 can assist you in planning. They include a sheet to record a week of meals, and a sheet to track your first critical fourteen days.

Chapter 4

The Resilient Brain: Other New Findings

In this chapter we'll explore six areas that affect the functioning of the brain in important ways. These are substances, common medical conditions, medications, light, recreation and lifelong learning, and managing stress.

Substances

The single photon emission computed tomography, or SPECT, is a nuclear brain image that shows brain flow and activity levels in the brain. As such, SPECT reveals brain function, not anatomy. According to Daniel Amen, M.D., who has performed thousands of such studies, SPECT can reveal brain abnormalities years before reduction in brain volume is visible. A healthy, well functioning brain will appear smooth on the SPECT scan, as on the two center scans in Figure 4.1. Any drug, in excess, increases the harmful scalloping effects seen around the perimeter of Figure 4.1. Clockwise from top center, the scans show excesses in alcohol, marijuana, tobacco, inhalants, cocaine, and methamphetamine. We'll briefly mention the more common substances.

Figure 4.1
THE EFFECTS OF SUBSTANCES ON BRAIN FUNCTION

Reprinted by permission of Dr. Daniel Amen. www.AmenClinics.com. ©2005 Daniel G. Amen.

Alcohol

In excess, alcohol is toxic to neurons, reduces the growth of cells in the hippocampus, increases the risk of memory loss and dementia, and reduces resilience. In moderation, alcohol might reduce the risks of dementia and Type 2 diabetes. However, most drinkers indicate that they exceed the recommended limit of one drink per day for women or two for men. Dr. Amen reports that daily drinking is associated with smaller brain size. Excessive drinking is also associated with higher blood pressure, abdominal fat, and triglycerides. Having more than five drinks a day for men and four for women, even occasionally, is particularly risky. Abstinence stops the damage to neurons and probably reverses it. For brain function, it is better not to drink than to drink excessively. Harvard psychiatrist Dr. George Vaillant offers this simple test to see if drinking is a problem (Baylis, 2009, p.196). Ask yourself:

- Is alcohol causing problems in any areas of my life: work, social, personal, or physical?
- Does alcohol interfere with hobbies or other leisure pursuits?
- Does drinking interfere with my emotional development (e.g., does it stop me from facing and solving problems)?
- Does it seem to help me to be myself, or does it dilute my identity?
- Does it help me relax, or does it leave me feeling tired and irritable?
- Does it help me to socialize, or does it blur my interactions with others?
- Does alcohol improve my relationships or does it say, "I can't appreciate you when sober."

Smoking

Smoking tobacco impairs memory and cognitive functioning. It raises the yearly risk of cognitive decline, while also increasing the risk of dementia, high blood pressure, stroke, diabetes, and heart disease. Smoking greatly increases the risk of depression and anxiety, including panic attack. People with mental disorders are about twice as likely to smoke, and find it difficult to quit—in part because mental symptoms become more apparent after quitting. So if you are contemplating quitting, ensure that any existing mental disorders are being effectively treated.

Like tobacco smoking, smoking marijuana also decreases blood flow to the brain and impairs memory. Smoking tobacco or marijuana impairs our ability to grow after experiencing traumatic events.

Caffeine

Caffeine, like nicotine, is a stimulant that causes vasoconstriction in blood vessels supplying blood to the brain. Reduced blood flow to the brain impairs cognitive functioning. Caffeine is found in coffee, tea, cola and other caffeinated soft drinks, and some medications (check the label of weight loss aids, cold medications, and pain medications). Coffee is a mixed bag. Its high antioxidant content might protect against dementia and mild memory problems. Three cups or less daily appears safe. The stimulant effect on the brain also seems to work best when caffeine is used less frequently, thus preventing caffeine tolerance.

Medical Conditions

A number of medical conditions can directly affect brain function in harmful ways. We'll discuss some of the most common ones.

Sleep Apnea

About 10% of adults are affected by obstructive sleep apnea. In this condition, the airway becomes blocked as soft tissue collapses in the throat during sleep. It is characterized by loud snoring, the stoppage of breathing as the airway closes, and loud gasps for air as people partially awaken in order to breathe. This pattern of blocked breathing and partial awakening can be repeated scores of times throughout the night. The affected individual will awaken deprived of both sleep and oxygen. As a result, the person might experience fatigue, mental sluggishness, depression (20% of depressed people suffer from this condition), sexual disinterest, headaches, insomnia, and nightmares. In addition, apnea is a risk factor for high blood pressure, heart attacks, diabetes, and strokes. This condition is more prevalent in overweight, older males. Sleeping pills worsen the problem. Apnea is also common in people with PTSD; treatment often improves nightmares and other PTSD symptoms.

Fortunately, apnea is very treatable. Ask your doctor for an evaluation at a sleep center (see Appendix 9 for help in finding an accredited sleep center). The most common treatment is a device that pumps air into the airways at sufficient pressure to keep the airways open. (A continuous positive airway pressure, or CPAP, machine pumps air at a steady pressure through a mask that fits over the nose, and sometimes the mouth. Other devices adjust the pressure to make breathing somewhat easier.) Losing weight (sometimes only five or ten pounds) might help, as does limiting alcohol, sedatives, sleeping pills, and muscle relaxants. Surgery to remove, shrink, or stabilize excess tissue is sometimes tried. Devices that pull the tongue and jaw forward during sleep might help mild to moderate apnea. Antidepressants might slightly improve muscle tone in the airway, and might help mild apnea.

Elevated Cholesterol

Elevated cholesterol can put one at risk for depression. Lowering cholesterol levels through diet, exercise, and/or medication can often improve depression that is related to elevated cholesterol. Adding fiber through supplements like Metamucil can increase the effectiveness of statins, which are cholesterol-lowering medications. Statins might also help to prevent cognitive decline and dementia.

Thyroid Disorders

The thyroid gland sits like a bowtie on the neck below the Adam's apple. It secretes thyroxine, a hormone that affects cell functioning throughout the body—including neural functioning, heart rate, and respiratory rate. Even slight irregularities in thyroxine can cause symptoms that mimic a wide range of medical and psychological disorders. Either too much or too little thryroxine can interfere with memory and learning, perhaps by causing changes in the hippocampus.

Too little thyroxine (hypothyroid) is associated with depression, worsening of PTSD, fatigue, weight gain, high cholesterol, and sleep problems. Too much thyroxine can lead to confusion, anxiety (or anxious depression), insomnia, and weight loss.

The good news is that thyroid disorders are very effectively treated. The bad news is that more than 10% of adults have a thyroid disorder, mostly undiagnosed. Among those who are medicated for an under-active thyroid, more than a third are receiving improper doses.

Typical blood tests can measure levels of thyroxine in the blood. However, the inexpensive thyroid stimulating hormone (TSH) test is a more sensitive test. TSH is secreted by the pituitary gland in the brain. TSH causes the thyroid gland to secrete thyroxine. If, for example, thyroxine is in the low normal range, but TSH is elevated, this indicates that the brain is trying to stoke a sluggish thyroid. Elevated TSH is associated with decreased blood flow to the brain, especially in the pre-frontal cortex, as well as memory and concentration problems. Get a TSH test if there is any mental disorder, old-age memory loss, elevated cholesterol, or other unexplained symptoms. You might also suspect a thyroid problem if there appears to be swelling at the base of the neck (the thyroid can be enlarged in either thyroid condition), or if the eyes bulge. If you are taking thyroid medication, monitor TSH and thyroxine levels to ensure that the dosage is correct. Avoid smoking, which can interfere with thyroid functioning.

High Blood Pressure

Maintaining normal blood pressure might prevent or limit age-related cognitive decline and dementia. In addition to following the health practices already discussed for brain health, hypertension risks can be reduced by:

- *Reducing sodium intake.* The average American adults gets two to three times the recommended upper limit of 1500 mg of sodium per day (which amounts to 2/3 teaspoon of table salt). Sodium is found in processed foods, such as canned soup, pasta sauce, and many baked goods. For example, a bagel or a half-cup of cottage cheese has about 450 mg of sodium, twice the amount of a medium McDonald's French fries.
- *Reducing the use of oral contraceptives*
- *Increasing intake of potassium-rich foods.* These include: fruits such as orange juice, bananas, cantaloupe, prunes, raisins, avocados; vegetables such as tomatoes, spinach, winter squash, potatoes with skin; beans; dairy; and white meats.

Diabetes

Diabetes is associated with heightened risks for dementia, slower mental function, memory problems, and smaller hippocampi. Prevent Type 2 diabetes by following the guidelines in this and the previous chapter. Should you have diabetes, keep in under the best control possible through proper treatment and blood sugar monitoring.

Gum Disease

There does appear to be a mind/mouth connection. Poor oral health can lead to gum disease and the release of toxins into the bloodstream. These toxins might increase the risk not only of cardiovascular disease and diabetes, but also Alzheimer's disease. So brush and floss each day, and treat gum disease—especially if you notice blood when brushing or flossing. Consuming just a quarter cup of yogurt containing live bacteria (such as Lactobacillus) might reduce the risk of gum disease. And don't smoke tobacco or marijuana. The toxins in smoke hinder the body's ability to fight inflammation.

Medications

Acetylcholine is a chemical that enables neuron-to-neuron message transmission. Anti-cholinergic medications block the action of acetylcholine and can interfere with cognitive functioning. Medications with anti-cholinergic effects include antihistamines, tranquilizers (such as benzodiazepines), sleeping pills, Tagamet, Zantac, and tricyclic antidepressants. Ask your doctor or pharmacist if your medications have anti-cholinergic effects. Try to take such medications no longer than needed and ask if alternative medications could be used. Conversely, most of the newer selective serotonin reuptake inhibitors used to treat depression appear to increase hippocampal neurogenesis—as do other treatments for depression, including cognitive therapy and exercise.

Light

Up to an hour of light therapy might help to reduce both seasonal and year-round depression. Light therapy usually consists of sitting in front of a light box whose brightness equals that of a window on a spring morning. Preliminary research suggests that bright light might also improve cognitive performance. Exposure to sunlight can be increased through exercising outdoors in the daytime, opening curtains, trimming bushes by windows, and installing skylights. You might also try sitting in front of a light box in the morning for 30-60 minutes, perhaps while reading.

Recreation & Lifelong Learning

Recreation and lifelong learning improve brain health. Recreation helps us to reduce stress and to improve energy and mood levels. Lifelong learning helps to build neural pathways that improve cognitive function and adaptability under stress. People who are mentally and socially active are less likely to develop mild cognitive impairment or dementia. Look for enjoyable activities that pleasantly engage your attention and require concentration. The more activities you try and the earlier in life that you start, the better. You might consider:

- *Music.* Listen to it, play an instrument (or learn a new one), sing, or create it. Choose the type of music you enjoy most.
- *Reading.* Try favorite topics or a new adventure. Book clubs or other discussion groups elicit mental and social engagement.
- *Taking a class related to a new interest*

- *Board or card games*
- *Puzzles*
- *Cooking*
- *Exploring*
- *A new fix-up or decorating project at home*
- *Hobbies*
- *Computer games*
- *Ping pong*

Managing Stress

Managing stress helps to reduce stress hormones that are harmful to the brain and promote weight gain. The rest of this book will help you to master coping tools that will help you to handle stress confidently. In addition, use organization techniques to help you remember. These include: designating spots for frequently used items, such as keys; having a calendar and To-Do list; making lists for contact information and vital or easily-forgotten information, such as birthdays, gifts and sizes, goals, recreation ideas, things to buy, etc.; and having a file or retrieval system.

Table 4.1 below might help you remember the steps toward optimizing brain functioning that have been discussed in this and the previous chapter.

Table 4.1
THE RESILIENT BRAIN: STEPS TO OPTIMIZE COGNITIVE FUNCTION & PROTECT AGAINST DEMENTIA[1]

Healthy behaviors prepare the brain for learning. Learning then grows and strengthens new adaptive neural pathways.

1. ***Exercise***. Morning exercise is associated with maintaining an exercise program and regulating sleep cycles. Exercise before difficult learning or brainstorming activities.
2. ***Engage in lifelong learning to keep brain circuits sharp*** (e.g., hobbies, classes, music).
3. ***Don't smoke or use drugs. Minimize caffeine.***
4. ***Moderate drinking***. No drinking is better than excessive drinking; most drinkers drink excessively/binge.
5. ***Healthy diet***.
   - Avoid caloric excess; maintain normal weight. Include protein at breakfast to feel fuller throughout the day. Eating six smaller meals lowers cholesterol (e.g., between meals try veggies with hummus, yogurt, a tablespoon of peanut butter).
   - Choose good carbs (whole grains, beans, vegetables, fruits), good protein (fish, lean meat, nuts, beans, eggs), and good fats (in fish, olive or canola oil, nuts, seeds, avocados).
   - Eat many colorful vegetables (e.g., dark green) and fruits, and whole grains. Remember apples, which especially reduce the risk of metabolic syndrome.
   - Drink much water (the brain is 80% water).

- Eat high water volume/fiber foods (fruits, vegetables, soups, whole grains, cooked dry beans, low-fat dairy).
- Spare fatty meats, fried foods, cheese, pretzels, chips, cookies, dried fruit, and processed foods.
- Eat spices, which are rich in antioxidants that reduce the inflammation associated with a range of chronic diseases. Think cloves, cinnamon, allspice, saffron, fennel, oregano, cumin, garlic, rosemary, turmeric (a component of curry), basil, ginger, red and black pepper, etc.

6. ***Take a good quality multivitamin supplement.***
7. ***Get consistent, sufficient sleep.*** Aids include: morning exercise, avoidance of caffeine, no or sparing use of sleeping pills, and warm milk (tryptophan) and honey before bed. Poor sleep is associated with smaller hippocampi, diabetes, weight gain, high blood pressure, periodontal disease, and impaired mood and cognitive function.
8. ***Socialize.*** Get away from the computer and digital games. Relationships that nurture change the brain.
9. ***Protect the brain from head trauma*** (use seat belts, helmets for biking/skiing, mouth guards for contact sports; avoid cage fighting/boxing) ***and toxins*** (tobacco smoke, lead, mercury, carbon monoxide, paints, dyes, inks, solvents, pesticides, PCBs, car exhaust, glues, preservatives).
10. ***Treat medical conditions.*** Especially thyroid disorders, diabetes, depression, anxiety, post-traumatic stress disorder, high cholesterol, obesity, gum disease, high blood pressure, and apnea. Statins protect against cognitive decline.
11. ***Organize.*** Keep written time management plans (goals, calendar, to-do's) and lists of important information. Refer to these and revise often.
12. ***Keep belly fat down.*** Stay lean by exercising, getting enough sleep, and eating in a healthy way.
13. ***Maintain healthy gums.*** Gum disease is a risk for diabetes, Alzheimer's, and heart disease. Brush, floss, and eat small amounts of yogurt daily (1/4 C).
14. ***Small amounts of dark chocolate or cocoa increase blood flow to the brain.***
15. ***Get some sun or use bright lights (phototherapy) daily.*** This can improve mood and cognition.
16. ***Manage stress.***

Activity

After reviewing this chapter, make a written list of any of the factors that might be impairing your ability to function at your best. Consider:
- Unhealthy substance use
- The need for a physical exam to rule out or treat medical conditions
- The need to get sufficient sunlight (or high-intensity artificial light)
- Recreation and lifelong learning
- Getting organized. Have a system for recording and retrieving important information—such as a file cabinet, file folders, shelves, and labeled boxes.

Then indicate steps you plan to take to address these factors.

PART III

CALMING SKILLS

Chapter 5

Basic Calming Skills

This chapter introduces skills that help us be calm under pressure. Calming skills, as do all the skills in resilience training, rest upon the relationship depicted in the diagram below. The mind and body affect each other for good and bad. So a calm body tends to calm the mind, while an overly aroused body tends to overexcite the mind. Conversely, one's thinking can either calm or arouse the body.

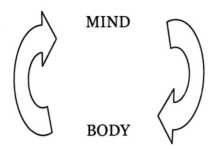

MIND

BODY

Have you ever noticed what your body does when you sit at a computer? It is estimated that 95% of people tense their muscles, particularly around the shoulders. This often leads to subtle shifts in breathing and thinking patterns that can significantly impair performance. If these changes in mind and body result from simply sitting at a computer, can you imagine what can happen during a crisis? Whether sitting at a computer or navigating a crisis, the objective is to calm breathing, reduce muscle tension, and control disruptive thoughts.

Only 10-20% of people stay calm during emergencies (Gonzales, 2003). Excessive arousal not only impairs our ability to think and perform under pressure, but it can result in mental illness. Psychologist Thomas Marra (2005) has described the diseases of arousal, which include anxiety, depression, excessive anger, and substance use disorders. These acute mental disorders share the following characteristics of high arousal and reactivity:

- *Physical.* Muscle tension, short and rapid breathing, increased heart rate and perspiration
- *Mental.* Negative and pessimistic thoughts, including worry, which hinders a person's ability to calm down
- *Emotional.* Heightened intensity of strong feelings

The goal for preventing and recovering from these disorders is to learn how to calm excessive physical, mental, and emotional arousal and reactivity. Resilient survivors have a variety of tools to do so.

Heart Rate and Performance

The normal resting heart rate is about 70 beats per minute (bpm). This heart rate increases with stress. An instructor at the police academy in St. Louis, Bruce Siddle, notes that in combat situations (Grossman, 2004):

- 115-145 bpm on average is optimal for vision, reaction time, and the performance of complex motor skills. However fine motor skills begin to deteriorate at 115 bpm.
- Beyond 145 bpm performance deteriorates significantly. As part of the stress response, blood is shunted to the body's core. As a result:
  - Complex motor skills deteriorate
  - Hands become clumsy
  - Blood drains from the face
  - The voice shakes
  - Vision deteriorates (loss of near vision and depth perception; tunnel vision), as does hearing (e.g., some sounds are not heard)
  - Decision making becomes irrational (e.g., a cop fires at everything, or throws away his gun and charges an armed perpetrator as strength increases for a few seconds before falling off sharply)
  - Freezing can occur
  - Some memory loss can occur afterwards, along with exhaustion, nausea, and/or dizziness

With training we can condition our mind and bodies to keep our heart rate within optimal limits—and even bring it lower when fine motor skills are needed. One way to do so is to practice calm breathing and systematic relaxation. A second method is to gain control over negative, worrisome thoughts. We'll explore calming breathing and systematic relaxation in this chapter, other effective relaxation techniques in the next chapter, and the control of negative, arousing thoughts in chapter 7. (Another way to regulate heart rate is to condition the cardiovascular system through aerobic exercise. Exercise doesn't involve fear and loss of control, and thus does not lead to most of the harmful effects noted above.)

Calm Breathing

The U.S. Army (Department of the Army, 2003) recommends that all individuals learn at least two relaxation techniques, including a quick one for pressure situations. Calm breathing is one very effective strategy for pressure situations. When under pressure, the adage is, "Stop, breathe, look around, think." Breath control has been a standard tool for warriors and other high-risk professionals, martial arts, Lamaze birthing, and meditation practices for many years. As breathing calms, the ability to think, remember, and perform effectively improves.

Under stress, breathing often becomes rapid and shallow as we tighten muscles in the throat, chest, and abdomen in preparation for fight or flight. Even subtle shifts in breathing can result in less oxygen reaching the brain, heart, and extremities—and a shift in blood acidity. Among the scores of possible resulting symptoms are: racing heart, elevated blood pressure, panic attacks, dizziness, unsteadiness, visual disturbance, headaches, shortness of breath, muscle tension and cramps, weakness, unreal feelings, catastrophic thinking, exhaustion, nightmares, and impaired concentration, memory and performance. Symptoms can worsen if we remain immobile while under stress, say while sitting in traffic, watching TV, or working at a computer.

Although there are several variations, the basic calming breath is very simple:

1. First, select a calming word or phrase, such as "relax," "calm," or "easy does it." As you practice pairing the calming word or phrase with calm breathing, both the word or phrase and the calm breathing will elicit relaxation.
2. To begin, sit in the "meditator's posture," with feet flat on the floor with your back comfortably erect, supported by the chair. Take a moment to consciously relax the muscles of your mouth, jaw, throat, shoulders, chest, and abdomen. Place your hands over your navel. Breathe naturally. On the in-breath notice your hands rising, as if you were filling a balloon in your belly. On the out-breath your hands fall as the imaginary balloon deflates. Keep your chest and shoulders relaxed and still. Once you are breathing abdominally (low and rhythmically), allow your eyes to close. Simply closing one's eyes and attending to breathing is usually very calming. (Keep your eyes open if closing the eyes is uncomfortable or unsafe for any reason.)
3. Take two continuous, smooth, slightly deeper calming breaths—filling, as it were, the imaginary balloon in your abdomen as you breathe in, and deflating the balloon as you breathe out. Say the calming word or phrase as you breathe in and as you breathe out. This is an easy, gentle breath, with no gasping or abrupt movements. Ensure that your upper body is still and that only the abdominal area moves with the breathing.
4. After completing the two calming breaths, breathe normally for a few seconds before opening your eyes.

Activity

With practice, calm breathing becomes more effective. Calm breathing is also the first step in more structured relaxation strategies that we'll explore later. For this activity, practice two deeper calming breaths seven times a day: upon awakening, before going to sleep, before meals, and at other times of your choosing. (Initially it is best to practice when you are not stressed. Then you can practice during slightly stressful times. After gaining confidence with this skill, you can try it during times of great stress.) It will take you less than thirty seconds to practice two calming breaths.

Keep a log for seven days, recording the effectiveness of each practice, ideally right after you complete the two calming breaths. A log can reveal patterns (e.g., at what time of the day calm breaths seem to work best) and can motivate you as improvement is noted. Rate physical and emotional effectiveness on a 1-10 scale, where 0 = no effect, 5 = somewhat relaxing, and 10 = very relaxing. The log would begin like this (allow for forty-nine entries):

7-Day Calm Breathing Log

Date	Time	Situation	Effectiveness	
			Physical	Emotional

Combat (or Tactical) Breathing

Combat (or tactical) breathing is a variation of calm breathing that has been taught to and successfully utilized by many high risk professionals, including elite military special operations and law enforcement units. This variation includes counting, which helps keep the mind focused under stress. The instructions are (Grossman, 2004):

1. Relax your shoulders and upper body.
2. Breathe in through the nose for the count of four, expanding your belly.
3. Hold the breath for a count of four.
4. Breathe out through the lips for the count of four.
5. Hold for the count the four.
6. Repeat steps 1-4 about three times.

The more you practice the better you get at staying calm under pressure, as these stories relate:

- A SWAT team member took one deep breath before popping up and hitting a dangerous, armed criminal. He said it was *practicing* combat breathing over the years that enabled him to breathe calmly under pressure (Grossman, 2009).
- Police officer Keith Nelson Borders was shot ten times in six shoot-outs in Oklahoma and Nevada over an eleven-year period. Each time, he breathed deeply and calmly. "It keeps you very calm. You don't start to hyperventilate or panic...You say, OK, here's what's going on, I can handle this. I got shot in the head, and I'm still alive, things are working, so it's not that bad" (Ripley, 2008, p.78).
- Charles Humes, a Toledo, Ohio, police officer, became dangerously aroused during high-speed chases, when he experienced tunnel vision and his voice would raise several octaves and become unintelligible over the radio. Every day he played a tape recording of a siren as he practiced tactical breathing. Soon the siren became a cue to relax. After a month his voice was noticeably calmer and he was more under control when he radioed from his patrol car during a pursuit (Ripley, 2008).

Activity

Practice combat breathing and keep a log for a seven-day period. If it is effective, continue to practice it at least once a day.

Progressive Muscle Relaxation

Dr. Edmund Jacobson, the originator of progressive muscle relaxation (PMR), demonstrated that when people relaxed their muscles they became mentally calmer. He found, however, that attempts were only partially effective when people consciously tried to relax their muscles. Paradoxically, people can relax more deeply when they first tense their muscles. The brain senses increased tension and responds by triggering the relaxation response.

      PMR is a very active relaxation strategy that is effective fairly quickly for nearly everyone who tries it. In PMR you'll tense various muscle groups, then relax them, paying close attention to the difference between tension and relaxation. As you progress from the feet to the head, your body becomes more and more relaxed. With practice the nervous system becomes increasingly calmer, and the brain becomes better at recognizing and reducing arousal. Try it once or twice a day for about twenty minutes per session and see if cognitive functioning improves. Done before bedtime, PMR is a very effective treatment for insomnia.

Progressive Muscle Relaxation Instructions

Read through these instructions before practicing PMR. You might then wish to follow the summary instructions, audio-record these instructions, or have someone else read them to you.

Prepare by getting comfortable. You might remove glasses, contact lenses, and/or shoes. Loosen any tight clothing, such as belts or collars. Lie down in a comfortable place, with your arms at your sides. For comfort, you might wish to place pillows under your knees, the small of the back, and/or your head. (You can also do PMR in a seated position, with obvious adaptations of the instructions.) Stay alert and avoid sleeping as you practice (unless, of course, you are practicing this in bed with the intent to fall asleep). Starting with the feet, we will progressively tense, and then deeply relax, the major muscle groups of the body. It is important to fully concentrate on each muscle group—first on the sensation of tension, and then on the state of relaxation. This trains the brain to distinguish the two contrasting states and elicit the relaxed state. Tense relatively hard for about 5-10 seconds, but always stop short of discomfort or cramps. Then relax each muscle group for at least ten seconds.

1. *To begin, close your eyes, if that is comfortable, and breathe abdominally.* Allow the soothing rhythm of the breath to relax you. Take two deeper calming breaths, saying your calming word or phrase slowly as you breathe in, and as you breathe out. Then return to the gentle rhythm of quiet, normal abdominal breathing. Be aware of your body for a moment. Simply notice any areas of tension in the body, and any areas that feel relaxed

2. *Point both of your feet and toes away from the head at the same time, leaving the legs relaxed.* Notice the tension in the calves and the bottoms of the feet. Form a clear mental picture of this tension. Now relax all at once. Feel the relaxation in those same areas. When muscles relax, they elongate, and blood flow through them increases. So you might feel warmth or tingling in areas of your body that you relax. Pay close attention to the feelings of relaxation in those muscles that you previously tensed.

3. *Now bend your feet at the ankles so that the toes move toward your head.* Observe the tension in the muscles below the knee, along the outside of the shins. Now relax all at once and study the difference as those muscles fully relax and warm up.

4. *Next, tense the quadriceps muscles on the front of the leg above the knee by straightening your leg and locking your knees.* Leave your feet relaxed. Concentrate on the pulling in these muscles. Notice it clearly in your mind. And

relax. Sense your quadriceps as you relax. Feel them softening and warming, as though they are melting.

5. *Tense the back of your legs.* Imagine now that you are lying on your back on a beach blanket and you press the back of your heels against the sand, with your toes pointing toward the sky. Keep your feet relaxed. Sense the tension along the backs of the entire legs. Now relax and pay attention to the experience of those muscles loosening and relaxing.

6. *Squeeze the buttocks or seat muscles together while contracting your pelvis muscles.* Keep your stomach relaxed as you do this. Notice the tension in these muscles. Then relax and observe what relaxation in those muscles is like—perhaps a pleasant warm and heavy feeling.

7. *Tense your stomach muscles.* Imagine that your stomach is a ball that you are squeezing into a tiny ball and pulling back toward the spine. Sense the tension there and notice how tensing these muscles interferes with breathing. Now relax. Let the abdomen warm up and loosen up, freeing your body to breathe in the easiest, most calming way. Continue to breathe abdominally as you progress.

8. *Tense your back muscles.* Leave your shoulders and buttocks down on the surface as you gently and slowly arch your back. As you do, pull your chest up and toward your chin. Notice the tension in the back muscles along both sides of the spine. Then gently and slowly relax as your back sinks down, feeling very warm, relaxed, and supported. Pay close attention to the feelings of relaxation in those muscles.

9. *Shrug your shoulders.* Pull them up toward your ears and sense the tension above the collarbones and between the shoulder blades, where many headaches originate. Now deeply relax those muscles, paying close attention to what that feels like.

10. *Tense the muscles in the forearms.* With arms at your sides, place your palms down on the surface. Pull your relaxed hands back at the wrists so that the knuckles move back toward your head. Sense the tension on the top of the forearms. Relax all at once, and study the feelings of relaxation there.

11. *Tighten the fists and biceps.* Make tight fists and draw them up toward the shoulders as if curling weights. Study the tension in the fists, forearms, and biceps. Relax, letting your arms fall back to your sides, and notice closely the feelings as those muscles go loose. You might pause here to scan your body and notice how good it feels to give your muscles a break. Allow your entire body to remain relaxed as you move on.

12. *Tense the neck muscles.* Very, very slowly, turn your head to the right as if looking over your right shoulder. Feel the tension on the right side of the neck pulling your head around. Stop rotating before it becomes uncomfortable, and hold the tension for a while to observe it. Then turn back very slowly to the front and notice the difference as the muscles on the right side of your neck relax. Turn just as slowly to the left and sense the muscles on the left side of your neck contract. Rotating slowly back to the front, sense the left side relaxing.

13. *Tense the muscles at the base of the skull.* Press the back of your head gently against the surface you are lying on, while raising the chin toward the ceiling. Sense tension at the base of the skull, where the skull meets the neck. Much headache pain originates here, as well. However, just as we can create tension there, we can also let it go completely. Sense the tension. Then relax and allow those muscles to warm up and elongate, even more than they are now.

14. *Tense the forehead muscles.* Lift your eyebrows up and furrow your brow. Feel the tension across the forehead. Relax. Feel the forehead becoming as smooth as the surface of a pond on a calm and still summer's evening.

15. *Tense the chin and neck muscles.* Frown, pulling the corners of the mouth down as far as they'll go. Feel the tension on the sides of the chin and neck. Now relax, and notice how those muscles feel when they rest.

16. *Tense the jaw muscles.* Grit your teeth and sense the tension that you created from the angle of the jaw all the way up to the temples. Now deeply relax those muscles. Relax the tongue and let the teeth part slightly. Enjoy the satisfying feeling of creating relaxation in those same muscles that had been tense.

17. *Tense the muscles around the cheekbones.* Make a wide, open smile. Grin ear to ear, perhaps thinking of an amusing or pleasant moment. Observe the muscles around the cheekbone contracting. Now relax and let all the muscles of the face now be smooth and placid. Just notice that feeling for a few moments.

Allow a pleasant sense of relaxation to surround your body. Imagine that you are floating well supported on a favorite couch, bed, or raft—all your muscles pleasantly relaxed. When you are ready to end this session, count slowly to five, send energy to your limbs, stretch, sit up slowly, and move your limbs before standing slowly.

Activities

- Practice progressive muscle relaxation once or twice a day for at least one week. Many find it even more effective to tense each muscle group twice. Record your progress on the Relaxation Record on the next page.

- Throughout the day, try to become increasingly aware of tension in various parts of your body as it first arises, and cause those muscles to relax. Consciously relax your body as you are walking, working, driving, or talking to people. Notice how this affects your mood. Alternatively, when you want to calm down, tense an isolated muscle group and relax as you breathe out.

- One way to relax the body is through Qi Gong. Try this exercise. Sit down and concentrate. Now lift your arm straight up and notice what that feels like. Many say it feels very abrupt, almost violent. Now move your hand back to your side. Imagine that a string attached to your wrist gently raises your relaxed hand, and then gently lowers it. Notice how different that feels. Try this again, breathing in as you gently raise the hand, and breathe out as you lower it, paying attention to how this feels. Repeat this, this time saying, "I'm a really nice person and this is a fun place to be." This movement helps to relax the body, which is beneficial because relaxed muscles will move more quickly when called upon. The pleasant message also helps to calm the mind and keep it more open to mental demands.

RELAXATION RECORD

BODY:
Physical

Very Relaxed   Very Tense

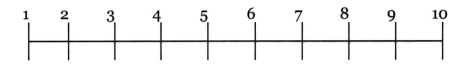

1   2   3   4   5   6   7   8   9   10

MIND:
Emotions

Very Calm   Very Anxious

DAY/ DATE	TIME OF DAY	LENGTH OF TIME	PHYSICAL before after		MENTAL/EMOT. before after		COMMENTS

Chapter 6

Other Calming Skills

This chapter adds two calming skills to your coping repertoire. Each takes about one to two minutes. The first, centering, is effective in its own right. It also prepares us for the powerful heart coherence skill that follows.

Centering

Centering effectively relaxes the body and mind in about two minutes. This strategy grounds in the body, helping us to get underneath racing thoughts, clear the mind, and gather useful energy. These instructions are adapted from *Emotional Intelligence in Action* (Hughes, Patterson, & Bradford, 2005)[1]:

1. Sitting, cross your left ankle over your right.
2. Extend your arms in front of you. Cross your left wrist over your right wrist and interlace your fingers.
3. Inhaling, draw your hands up toward chest. Rest your hands over your chest and rest your arms against your body.
4. Close your eyes. Exhale. Relax you shoulders. Feel your hands and arms resting against your body. Breathe abdominally, relaxing deeply, for a minute. Rest your mind, as it were, in your body—settling beneath your whirling thoughts, and grounding in your body.
5. When you are ready, uncross your legs. Touch your fingertips together. Breathe deeply for another minute.

Heart Coherence[2]

It has long been known that holding pleasant images in mind reduces physical arousal. However, what has not been as well established, until recently, is that calming the heart has profound effects on the mind and the rest of the body. New computer technology has enabled researchers, primarily at the Institute of HeartMath in Boulder Creek, California, to demonstrate the importance of heart coherence and the heart coherence skill that helps individuals be grounded and centered in the heart. The heart coherence skill rests on three premises:

1. *We experience emotions in our body, not our head.* Think of the ways we experience emotions in the *gut* (we say that an experience is gut wrenching; we sense a knot in the stomach; we are sick to the stomach; "I spilled my guts"; "My stomach flipped"), the *throat* ("There's a lump in my throat"; "I'm choked up"), or the *heart* ("I am broken hearted"; "My heart is down"; "He is cold-hearted"). The heart coherence skill focuses on experiencing *positive* emotions in the heart—as in warm- or tender-hearted, heartfelt, a heart full of love, or heartfelt appreciation.
2. *There is more communication from the heart to the brain than from the brain to the heart.* The heart communicates to other parts of the body via powerful neural, biochemical, biophysical (blood pressure), and energetic (electromagnetic)

messages. For example, the electrical field of the heart is fifty times stronger than that of the brain and the heart's magnetic field is 5000 times stronger than that of the brain. The electromagnetic field generated by the heart can be measured several feet away from a person and can influence the physical and emotional states of individuals nearby.

3. *Changing the heart changes the brain more than changing the brain changes the brain.* In other words, calming the heart very effectively calms the brain and the entire body.

What Is Heart Coherence?

While having a lower heart rate is linked to health and performance under pressure, heart coherence might be even more important. It is possible to record beat-to-beat changes in heart rate.[3] Heart coherence reflects the heart's ability to adjust speeds smoothly, flexibly, and quickly. Notice Figure 6.1 below, which depicts a coherent heart on the left, and a more chaotic heart on the right. Although both hearts have the same average resting heart rate of 70 beats per minute, the pattern on the left shows a balance between the two branches of the nervous system responsible for increasing and decreasing arousal. This heart speeds up and slows down with smooth regularity. Think of a finely conditioned basketball player who seems to effortlessly accelerate and slow down as the situation requires and you get a sense of heart coherence.

Figure 6.1
HEART COHERENCE vs. HEART INCOHERENCE (Childre & Rozman, 2003, p.21, adapted with permission)

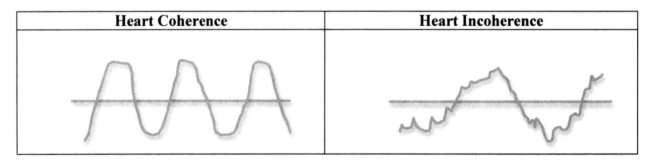

Heart Coherence	Heart Incoherence

Why Is Heart Coherence Important?

Heart coherence is linked to a wide range of benefits. Briefly summarized, the benefits are:

1. *Better mental health*: Heart coherence is associated with less depression, anxiety (including panic attacks and PTSD), anger, and stress. Dissociation is a particularly troubling symptom of PTSD, whereby one's mind tends to separate from the body. Heart coherence appears to help people reconnect the mind to the body by grounding in the body (see chapter 32 for more on dissociation). Heart coherence is also linked to greater general well-being and reduced employee turnover.

2. *Better medical health.* Heart coherence is associated with less hypertension, pain, chronic fatigue, metabolic syndrome, exhaustion, sleeplessness, migraines, fibromyalgia, diabetes, pre-menstrual disorder, and heart disease, and lower cholesterol, cortisol and weight levels.

3. *Better functioning.* Just as heart health equals brain health, so is heart flexibility linked to brain flexibility. Heart coherence is linked to improved listening ability, productivity, learning, thinking, and concentration.

It has been demonstrated that heart coherence can be improved through training within weeks to months, with many beneficial results.[4] Even people who may not be able to express emotions verbally can cut through mental constructions, notice what their heart is feeling, and calm it.[5]

The basic principle of the heart coherence strategy that follows is that any positive emotion experienced in the heart calms and synchronizes the heart, brain, and gut into coherent rhythms.

The Quick Coherence® Technique

This basic heart coherence technique only takes a minute, but has powerful effects. Here are the instructions (Childre & Rozman, 2005, pp.44-45):

1. *Heart focus.* Focus your attention in the area of your heart. If this sounds confusing, try this: Focus on our right big toe and wiggle it. Now focus on your right elbow. Now gently focus in the center of your chest, the area of your heart. (Most people think the heart is on the left side of the chest, but it's really closer to the center, behind the breastbone.) If you like, you can put your hand over your heart to help. If your mind wanders, just keep shifting your attention back to the area of your heart. Now you're ready for the next step, Heart Breathing.

2. *Heart Breathing.* As you focus on the area of your heart, imagine your breath is flowing in and out through that area. This helps your mind and energy to stay focused in the heart area and your respiration and heart rhythms to synchronize. Breathe slowly and gently in through your heart (to a count of five or six) and slowly and easily out through your heart (to a count of five or six). Do this until your breathing feels smooth and balanced, not forced. You may discover that it's easier to find a slow and easy rhythm by counting "one thousand, two thousand," rather than "one, two." Continue to breathe with ease until you find a natural inner rhythm that feels good to you.

3. *Heart feeling.* Continue to breathe through the area of your heart. As you do so, recall a positive feeling, a time when you felt good inside, and try to re-experience it. This could be a feeling of appreciation or care toward a special person or a pet, a place you enjoy, or an activity that was fun. Allow yourself to feel this good feeling of appreciation or care. If you can't feel anything, it's okay; just try to find a sincere attitude of appreciation or care. Once you've found a positive feeling or attitude, you can sustain it by continuing your Heart Focus, Heart Breathing, and Heart Feeling. It's that simple.

Some Tips for Heart Coherence

If there is time, or when first learning the heart coherence skill, it can be useful to do the following to prepare. Find a relaxing, comfortable place where you'll make three written lists.

1. *List the people you love most:*
   - First, think of the person you love best. Why do you love that person? How does he or she make you feel?
   - Then make a list of your favorite people, people who have made you feel loved, like a somebody. People, perhaps, in whose presence you felt safe, secure, or appreciated. Think of loved ones, friends, or even pets.

2. *Then make a list of experiences you've appreciated,* experiences that made you feel happy, content, peaceful, satisfied, or glad to be alive. You might recall moments in nature, such as a sunset at the beach, being on a mountaintop, or a picnic in a meadow. Perhaps you recall a meal with close friends or family, or a feeling of accomplishment for something you did. You might remember holding a child as she sleeps or nurses, or taking a vacation.

3. *Now make a list of moments where you felt caring, tenderness, respect, or compassion for someone.* Perhaps a loved one comes to mind, or someone in need.

4. *Pick one of these memories,* one that is relatively free of negative emotions, to use in the Quick Coherence® technique. If you can, try to remember an experience of genuine love. Love is usually the fastest way to heart coherence. Here we are referring to heartfelt, mature love, not fleeting infatuation. Loving takes courage, and courage springs from the heart. In fact, the word *courage* derives from Latin and French words for heart (Childre & Rozman, 2005). Love is at the heart of bravery and integrity. Courageous people are motivated by love—of freedom, country, family, comrades, or self. For example, Audie Murphy, the most decorated soldier in WWII, was asked how he had been able to be so courageous. He replied that the enemy was "killing my friends." In a Vietnamese prison, John McCain had the courage to resist his torturers because his first concern was not to fail his friends. It takes courage to open one's heart to feelings, but the returns are great.

   If you don't choose to work with love, another positive emotion such as appreciation, peace, contentment, quiet calmness, or wonder also works well.

5. *Take a time out.* You might use two calming breaths or the centering skill to calm down before starting.

Practice this skill for at least a week, at least five times a day: when you wake up, when you retire, and three more times. Try it initially when you are calm. Later, try it when you need a time out to recharge, calm down, think more clearly or less negatively, or comfort yourself. You can use it before, during, or after a stressful situation. Or try it when you want to perform well or be creative.

Heart coherence is contagious. Thus, the hearts of the mother and her baby tend to synchronize. Try this skill with co-workers or family members with whom you want to be in sync, such as before undertaking a difficult challenge or working on a task where creativity is needed. Keep a log of its effectiveness.

Visit the HeartMath website (see Appendix 9). If you have the means, you might purchase technology that enables you to monitor your heart rhythms on your computer or a handheld device. Seeing your heart coherence increase can be very motivating.

Chapter 7

Calm Thinking

Recall that the mind and body are connected. In this chapter we'll explore how the thoughts that we choose affect arousal. More importantly, we'll learn how to choose thoughts that help to lower arousal to appropriate levels.

The branch of psychology that deals with identifying and modifying unproductive thoughts is called cognitive therapy. Cognitive therapy began as a treatment for depression, and is now a mainstream treatment for all the stress-related disorders. It is also a mainstay in resilience training. The aim of cognitive therapy is to eliminate habitual negative thoughts that lead to excessive arousal. Excessive arousal can impair decision-making and performance. (Who hasn't made a bad decision or performed poorly when not thinking calmly?) Excessive arousal can also lead to any of the stress-related disorders. For example, excessive arousal can lead to dissociated traumatic memories, in which are usually locked unreasonable thoughts that increase suffering (more on this in chapter 32). On an everyday level, unproductive thoughts can simply dampen the mood and make life less enjoyable.

The originators of cognitive therapy are Drs. Aaron Beck and Albert Ellis. Ellis's ABC model is straightforward and sensible:

$$A \longrightarrow B \longrightarrow C$$
Adversity   Beliefs (or self-talk)   Consequences

In this model, **A** stands for adversity, or a challenging situation. **C** is the consequences. Originally this referred to emotional arousal. However, this also refers to physical arousal and impaired performance. **B** stands for the beliefs, or the things we tell ourselves about A. Most people think that A leads directly to C. However, it is B that exerts the greater influence on C. Think, for example, of a person who makes a mistake. Arousal is greater when he thinks, "This is awful. People will think I'm an idiot," compared to thinking, "Let's see, how might I solve this?" Common sense, right? This is why cognitive therapy is called common sense psychology. However, under pressure, common sense often does not prevail. Here is where training in this method is very helpful.

Dr. Beck originated the ideas of *automatic thoughts* and *distortions* to describe self-talk. Automatic thoughts are the thoughts that run through our minds so quickly that we hardly notice them, let alone test them for reasonableness. Distortions refer to automatic thoughts that are unreasonably negative, and hence result in excessive arousal. The goal is to stop, identify distortions, rebut them, and then replace them. Fortunately, there are only a handful of distortions. If you master them—meaning you can identify, rebut, and replace them under pressure—you will improve your ability to remain calm, perform better, generally maintain an upbeat mood, and prevent mental illness.

People often learn cognitive therapy when they go for treatment of a stress-related mental disorder. However, the best time to learn cognitive therapy is preventively—before crisis hits. When taught preventively, cognitive therapy is called *cognitive restructuring* or *rethinking*. Ellis noted that the skills of cognitive restructuring can be learned very readily from a good book or teacher.

The optimistic assumptions of cognitive therapy/restructuring are:
- *People are capable of calm thinking.* That is, we have the internal mechanisms to think logically and reasonably.
- *People, however, pick up faulty information because we are human, not sick or weak.* Faulty information might be picked up from parents, friends, peers, the media, or any other source in our environment. Faulty information leads to distortions. Since no one is perfect, we all think in distorted ways at times. This comes with being human, so we are all in the same boat.
- *When the faulty information is corrected, thinking improves.* With more rational thinking, arousal also diminishes.

Think, for instance, of where children believe babies come from before they learn the correct facts. Ask them and you'll hear some very interesting hypotheses (e.g., hospitals dispense them, they grow in Mommy's tummy, storks deliver them). Unproductive thought habits are learned, but more adaptive thinking patterns can be acquired through practice.

The challenge is to use our minds in the most effective way possible. Cognitive restructuring provides a systematic way to gain control over our thoughts under pressure and at other times. The more we practice, the better we become at calm thinking. Calm thinking leads to lower arousal and better performance under pressure.

The Cognitive Distortions[1]

Calm thinking starts with mastery of the cognitive distortions, which cause undue disturbance. Learn these twelve distortions well, so that even under great pressure you can recognize them, and eventually replace them.

1. **Flaw fixation.** Zooming right in on what is wrong, or what went wrong, and ignoring the positive aspects. ("How can I enjoy this day when I made a mistake?")
2. **Dismissing the Positive.** Negating the positives, which might otherwise lift mood and self-esteem. ("Oh, anyone could have done that—it's no big deal," rather than, "I did a good job under the circumstances")
3. **Assuming** (or jumping to conclusions without testing the evidence). There are two types:
   - **Mind Reading** ("I know the boss hates me")
   - **Fortune Telling** ("I know I won't enjoy the party"; "I know I'll do poorly")
4. **Labeling.** Giving yourself (or another) a name or label, as though a single word could describe a complex person completely—always and in every case. ("I *am* a dud"; "He *is* a loser")
5. **Overgeneralizing.** Concluding that your negative experience applies to all situations. ("I *always* flop"; "I *never* succeed"; "*Everybody* hates me—*nobody* loves me"; "Nowhere is safe"; "Nothing means anything")
6. **All-or-None Thinking.** Evaluating yourself in extremes—allowing for no middle ground. ("I'm a hero or a loser";" I'm on top or a flop")

70

7. **Unfavorable Comparisons**. Magnifying another's strengths and your weaknesses, while minimizing your strengths and another's weaknesses. ("Bill is brilliant. I'm just a teacher. Sure, he beats his kids and lots of people like me, but he's the one that *really* contributes to life.")
8. **Catastrophizing**. Making things much worse than they really are. ("This is awful and horrible. It couldn't be worse. I can't stand this!")
9. **Emotional Logic**. My feelings "prove" that that's the way it is. ("I feel bad/inadequate/too tired to move. Therefore, I must be inadequate, incapable, unlovable, a loser, etc.")
10. **Should Statements**. Rigid, unchallenged demands of ourselves and the world. ("He *should* know better"; "He *must* not behave that way": "I *ought* not to tire, mess up, get depressed, be afraid, etc.")
11. **Personalizing.** Seeing yourself as more responsible or involved than you really are. ("It's all my fault that my son is failing in school"; "That guy is trying to aggravate me")
12. **Blaming.** Putting all responsibility on externals, making us feel helpless. ("This job is ruining my life and turning me cynical"; "I'm the way I am because of my crummy childhood")

Identifying Distortions Drill

Calm thinking skills, like any other resilience skill, rely on practice. In a moment you'll see if you can identify common distortions drawn from real life examples, without looking at the answers. Notice that there can be overlap between some distortions. However, there is usually one best answer. To warm up, notice examples of the following distortions. If any of the distortions seem reasonable, you might ask how believing it might make a person feel.

Distortion	Examples
Flaw Fixation	• All I can think about is my screw up.[2] • You criticize your spouse for being late, ignoring the thoughtful things he/she did the rest of the day. • "One sin cancels out 1000 good acts."
Dismissing the positive	• "What I did was no big deal." • To a compliment you say, "Yes, but I could have done better."
Mind reading	• A cop thinks, "That suspect will respect the authority of my badge" (and thus isn't prepared to fire his weapon if necessary).[3] • "I know why my spouse is upset with me. She thinks I'm stupid."
Fortune Telling	• "I'm going to fail (so I might as well quit trying)."
Labeling	• "That person is bad through and through."
Overgeneralizing	• A police officer looks at children playing and thinks, "All bikes are stolen," ruining his pleasure.[4] • "All priests (scout leaders, teachers, youth leaders, etc.) are child molesters." • "Everyone who reminds me of my assailant is bad." • "My whole life stinks."

All-or-none thinking	• "Either I completely like and trust you or you are worthless." • "Either I'm perfect or not worthwhile." • "I'm totally resilient or I'm helpless." • "Without her approval I'm nothing."
Unfavorable comparisons	• "I'm not as smart or brave as Manny."
Catastrophizing	• "It would be awful if that crisis were to happen again." • "I couldn't stand losing your approval."
Emotional Logic	• "I feel so guilty—I must be bad and totally to blame." • "My anger feels justified. It must be." • "I feel overwhelmed. I must have no control or ability to solve my problems." • "I feel fat/ugly. I must be unlovable."
Should statements	• "I must always be hypervigilant." • "You should see things my way."
Personalizing	• "Your dissing me is personal."
Blaming	• "My children/spouse make me so mad!"

These examples come from combat. See if you can name the distortions. The answers are below.

1. After an eight year drunk to escape the pain, a veteran says, "I don't feel like a man anymore. I feel so bad, I must have really screwed up."[5]
2. "The war took my manhood away from me. I blame the Army for what it's done to me."
3. "I don't trust people anymore. In the war you learned not to trust women and children because they carried grenades."
4. "I'd like to talk to someone about my difficult war experiences, but I don't think there's anyone interested in talking about hell."
5. "God won't forgive me for what I did over there."
6. "I should be able to secure the release of my comrades who are missing in action and POWs. "
7. "I must be strong for the others."

Answers
1. *Emotional logic.* 2 *Blaming* (this leaves us feeling powerless). 3. *Overgeneralizing.* 4. *Mind reading* (e.g., most experienced counselors realize that talking is healing). 5. *Mind reading* (Where is it written that God doesn't forgive those who sincerely try to overcome their past?). 6. *Should statement* (The vet who expressed these sentiments was very active in the POW movement, getting his hopes up and then seeing them dashed, and drinking too much. He eventually concluded, "There are some things God has to handle. All I can do is pray.").[6] 7. *Should statement* (Sometimes we gain more by watching someone acknowledge fears or grief, then press ahead. For example, one sergeant in combat joked that he had urinated in his pants, as he carried on. That put the other men at ease and made them feel normal for also feeling fear (Broadfoot, 1974)).

Antidotes: Rational Alternatives to Distortions

The next step is to get good at replacing distortions that you identify. Note the possible replacement thoughts for each of the distortions:

1. **Flaw fixation.** "I won't allow a negative element to overshadow all the good fortune around me." Ask, "Is it really the negative element that is ruining things for me, or my choice to dwell on it?" Ask, "What could I focus on to enjoy; what would I see if I were having a better day; what *isn't* wrong?"

2. **Dismissing the Positive.** Instead of "Yes, but...," say "Thanks," and think, ""Yes, I really do deserve some credit for juggling so many demands, getting all these boring tasks done, shopping wisely, showing good taste, working hard, getting most things done well, etc." See which approach motivates you more.

3. **Assuming**
   - **Mind Reading.** Ask! Check it out. Think, "Maybe it isn't so; I won't know until I ask. Maybe there's another possibility."
   - **Fortune Telling.** Expect the middle ground, rather than extremes. Think, "I won't know for sure until I experiment. I'll probably have some success/enjoyment, as opposed to none. I might even surprise myself."

4. **Labeling.** Rate behavior, not the person. ("He is *driving* poorly.") Remind yourself that no one is always anything (dumb, rude, inept, etc.), and that the person probably is already suffering from his/her faults. Ask yourself why someone's faults should bother you or why you should punish the person further. Apply the same standard to yourself.

5. **Overgeneralizing.** Ask, "What is the evidence that I *never* do well and *always* do poorly?" Or, "What's the evidence that *all* people fit this profile?" Instead, use words like *sometimes, often, generally, usually, yet* (e.g., "I haven't mastered this *yet*"). Test the notion that you never do well; experiment and see how well you do (your *performance* is likely to be somewhere between 0 and 100).

6. **All-or-None Thinking**. Rate *performance or behavior*, not people (e.g., "I batted .850 today—my *performance* wasn't so hot"). A baby has worth, even though he/she doesn't perform well. Ask yourself, "Why *must* I bat 1000?" Accept the fact that those who don't win gold medals are not worthless, just human. (In fact athletes who aim for an excellent job usually perform better than those who shoot for perfection.) Remember that all people have both strengths and weakness coexisting alongside of each other, and still have worth. Enjoy the satisfaction of knowing you did your best, even though the outcome falls short of perfection.

7. **Unfavorable Comparisons**. Don't compare. Allow that each person is different and contributes in unique ways according to unique strengths (e.g., the contribution of a teacher, front-line soldier, or nurse is no less valuable than that of a doctor, commander, or CEO, just different).

8. **Catastrophizing.** Things really *could* be much worse and I *can bear* this, even if I don't like the inconvenience. If I don't avoid facing the difficulty of this challenge, I'll probably figure out a way to deal with it. Also, ask, "What are the odds of this 'awful' thing happening?"; "If it does happen, how likely is it to do me in?"; "How well am I preparing for or coping with this situation? (I'm probably somewhere in the middle, not at 0 coping)"

9. **Emotional Logic.** Remember that emotions are signals of upset, not statements of fact. Acknowledge the feelings, and allow that feelings change. Think, "Isn't it interesting that I'm experiencing this strong emotion. Don't go ballistic. It might change with rest, exercise, time, etc." If you feel worthless or bad, try to put a number to the reality (e.g., asking "What would 100% worthless or bad be?" helps avoid all-or-none thinking).

10. **Should Statements.** At least some of the problem is my expecting the world to agree with my perfectionistic expectations. People are just the way they *should* be, given their beliefs, distortions, experience, breeding, etc., and it's foolish to demand they be otherwise. It *would* be nice if they were different, and maybe I *could* influence them to change. In fact, maybe I would motivate myself more effectively if I used more "woulds," "coulds," and "want to's" (e.g., "I *would like to* improve, and *want* to," rather than "I *should*").

11. **Personalizing.** Distinguish influences from causes. Look realistically for influences outside of self (e.g., Instead of "What's wrong with me?" think, "The test was hard, I didn't prepare adequately, I was tired from two jobs, etc." In other words, focus on behavior and externals without judging yourself. Also, depersonalize ("Maybe I'm not the central figure in the other person's drama today").

12. **Blaming.** Acknowledge outside influences, but take responsibility for your own welfare. ("OK, I understand how these things have influenced me. Now I commit to get back on track and move on." Or, "Nothing makes me do anything—I choose how I respond.")

Rebuttal Exercise

Cover up the columns in the center and the right. Try to name the distortions and then come up with a rational alternative thought. Be patient. Coming up with replacement thoughts usually takes time and practice. This exercise lends itself nicely to group work, because individuals typically come up with many practical alternatives.

Example	Distortion	Possible Replacement Thoughts
You stew about a mistake, forgetting about years of dedicated, mostly successful service.	Flaw Fixation	Ask, "What *didn't* I do wrong? Maybe when my life is over people won't judge me solely by this isolated instance."
You dismiss a compliment or word of thanks, saying, "I just did my job."	Dismissing the Positive	Think silently, "I take satisfaction that I did the job well."
"My buddies think I'm a loser for freezing."	Mind Reading	"I could ask. Maybe they think I am human."
"Either I perform perfectly, or I am a failure."	All-or-None	"I won't always bat 1000. Sometimes batting 700 is doing well."

"I shouldn't be feeling distressed about this. My role model in the department doesn't get this way."	Should Mind Reading	"It *would* be good to be calmer. I wonder what *would* help." "I should be feeling exactly as I do, given the nature of the event and my present coping skill." "Maybe my role model feels distress, but has learned to calm it through years of practice."
"I feel so anxious. I must be going crazy."	Emotional Reasoning	"It's normal to be upset in these circumstances. With time, rest, or calming breaths, I might think more clearly and feel better."
"People always let you down."	Overgeneral-izing	"*Sometimes* they don't."
"I'm a coward."	Labeling	"I was frightened and made some bad choices. That makes me human, not a coward. I'll view fear as an opportunity to show courage."
"I lost 20 people in the fire."	Personalizing	"I didn't lose them. They were murdered by an arsonist."
"This job is turning me cynical."	Blaming	"I can choose to fight this (e.g., by taking a break, working less overtime, and investing in making my life overall more satisfying)."
"I'm not as capable as Joe."	Unfavorable Comparisons	"I have different strengths. It would be better to concentrate on doing *my* best, rather than *the* best."
"Either I'm the Energizer Bunny and put my children's needs first all the time or I'm a bad mother."	All-or-None	"If I don't take care of my physical, emotional, and spiritual needs, I won't be of much use to anyone. I'll strike a balance between their needs and mine."
"It's my fault that my husband doesn't confide in me and that I can't help him."	Personalizing	"It's not a sign of personal failure that he confides in peers who can relate to dangerous work. He may be trying to spare me from worry, or he might fear rejection. I'm not causing his work stress and I can't fix it. I can just be as supportive as I can."
"This is a disaster, utter chaos—how awful!"	Catastro-phizing	"This is a challenge, an opportunity, a beginning to my learning. Even if I'm knocked down, I can get up, learn, and improve something about me or the situation."
"My reputation is ruined—I can't stand what they are saying about me."	Catastro-phizing	"It's not what they call you, it's what you answer to."

"Everyone will judge me unkindly for what I did."	Fortune Telling	"Perhaps some will understand how difficult that situation was."
"My job is a test of my character, strength, manhood, etc."	Personalizing	"My job is my job, a duty I choose to perform well. It does not represent the entirety of who I am."

The Daily Thought Record

Once mastery of the distortions is achieved, you're ready to apply the central strategy of cognitive restructuring, the daily thought record (DTR), to your life. Remember, distortions pass through our minds so quickly that we hardly notice them, let alone challenge them. The DTR (see Figure 7.1) gives us the chance to slow down the action and systematically replace disturbing distortions. You can complete one as soon as things calm down a bit after an upsetting event. With practice you'll find that you choose more reasonable thoughts automatically under pressure. Completing the DTR takes about fifteen minutes. The instructions follow:

Step 1. The Facts

At the top, briefly describe the upsetting event and the resulting emotions. Emotions can be named with a single word, such as angry, sad, anxious, or guilty. Then rate the intensity of the emotions on a 1-10 scale, where 10 is extremely unpleasant. This step describes the **A** and the **C** in the ABC model.

Step 2. Analysis of Your Thoughts

- In the first column, lists the Automatic Thoughts, the **B** in the ABC model. Ask yourself, "What thoughts went through my mind?" List the thoughts separately. Change questions to statements. For example, one might change the question "Why is this happening to me?" (which keeps us feeling stuck and powerless) to statements such as "This shouldn't be happening to me," or "This is awful." Now the distortions become apparent. Then rate how much you believe each automatic thought from 0-10, where 10 means a thought seems completely believable.
- In the middle column, label the distortions. (Some automatic thoughts might be reasonable.)
- In the last column, write down more reasonable alternative thoughts. Your initial thought is only one possibility. There might be many more adaptive thoughts. (If you are working in a group, others can often be very helpful in suggesting alternative thoughts.) After you finish listing alternative thoughts, rate each one as to how much you believe it, with 10 meaning that it is completely believable.

Step 3. Results

Based on the analysis of your thoughts, go back to the Initial Responses column and re-rate how much you now believe the automatic thoughts. Then at the top re-rate the intensity of your emotions. Even small drops in emotional intensity are significant. More importantly, as you practice, you are learning to more automatically replace unproductive, needlessly arousing thoughts.

Remember to work out your thoughts on paper. For most people, it is too complex to do this in your head for difficult situations.

Completing the DTR: An Example

Figure 7.2 is an example of a completed DTR.[7] Police officers often state that dealing with supervisors is the most stressful aspect of their work. An officer named Bob decided to tackle unfair treatment by his supervisor. He could have worked with a letter of reprimand, days off without pay, failure to get a deserved promotion, favoritism, or cronyism, but chose instead to work with an involuntary transfer.

Perspective Taking

Behavioral scientist and former police officer Kevin M. Gilmartin, Ph.D., (2002) notes that it is a great revelation to realize that life isn't fair. The one true overgeneralization, he states, is that *everyone* gets screwed by the agency at least once. The victim gets rigidly stuck on resentment, righting the wrong and making it all fair, and getting even. He digs in his heels and insists that he is always entitled to fair treatment, forgetting that rain falls both on the deserving and undeserving at times. This victim posture makes one feel agitated and powerless. In contrast, the thriver is more flexible, knowing when to let go. She continues to invest in her job, to care, and to live her values. She accepts loss of control, knowing that no one has full control of her job, including the boss. We can give up control without losing our true self. The boss controls assignments, but we control our response. Paradoxically, relinquishing control of the uncontrollable liberates and empowers.

Personalizing and Applying the DTR

- It's great to practice in a small group. If you can, form a group of two or three people. Each person in the group shares a stressor. Then the group agrees on a stressor that the group would like to work with. The helper(s) fill out the DTR. After completing the top regarding a person's stressor, they ask the individual, "What goes through your mind when you think about that event? And what else?" Helpers don't play the role of all-knowing expert, but of collaborator and coach. They might ask if a certain thought could be a distortion, checking it out with the individual. They might ask, "How might this thought work as a replacement thought?"
- Another group activity is the reverse role-play. Here a helper takes on the role of the person with the upsetting event. The latter then becomes the helper as a DTR is completed. Helping another work through the DTR is a great way to learn the process.
- On your own, complete a DTR for a different stressor each day for a week.

Figure 7.1.
DAILY THOUGHT RECORD

DATE _____

The Facts

Adversity (Describe the event that "made you" feel bad/unpleasant)	Impact of Event (Describe the emotions you felt)	Intensity (Rate the intensity of these emotions from 1-10)

Analysis of Your Thoughts

Initial Responses (List the automatic thoughts or self-talk. Then rate how believable each is from 1-10).	Ratings	Thought Fallacies (Find and label the distortions)	Reasonable Responses (Talk back! Change the distortions to more reasonable thoughts. Rate how much you believe each from 1-10)	Ratings

Results

Based upon the analysis of your thoughts, re-rate how much you believe your initial responses. Then re-rate the intensity of your emotions.

Figure 7.2.
DAILY THOUGHT RECORD EXAMPLE   DATE <u>June 20</u>

The Facts

Adversity (Describe the event that "made you" feel bad/unpleasant)	Impact of Event (Describe the emotions you felt)	Intensity (Rate intensity of emotions from 1-10)
Boss involuntarily transferred me.	Angry, frustrated Cynical Sad Anxious	10 ➤ 7 9 ➤ 6 7 ➤ 5 8 ➤ 6

Analysis of Your Thoughts

Initial Responses (List the automatic thoughts or self-talk. Then rate how believable each is from 1-10).	Ratings	Thought Fallacies (Find and label the distortions)	Reasonable Responses (Talk back! Change the distortions to more reasonable thoughts. Rate how much you believe each from 1-10)	Ratings
I am consumed by the boss's unfair acts, to the exclusion of good things about him and the agency. It's all I can think about.	9 ➤ 6	Flaw fixation	What's left? I can still enjoy other aspects of my life and job.	8
He shouldn't be that way.	8 ➤ 6	Should	He is as he is. It would be nice if he were different, but I'll make myself crazy by getting stuck on fairness.	7
He's screwed up my life. I'm going to quit being a good cop.	7 ➤ 5	Blaming	I won't justify my cynicism or bad behaviors by blaming him. The effects of cynicism and loss of integrity will live on long after I retire.	9
The commander has it in for me.	8 ➤ 7	Personalizing	Maybe he doesn't.	4
I can't stand this.	8 ➤ 4	Catastrophizing	It will be an adjustment to get used to this new assignment. I'll view it as a stepping stone, a challenge to do some good in a difficult environment.	8

Getting to the Underlying Core Beliefs: The Questioning Technique

Replacing distortions goes a long way toward reducing undue arousal. Replacing the deeper *core beliefs* gives even greater relief. Core beliefs are usually acquired early in life. Like distortions, they typically go unchallenged. Core beliefs come in two basic forms:

- I'm inadequate (incapable, incompetent, helpless, weak, powerless, out of control, etc.)
- I'm unlovable (unlikable, no good, rejectable, unworthy, different, defective, etc.)[8]

These core beliefs will drive our behaviors and thought processes until they are neutralized. For example, let's assume Bob was severely criticized and neglected as a boy. Feeling that he is inadequate and unlovable, Bob as an adult becomes driven to perfection in his job in order to compensate for this basic insecurity, and is overly sensitive to criticism. Fearing rejection, he might keep people at a distance (e.g., becoming a loner, distrusting and rejecting others, fearing authority). From the core belief arises distortions, such as "It's awful to make a mistake (or be criticized or rejected)," because these events bring him back to the painful core beliefs. Cognitive restructuring provides a way to identify and modify the core beliefs. In the questioning technique, you start with an emotionally charged distortion. Then you ask questions such as "What does that mean?" or "Assuming that's true, why is that so bad?" Eventually you ask the question, "What does that say about me?" Here's how it works. Going back to the example on the previous page, Bob decides to work with the difficult distortion, "The commander has it in for me." The questioning technique would look like this:

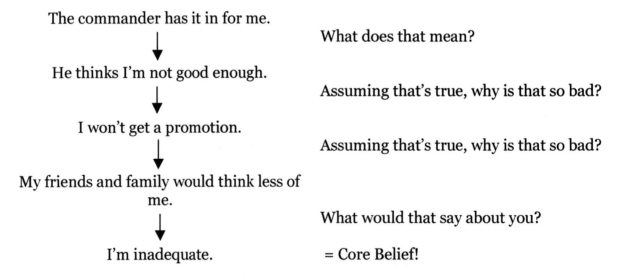

The commander has it in for me.

↓   What does that mean?

He thinks I'm not good enough.

↓   Assuming that's true, why is that so bad?

I won't get a promotion.

↓   Assuming that's true, why is that so bad?

My friends and family would think less of me.

↓   What would that say about you?

I'm inadequate.   = Core Belief!

Now you challenge the core belief. You might reason: "Inadequate is a relative term. Everyone is inadequate (meaning not equal to the task) in certain areas and at certain times, but everyone is capable of growing and improving. There is no shame in being imperfect. I'll motivate myself more by focusing on and growing my strengths rather than by being self-critical. I'll find satisfaction in giving my best personal effort. Just because Dad was judge, jury, and executioner doesn't mean I have to be that way."

Another way to uncover core believes is to answer the following questions, posed by Follette and Pistorello (2007, p.124):

- I secretly fear that I am____, but most people around me would not know that about me.
- I get angriest when people imply or say that I am____.
- To my parent figure, the worst quality for someone to have was /is_____

The Devil's Advocate Drill

This drill is a very effective way to test your cognitive reflexes under pressure. Read the distortion on the left. See how many rational responses you can come up with. There can be more than one answer.

Distortion	Comment	Replacement Thoughts
My worth equals my wages.	This all-or-none fallacy can lead to excessive overtime, which strains the family.	My worth as a person is innate and independent of my salary.
My worth equals my success rate in saving people—my buddies in battle, those trapped in a burning building, etc.[9]	This leads to unhealthy shame when we fail to save everyone.	Human worth does not equate to perfect performance. I'll try my best to protect others, but recognize that we all have limitations.
I am invincible.	What happens when you realize that you're not?	I am a vulnerable, fallible human—and still capable of very good work.
I'm inadequate. How awful!	This thought can lead to fear-driven perfectionism and anxiety.	I am imperfect and human, and that is OK. My peace of mind comes from knowing that I am making the effort to do my personal best.
A mistake means I am inept, a fraud.	George Washington experienced numerous serious military defeats before triumphing.	A mistake makes me human, just like even the legends on the force. You can't do this kind of work without upsetting someone. I'll do my best and not get too attached to the outcome.
I must not be mediocre.	Half of all cops (soldiers, doctors, etc.) are below average.	I'll be the best I can and not worry about keeping score. In other words, I'll focus on the process, not the outcome.

I must not feel, admit to, or show fear.	Fear happens. Sometimes it encourages others to know that a leader is feeling fear, but pressing forward anyway.	Fear is normal. Survival isn't about not feeling fear—it's about acknowledging it and then turning it into productive, determined behavior. Some fear may enhance my judgment and performance. Even freezing is normal. Should this happen, I'll breathe, and focus on what I intend to do.
To function effectively, I must smother all feelings.	It is not possible to smother feelings. Trying to do so wastes much energy.	I can acknowledge feelings, suppress and/or calm them, carry out the mission, and then deal with them later.
This crisis is insurmountable.	This could lead to prematurely giving up.	It might be partly solvable if I persist and move ahead in small ways. If not, I'll accept it.
I'm either on a high at work or I'm down at home to recover.	This can create distance at home when one returns from work and sits in front of the TV for hours.	There's a middle ground. When I get home I can take a breather for a few minutes, then engage with my family in enjoyable ways.

Research indicates that when self-defeating distortions are eliminated, we become more open to the positives that will follow later in the book.

PART IV

MANAGING DISTRESSING EMOTIONS

Chapter 8

Defusing

During the course of our work and our lives, adversity will inevitably trigger strong negative emotions, such as fear, grief, anger, sadness, or shame. Such emotions can overwhelm your resilience if you don't have strategies to effectively manage them. This part of the book will teach a number of skills that will help you manage these intense emotions that your experiences trigger. We'll explore the first of these skills in this chapter, the defusing technique developed by psychologist Steven Hayes.[1] Defusing is based on three principles:

1. *Almost everyone suffers intense pain sometime.* Nearly all of us experience depression, anxiety, or self-dislike, or battle substance abuse or thoughts of suicide at some point in our lives

2. *Most suffering results from the endless battles that we fight against our histories.* We get locked, or fused, in a battle against our painful memories—trying to fix, solve, or end the memories. Often our attack weapon is thinking. Say someone treated you harshly and made you feel incompetent. You might think, "I hate that feeling. I don't want to feel that way. What if I really am incompetent? I don't want to live with that feeling. I'll do something so competent that I'll no longer feel incompetent. That will get rid of these feelings of incompetence. But what if I fail? Then I'll feel even more incompetent." And the battle goes on and on. Even the word *incompetence* is enough to throw you back into the battle and dredge up the old pain.

3. *Although we can control 95% of our outer problems (leaky faucets, flat tires, bad hair), we cannot get rid of our histories.* Thinking about a memory doesn't eliminate it, nor does trying not to think about it. Test this by thinking in detail about a chocolate cupcake. Visualize it. Smell it. Taste it. Feel it in your mouth. Now try not to think about it. After all, it adds lots of empty calories so it would be good not to think about it. Of course, you will now think about it. You might even count how many times you think about it over the course of the next minute. It works the same way with a painful memory. Once you experience it strongly, it is unlikely that "not thinking about it" will work. In fact, the more you try not to think about it, the more you will think about it. Ron is an intelligent, accomplished Marine, a Vietnam veteran. He told me that he wished he could laser out of his mind his memories of combat. Of course, memories can't simply be erased. Ironically, the more we fight against the memories the more emotional charge they absorb. For a respite, we might try to escape the battlefield. We try to run from the memory by trying not to think about it. Or we try to distract with sleep, working, shopping, sex, gambling, TV, painkillers, or other attempts to numb the pain. However, the memories return because they haven't changed.

What is required is a change in tactics! Paradoxically, we can better defuse or separate from the battle by fully joining the battle. That is, we learn to fully let the pain into awareness with a completely accepting and kind attitude. Then we step away from the battlefield and move on with our lives, without wasting energy trying to change the memory.

Activity: Identify a Painful Memory

This activity prepares you for the defusing technique that follows.
1. *Identify a moderately painful memory.* Perhaps you'll recall a situation that made you feel embarrassed, rejected, shamed, disrespected, abused, ridiculed, inadequate, or unloved. Perhaps you made a mistake or a bad decision. Perhaps you were mistreated. Maybe a parent or "friend" labeled you lazy or a coward, and you've tried to run from that memory for years. Maybe you experienced adversity more recently.
2. *Write down how that situation bothered you.* Describe the thoughts, feelings, images, and bodily sensations.
3. *Write down how long the memory has bothered you?* Has thinking gotten rid of it?

The Milk Exercise

This activity demonstrates why the defusing technique works.
1. *Think about milk.* Fully experience it in your mind. See what that word pulls up. Do you think of something white in a big glass? In a bottle? On cereal? Do you feel it coating your mouth, feeling cold and creamy? Do you hear "glug, glug" as you swallow, and feel it going down into our stomach? Does that feel good? Do you think, "I like the taste of milk," or "I'm lactose intolerant," or "Mom put milk on my cereal"? Just see what comes up.
2. *Say the word "milk" aloud as fast as you can for 45 seconds.* Then notice what happens. People often say that the way they experience the word "milk" changes. "Milk" just becomes a sound, without the meaning or sensations connected to the memory of milk.

The Defusing Technique

Go back to the moderately painful memory that you identified above.
1. *Pick a single word that describes what the memory makes you feel about yourself.* The word might be *bad, inept, dumb, loser, helpless, powerless, inadequate, coward, lazy, disgusting, shame, guilt, stupid,* or *clumsy*.
2. *Rate how distressing that word is, from 1-10.*
3. *Now, welcome that memory into full, accepting, kind awareness*—not as an enemy you are fighting, but as a friend you are welcoming into your home. Not with the thought, "I'll grit my teeth and tolerate this for a minute so I can get rid of it," but rather, "I welcome this memory fully into kind awareness." Let your body be soft and relaxed.
4. *With this kind and open attitude, repeat aloud the single word that you selected in step one as many times as you can in 45 seconds.* When finished, re-rate the distress level. Notice what has happened. Do you notice that the word loses some of its emotional impact? Do you feel less fused with the word? Is the memory

and/or the word less distressing? Do you realize that you really *can* bear it? If so, this might be a good skill to use with other distressing experiences. It is powerful to invite our pain into open, kind awareness, and notice how the way we experience the memory shifts.

You can try this again, this time varying how you repeat the word. You might say it loud, then soft. Slow, then fast. Falsetto, then low in pitch. Try it in a scolding tone, like nasty old Aunt Edna would use, then in a playful tone. These variations can further help to change the way you experience the memory.

Other Defusing Strategies

Try the defusing technique with upsetting words. Often we become fused with these words at an early age. Some would argue that early memories are more emotional than verbal, and it is difficult to reason someone out of a core belief that they were not reasoned into. The defusing technique can be useful here. Recall the questions posed in chapter 7 (Follette & Pistorello, 2007, p.124):
- I secretly fear that I am____, but most people around me would not know that about me.
- I get angriest when people imply or say that I am____.
- To my parent figure, the worst quality for someone to have was /is_____.

If you don't remember the specific memory that triggers these words, simply bring the word into kind, open awareness, experiencing all the emotions and bodily sensations. Then repeat the word for 45 seconds and notice what happens.

To further solidify the idea that you can let your pain into awareness, and then leave the battlefield to carry on with your valued life, try this exercise. On a sheet of paper, draw a picture of a big head. Inside place everything that is going on in your head—the feelings, thoughts, and images. Again, do this with a kind, accepting attitude and a soft, relaxed body. Then fold the paper up and put it in your pocket as you go about your day. This symbolizes the fact that you can bear your pain and carry on with your life. You can acknowledge the pain without letting it hold you back from the things you most want to do.

Another defusing strategy is journaling. This will be discussed in chapter 10.

Chapter 9

Rapid Relief Techniques

The techniques in this chapter can be very useful to gain temporary and fairly rapid relief from intense, distressing emotions.[1] Such emotions might arise from adversities ranging from an argument with the boss or a spouse to getting shot at or witnessing a traumatic scene. These techniques are eye movements and thought field therapy. For overwhelming or potentially overwhelming emotions, it is best to try these techniques within the context of a therapeutic relationship with a mental health professional. For events involving moderately intense emotions, you might experiment with these on your own.

Eye Movements

This technique, described by Dr. Larry D. Smyth,[2] is not to be confused with Eye Movement Desensitization and Reprocessing (EMDR), a comprehensive treatment for PTSD and other stress-related mental disorders. Eye movements help about two-thirds of people who try it.[3] The instructions follow:

1. *Identify a past or present situation that distresses you and is difficult to shake.* Remember, go easy. Do not try this at first for a situation or memory that is extremely intense for you. Rather, pick a moderately distressing event at first to gain confidence in the technique. While this technique does not usually lead to negative side effects, there is always the possibility that one might be overwhelmed by trying to go too fast too soon. In a moment you will think about the situation to the point that you feel five to six subjective units of distress (SUDs), where 0 means you feel pleasantly relaxed with no distress, and 10 is the most intense discomfort you could possibly feel.

2. *Imagine the upsetting situation.* Notice the feelings, bodily sensations, images and thoughts that go along with this. Stew about it, adding the negative thoughts ("Oh no....this is the worst...why did this have to happen?") until the SUDs level reaches 5-6. Don't' allow the SUDs to go higher, because we don't want this to become overwhelming. A level of 5-6 is moderately distressing—uncomfortable but tolerable. At this level you can think clearly.

3. *With eyes open and head still, move two extended fingers of a hand back and forth.* The hand is about 14 inches in front of the eyes, and the back and forth movement covers a distance of about two feet. Move back and forth about twenty-five times.

4. *Notice where your SUDs are now.* Typically you might notice them drop to 4 or 4½. Notice any shifts in the thoughts, images, bodily sensations, and/or emotions. People often notice that thoughts, emotions, or bodily sensations change or lessen in intensity, images shrink or fade, and so forth. If your SUDs dropped a little, then this technique seems like a useful skill for you. Repeat the back and forth movements.

5. *If you wish to use this in places where back and forth hand movements are inconvenient, be creative.* You might pick two spots on the wall or on your knees

and move your eyes between those spots. You might wish to move your eyes back and forth with your eyes closed, or with your hand over your eyes as if you were in deep thought.

6. *If this technique dropped your SUDs, try practicing it several times a day over a one-week period to gain mastery of the skill.* Use it as a rapid stress reducer when you want to soothe your nerves, or perhaps before returning home from work.

Thought Field Therapy

Thought Field Therapy (TFT) is another simple technique that can bring rapid relief from strong and distressing emotions. Its originator, Dr. Roger Callahan, asserts that it is a self-help technique that can decrease emotional distress related to anxiety (including panic, phobias, worries, fears), depression, stress, troubling memories, guilt, grief (e.g., from death or a broken relationship), fatigue, and embarrassment. He notes that it also dramatically improves heart rate variability[4] typically within minutes, while helping to reduce pain and symptoms of certain chronic diseases, such as fibromyalgia and asthma. There are, he states, no apparent risks or side effects—it either works or it doesn't. One using the technique does not have to talk about, analyze, or disclose any details regarding the adversity. The technique is easily learned and can be taught easily to others. Thus, you can become a greater resource for others. Preliminary research appears to support the favorable clinical impressions regarding its use.[5] The instructions that follow are an adaptation developed by Dr. Robert L. Bray.[6] In this technique, you will tap solidly with the balls of two fingers of either hand—firmly but not so hard as to be uncomfortable. To prepare, locate the tapping points as follows (it does not matter which side of the body you use):

1. *Side of hand.* This is fleshy part where one would do a karate chop.
2. *Under nose.* Between the lip and the nose.
3. *Beginning of eyebrow.* Just above the bridge of the nose.
4. *Under eye.* On the bone about an inch beneath the pupil, when looking straight ahead.
5. *Under arm.* On the side of the torso, about four inches below the pit of the arm.
6. *Under collarbone.* Place your two fingers at the notch at the base of your neck. Drop your fingers down an inch and slide them over about an inch.
7. *Little finger.* Along the nail line on the inside of the finger, next to the ring finger.
8. *Under collarbone.* Same as in step 6.
9. *Index finger.* On the nail line on the side near the thumb.
10. *Under collarbone.* Same as in step 6.

The *gamut spot* is so-called because you carry out a sequence of activities while continuously tapping there. Make a fist, then place the index finger of the tapping hand between the knuckles of the little and ring fingers. Slide the index finger an inch toward the wrist. You'll tap this gamut spot while the hand that you are tapping is flat.

Here are the instructions for TFT:

1. *Think about/remember a situation that had a negative impact on you.* Rate the upset, using SUDs ranging from 1-10. If you can't remember a situation, focus on an image, feeling, sensation, or sound.

2. *Tap in succession each of the ten major points about 6-10 times:*
   a. Side of hand
   b. Under nose
   c. Beginning of eyebrow
   d. Under eye
   e. Under arm
   f. Under collarbone
   g. Little finger
   h. Under collarbone
   i. Index finger
   j. Under collarbone

3. *While continuously tapping the gamut spot, do the following:*
   a. Close eyes
   b. Open eyes
   c. Look down and left
   d. Look down and right
   e. Whirl eyes in circle
   f. Whirl eyes in circle in the opposite direction
   g. Hum any tune
   h. Count to five
   i. Hum again

4. *Repeat Step 2 above.*

5. *Re-rate upset. Repeat the whole sequence (steps 2-5) until there is no further drop in the upset.* Stop if there is no drop in upset after several repeats.

6. *End with floor to ceiling eye roll if the SUDs rating is two or less.* That is, while tapping the gamut spot and holding your head level, rotate your eyes on a vertical line from floor to ceiling over a period of 6-7 seconds.

Why Do These Techniques Work?

There are various theories as to why these techniques can be effective. First, both techniques help us to confront the pain. Exposing ourselves to distress is the first step toward desensitizing the nervous system, whereas avoidance maintains memories and resulting arousal. Stimulating both sides of the brain helps the brain process distressing memories that are "stuck." It is likely that the brain already contains thoughts and images that help to neutralize distressing memories. More fully activating the brain likely stimulates the healing process. Both techniques disrupt racing, worrisome thoughts—and focusing on bodily sensations, either by noticing them or by tapping, tends to ground one in the body and calm. Further, in tapping energy meridians, TFT is thought to unblock energy "perturbations."

Chapter 10

Opening Up

Give sorrow words: The grief that does not speak whispers the o'erfraught heart, and bids it break.
Shakespeare, *Macbeth*

Are your ever troubled by the memories of difficult times? Do you stew or ruminate over current concerns? This chapter will explore very useful ways to help neutralize negatively charged memories and worries, and take better care of yourself emotionally. Let's begin by putting trauma in perspective.

The Effects of Unresolved Trauma on Health and Performance

Every once in awhile you come upon research that hits you squarely between the eyes. One significant line of research has highlighted the impact of unresolved emotional wounds. Vincent J. Felitti, M.D., and colleagues (Felitti, 2002) studied 17,421 adults who came to an HMO with medical complaints. He found that more than 50% of these patients had experienced at least one adverse childhood experience (ACE), which consisted of growing up with abuse, domestic violence, an absent parent, or someone who was mentally ill, suicidal, a substance abuser, or imprisoned. ACEs rarely occurred in isolation. For instance, an alcoholic parent was also likely to abuse a child. Further, the researchers found that ACEs predicted a wide range of medical, psychological, and functional problems. Thus, the more ACEs one experienced as a child, the more likely one is as an adult to experience obesity, depression, suicide attempts, tobacco and intravenous drug use, alcoholism, heart disease, diabetes, fractures, chronic obstructive pulmonary disease, hepatitis, unintended pregnancy, sexually transmitted infections, and poorer occupational health and job performance. These researchers concluded that we are treating the smoke (the physical symptoms) when we'd be wiser to treat the flames (the traumatic emotional wounds).

Felitti's findings are consistent with other research. ACEs predict PTSD and depression in active duty soldiers (Gahm, Lucenko, Retzlaff, & Fukuda, 2007), while combat veterans with PTSD suffer more medical, psychological, physical, and work impairments (e.g., Zatzick et al., 1997). Furthermore, unresolved traumatic grief predicts cancer, heart trouble, hypertension, and suicidal ideation even within a period of about 1-2 years (Prigerson et al., 1997).

It appears that old emotional wounds don't necessarily heal with time alone. Unresolved, they can exert an influence that affects present heath and functioning for many people, regardless of when the traumas were experienced.

Confiding Concealed Wounds

Samuel Taylor Coleridge echoed Shakespeare when he penned these words in "The Rime of the Ancient Mariner": "Since then, at an uncertain hour, that agony returns, and till my ghastly tale is told, this heart within me burns." A psychologist at the

University of Texas at Austin, Dr. James W. Pennebaker (1997), reasoned that "keeping it all inside" is not healthy. Undisclosed wounds that are not processed and expressed verbally often intrude painfully into awareness and find expression in bodily symptoms.

Pennebaker asked various groups, ranging from students to survivors of the Holocaust, the San Francisco earthquake, the Gulf War, and job firings, to simply write about their most difficult adversities. He instructed them to put down their deepest thoughts and feelings surrounding the event, writing continuously for 15-30 minutes on each of four days. Pennebaker was surprised by the amount of traumas experienced by people who appeared "normal" on the outside. Traumas ranged from accidentally causing deaths to rape, physical and sexual abuse, and being blamed for parents' divorces. Childhood traumas were least likely to have been confided, and the most likely to cause illness later in life. Those who confided in writing showed better physical and psychological health. Understandably, mood slipped during the four days of writing. Thereafter, those who disclosed showed less depression, anxiety, and stress, while experiencing greater self-esteem, stronger immunity, and fewer illnesses. Those who had lost their jobs found new employment quicker if they had written about the firing. Writing about past adversities has also been linked to improved sleep, job satisfaction, working memory capacity, and grades, and reductions in symptoms of arthritis and asthma.[1]

The pioneer trauma investigator Pierre Janet first observed that the freezing, helplessness, "unspeakable terror," and other vehement emotions accompanying traumatic events interfere with the proper storage of memories.[2] He observed that the trauma survivor must calm down and tell the story. Verbalizing helps the brain process, integrate, neutralize, and complete the story, allowing the memory to be stored in a normal way. In short, telling the story helps to organize, resolve, and heal the memory. People often find that confiding in writing yields greater understanding and helps to settle the traumatic memory so that it no longer hurts to think about it. Writing forces us to slow down and face the event fully, without fear or avoidance. In so doing, we might see details previously missed that lead to understanding. We might see ways to improve upon the worst, or simply accept the event as just one part of our lives. Putting the pain down on paper frees us to go on with life less encumbered. Resilient people tend to be comfortable with telling their stories. Most of the resilient survivors of WWII combat whom I interviewed had written their stories in books or other media (Schiraldi, 2007).

Avoiding the trauma prevents the brain from processing and neutralizing the memory. We avoid by pretending it doesn't hurt, avoiding people who remind us of the trauma or might talk about it, sedating our troubles (for example, with drugs, alcohol, shopping, work, gambling, sex, or adrenaline rushes) or by shutting down all emotions so we don't have to feel. (Even constant worrying can be an attempt to avoid pain if we think, but don't fully feel. This only serves to maintain arousal and symptoms of PTSD, without bringing any healing.)

Some people avoid the trauma for fear of feeling. Perhaps they fear being overwhelmed by feelings, when in fact even painful feelings can be expressed, even with tears—and then they realize that things return to normal. Perhaps they were raised in an environment where feelings were not permitted or expressed, or they lack a vocabulary for feelings. However, with practice we can get used to acknowledging feelings as part of what make us human, and become comfortable expressing them in constructive ways.

94

Perhaps the workplace does not permit the expression of feelings. However, we can learn to function on the job while keeping our feelings in check, and later process those feelings when the time is right. Writing privately about feelings is one way to do this without risking the negative judgments of others. Writing promotes the ability to feel emotions fully and appropriately and then recover. *The U.S. Army Combat Stress Control Handbook* notes that physical symptoms are magnified when emotions can't be expressed. As bullet wounds need to be opened and drained before they are closed, so must emotional wounds be opened and the pain expressed before healing can occur. Interestingly, dealing with negative emotions also opens us up to feeling positive emotions more fully.

Confiding in writing seems to particularly help those who have never told anyone about a distressing event (e.g., for fear of embarrassment or punishment), but wish they had or could have. You might try confiding in writing for any past trauma or adversity that still troubles you, including the loss of a loved one, a breakup, moving, parents divorce, or anything else you'd like to forget, avoid, or resolve. It is comforting to realize that we can confront what we have run from, and in so doing overcome our aversion to the memories.

Confiding in Writing: Some Practical Guidelines[3]

Dr. Pennebaker has offered the following guidelines for disclosing in writing:

1. *Getting ready to write.* Find a time and place where you won't be disturbed. Ideally, pick a time at the end of your workday or before you go to bed. Promise yourself that you will write for a minimum of 15 minutes a day [15-30 minutes usually works well] for at least 3 or 4 consecutive days. Once you begin writing, write continuously. Don't worry about spelling or grammar. If you run out of things to write about, just repeat what you have already written. You can write longhand or you can type on a computer. If you are unable to write, you can also talk into a tape recorder. You can write about the same thing on all 3-4 days of writing or you can write about something different each day. It is entirely up to you.
2. *What to write about.* Something that you feel is affecting your life in an unhealthy way. Something that you have been avoiding for days, weeks, or years. Something that you are dreaming about. Something that you are thinking or worrying about too much.
3. *Instructions generally given in Dr. Pennebaker's research:*
   Over the next four days, I want you to write about your deepest <u>emotions and thoughts</u> about the most upsetting experience in your life. [Start by describing the facts, then the emotions and thoughts.] Really let go and explore your feelings and thoughts about it. In your writing, you might tie this experience to your childhood, your relationship with your parents, people you have loved or love now, or even your career. How is this experience related to who you would like to become, who you have been in the past, or who you are now?

   Many people have not had a single traumatic experience but all of us have had major conflicts or stressors in our lives and you can write about them as well. You can write about the same issue every day or a series of different issues. Whatever you choose to write about, however, it is critical that you

really let go and explore your very deepest emotions and thoughts.
<u>Warning:</u> Many people report that after writing, they sometimes feel somewhat sad or depressed. Like seeing a sad movie, this typically goes away in a couple of hours. If you find that you are getting extremely upset about a writing topic, simply stop writing or change topics.

4. *What to do with your writing samples.* The writing is for you and for you only. Their purpose is for you to be completely honest with yourself. When writing, secretly plan to throw away your writing when you are finished. Whether you keep it or save it is really up to you. Some people keep their samples and edit them. That is, they gradually change their writing from day to day. Others simply keep them and return to them over and over again to see how they have changed.

5. *Here are some other options:* Burn them. Erase them. Shred them. Flush them. Tear them into little pieces and toss them into the ocean or let the wind take them away.

Some Other Tips

- *Use a rich range of emotions, both negative and positive as you write.* Naming emotions calms the amygdala. Use statements such as "I feel sad because..."; "I feel like my world shattered"; "I was so scared that..." Younger men especially might have to persist longer in order to feel comfortable with this technique.[4] To prime the "feelings vocabulary pump," you might wish to refer to Table 10.1.

- *Try to add insight words* (e.g., *realize, know, understand*) and causal words (e.g., *reason, because*). The use of such words in writing is tied to greater benefits.

- It is good to use writing for adversities that you can't control, especially if you can accept having imperfect control.

- *If you feel distressed after writing, remember to try the techniques you have learned so far*: abdominal breathing, progressive muscle relaxation, centering, heart coherence, eye movements, or thought field therapy.

- *Remember, if writing is overly distressing, ease up.* Approach the event gradually or write about a different topic.

- *On the fourth or fifth day, you might also discuss in writing how you have or could have benefited from the adversity.* What good can come out of this experience? What lessons, if applied, would make this event more meaningful? What advice would you give to an imaginary friend undergoing a similar situation regarding how to deal with this adversity? Were there bright spots in the darkness? (Did you somehow persevere and show certain strengths? Did you or others demonstrate nobility of character?) Could you give the story a new twist—could the event signal a new beginning with a positive ending?

- *If writing about a traumatic event doesn't help, see a mental health professional who specializes in treating trauma.* A trauma specialist will help you learn other healing strategies. As with the other techniques in this book, you might also seek the help of a mental health professional if you feel that remembering the event might be too overwhelming.

- *If your life is chaotic you might wish to wait until things settle down before trying this method.*

Table 10.1
FEELINGS VOCABULARY

Emotional Intelligence means taking the time to acknowledge feelings, understand how they arise, accept that they exist, and express them in appropriate ways. Scan this list of words that describes a full range of feelings.				
Accepted	Depressed	Haunted	Overwhelmed	Stuck
Afraid	Dirty	Healed	Peaceful	Supported
Aggravated	Disappointed	Hopeful	Playful	Sympathetic
Alone	Discouraged	Heartbroken	Rage	Terrified
Angry	Disgusted	Helpless	Raw	Thoughtful
Anxious	Embittered	Hopeful	Rebellious	Threatened
Ashamed	Empowered	Hurt	Reckless	Tortured
Awestruck	Empty	Impatient	Relieved	Trusting
Betrayed	Encouraged	In control	Remorseful	Ugly
Broken	Enraged	Insecure	Renewed	Unworthy
Calm	Enthused	Isolated	Resentful	Used
Capable	Excited	Jealous	Respected	Validated
Changed	Exhausted	Joyful	Ruined	Valued
Cleansed	Fearful	Lost	Sad	Violated
Comforted	Forgiven	Loved	Safe	Violent
Confident	Frozen	Loving	Satisfied	Vulnerable
Confused	Furious	Miserable	Secure	Weak
Content	Frustrated	Needy	Selfish	Welcomed
Curious	Glad	Neglected	Serene	Worthless
Cynical	Gloomy	Numb	Shocked	Worthwhile
Defeated	Grateful	Obsessed	Sick	Wounded
Defensive	Grieving	Out of control	Spiritual	Yearning
Determined	Guilty	Optimistic		

Writing About Present Worries

Whereas Pennebaker found that writing about distressing past events can be very beneficial, Dr. Thomas Borkovec (Borkovec, Wilkinson, Folensbee, & Lerman, 1983) found that writing about everyday worries concerning the present and future can also be very useful. Worry keeps us aroused and distracted from performing our best, and worsens symptoms of anxiety, depression, and PTSD. If simply trying to stop worrying hasn't worked, then you might try worrying more efficiently—in writing. Investigating insomnia, Borkovec found that worrying keeps people awake. Borkovec reasoned that writing about current worries each day during a thirty-minute worry period—again, facts, thoughts, and feelings—and then postponing worries until the next day's worry period, would substantially reduce worry. Indeed, this approach reduced worries an impressive 35-50% in a matter of four weeks. Other researchers found that a thirty-minute worry period led to fewer medical complaints, such as pain and breathing difficulties (Brosschot & Van der Doef, 2006). This technique can lead to even greater psychological benefits than writing about past traumas (Smyth, 1998).

Putting current worries on paper seems to:

- Give distance and perspective. We realize that we have a finite number of worries, and they are understandable (we're not crazy for worrying).
- Provide a release (*expression*) for the negative energy of worry.
- Desensitize us to the worries as we calmly and continually expose ourselves to them (after awhile they don't seem to trouble us or matter as much).
- Help us focus on concerns we may have been avoiding—either helping us to problem solve or accept what can't be changed.

Dr. Borkovec recommends doing these steps every day for several weeks. Thereafter, you can do this whenever you notice worries building:[5]

1. *Find a unique place to use only for worry.* You do not want to associate worrying with certain places, so a kitchen table, bed, or favorite sofa would not be appropriate. But a chair placed in a corner could be.
2. *For 30 minutes, at the same time each day and in this same place, write down the facts, thoughts, and feelings about your worries.*
3. *Don't worry too near bedtime to avoid associations with sleep.*
4. *Postpone worries to the worry period when you can devote your full attention to problem solving.* If you're worried about forgetting the worry, write it down. Then, instead of worrying, fully focus on your present-moment experience. That is, instead of concentrating on worries, focus on what you are doing, on your surroundings, what you can see and feel, who you are talking to, and so forth.

Twists and Tips

1. *You might choose to use some of your worry period to problem solve.* Distinguish between those worries that will respond to action and those that won't. Ask, "What can I do about this?" If you can do something, identify steps to take and information you need to help you better understand and solve the problem. Break down the steps into small steps. You might want to have your calendar handy so that you can write down your "To Do's."
2. *Reframe.* Notice what you are telling yourself. Check out your worries.
   - Ask yourself:
     - Are my thoughts reasonable?
     - Is there another way to look at this?
     - What's the worst that could happen? What's the best that could happen? What's the most likely outcome?
   - Then:
     - Anticipate how you will cope, should the worst happen. Tell yourself, "I'll cope with it. It won't kill me. One hundred years from now, will anyone care?"
     - Test the evidence that things will turn out as badly as you expect.
   Note: This step is more effective after mastering the cognitive restructuring skills in chapter 7.
3. *Reduce bodily disturbances through relaxation before you begin, and maintain the relaxation as you write.* This helps desensitize your nerves. It also helps you think

reasonably. In addition, remember to consciously relax during the day. Focus on the task before you and on the environment.

4. *Some people find it extremely helpful to imagine a very pleasant memory for fifteen minutes following their worry period.* Recall the memory in vivid detail, using all the senses. Doing this will help you gain a sense of control and mastery as you realize that you can invite worries in and then end up feeling good.

The Bottom Line

If you want to reduce distress, try keeping a journal that no one but you will see. Write the facts, thoughts, and feelings regarding either past adversities or present worries. It is rare to find that such a simple, inexpensive strategy can be so effective. Remember to add this tool to your coping strategies.

Activities

- Confide in writing for a past adversity for a period of four days.
- Worry in writing for a week.

To Ponder

Coast Guard chaplain Jim Ellis once told me that he spoke to divers who were preparing to descend from a dive platform to retrieve bodies from Egypt Air 990, which had crashed into a large body of water. Using the principles we've discussed above, he briefly asked them, in effect, "What is the situation? What are you thinking? What are you feeling? What are you going to do?" Are there situations where you can stop, take a breath, and briefly consider these questions?

Chapter 11

Managing Distressing Dreams

All things one has forgotten scream for help in dreams.
Elias Canetti

Many people who experience a traumatic event, even those who do not develop PTSD, are nevertheless distressed by recurring nightmares. For example, among the resilient WWII combat survivors I interviewed were those who still experienced distressing nightmares of liberating the concentration camps decades after the war's end. Terrifying nightmares can jolt people awake in a cold sweat. They can lead to insomnia and reluctance to go to bed for fear of having another nightmare. Because nightmares disrupt sleep, they frequently lead to fatigue and impaired performance during the day. Nightmares can also raise arousal levels generally. Fortunately, one can learn to process and settle nightmares in waking life in much the same way as other highly distressing memories are processed consciously. This chapter will provide skills to help the individual neutralize nightmares. These skills are especially important to high-risk individuals.

You might regard a nightmare as simply distressing memory material that needs to be processed and settled. The brain often presents this memory material in more creative ways than it does in waking life. Sometimes nightmares replay the distressing events in a more or less literal way. At other times, symbols or twists are woven into the dream. The principle is to bring all aspects of the nightmare into calm awareness and to change both our response to the nightmare and the nightmare itself. Here are the steps to managing troubling nightmares.[1]

1. *Normalize them.* Nightmares are a very common result of being exposed to very distressing events, such as combat, witnessing death or injury, abuse of any kind, rape, or a perceived personal failure that leads to guilt or shame. Nightmares are the brain's attempt to sort out and make sense of the event. Common themes occur in nightmares. It can be reassuring to just realize that many others have experienced these themes. Dr. Deidre Barrett, a Harvard psychologist and president of the Association for the Study of Dreams, and her colleagues have identified the following themes and symbols in nightmares:[2]
   - Danger
   - Monsters
   - Being chased
   - Being rescued
   - Dying
   - Revenge
   - Being threatened again by an assailant or other traumatic event
   - Being punished or isolated
   - Being trapped or powerless

- Sexual abuse (dreams might include shadowy figures, snakes going in holes, worms, blood, good and bad sex, injury, being trapped, being paralyzed, shame, guilt, anger, violence or death)
- Filth, excrement, and garbage (can symbolize evil, lack of purpose or dignity, disgust or shame)
- Physical injury (losing teeth is fairly common, which might symbolize losing control, being powerless or unattractive, or being wounded emotionally)
- Being visited by the deceased

2. *Realize that nightmares require attention.* Normally, dreaming helps to process and settle challenges that we are facing. However, when one is depressed or for highly disturbing memories, processing can get stuck as the nightmares recur.[3] Avoiding the memory material doesn't work. We can't simply erase or "laser" out the memories. Neither can our normal active, problem solving coping methods change what happened.[4] Instead, we can turn toward the nightmare and process it until the memory loses its emotional intensity.

3. *Confide your dreams.* Sometimes all that is needed to diminish the intensity of nightmares is to share your dreams verbally with a supportive person or in a journal. Verbalizing in a supportive environment helps to neutralize the intense emotions and integrate the memory fragments—so that the entire memory can be settled. Notice that the confiding process is similar to that described in the previous chapter.
   - Relax and describe your dream in detail. Break it down into the following specifics:
     - What is the setting?
     - Who are the characters?
     - What is happening?
     - What are you doing? Feeling? Thinking? What are your physical sensations?
     - What are the symbols?
     - What are the symbols saying?
   - Create a system to recall your dreams. You might not remember the content of your dreams, especially if you are not in the habit of paying attention to your dreams. So you might keep a dream journal to help remember the details of your dreams. Try keeping a pad of paper and a pen, or an audio-recorder, beside your bed.

4. *Rehearse a different, calmer response.* Imagine that you see yourself at a specific, intense point in the dream carrying out a simple task, such as looking at your hands, and saying in the dream, "This is just a dream." Practice this before you go to sleep, to serve as a cue to remind yourself that this is just a dream, should the dream recur.[5]

5. *Modify the nightmare in an appropriate way.* Starting with dreams of lesser intensity, you might, for example:
   - Confront the monster chasing you and ask in a direct and friendly way, "What is it you want—what are you trying to tell me?" One person confronted the monster and discovered that it represented himself and his guilt. He assessed his guilt and made some growth-promoting changes. See if you can make the monster laugh or smile, or get it to dance.

- Create a new ending. For example, see the assailant being caught. See yourself coping. A combat veteran sees his buddy, "now with God." You might simply visualize yourself saying, "I am safe now, I survived," or any other positive cognition. Write out or talk out what you did. Rehearse the revised dream in your imagination for about fifteen minutes daily for a week.[6]
- Use art to draw the nightmare and then the more positive ending. Consider all the positive choices you now have. For many it is easier to talk about memory material once it is on paper, "out there" at a distance. Once you have drawn pictures relating to your dreams, try to discuss them or write about them in a journal, since verbalizing helps to settle the memory material. One couple hadn't slept throughout the night for four years because their son Jake came to their room terrified by nightmares each night. The boy had merely seen a commercial for a scary movie. In the course of an hour's time, I asked the boy to draw his nightmare. He drew the picture at Figure 11.1. The drawing depicted the scary movie character Chucky. Notice the eyebrows and the scars. I asked him how he felt when he looked at the picture. He replied, "Scared, mad, sad." I asked what went through his mind as he looked at the picture, to which he replied, "I'm not strong; I'm weak. I can't do anything." He rated the intensity of those feelings and thoughts using smiley faces on a 1-10 scale. I then asked him to draw pictures of how the dream made him feel in his body, and he drew the pictures at Figure 11.2 and 11.3. Notice the rating scale for his heart rate. I didn't know what that meant, and it didn't matter because it made sense to him. Next I asked him to change the dream in a way that felt good. He drew Figure 11.4. Notice that the scars are healed and that Chucky is smiling and friendly. In Figure 11.5 the young boy depicted the way that new drawing made him feel in his body. He said he felt "Strong and recharged, like I can do almost anything." I then asked him to think on the new drawing and the new thoughts, feelings, and sensations as we did a relaxation exercise. After doing this, Jake said he felt great and that he didn't think the memory was as scary anymore. The ratings of his negative thoughts and feelings dropped greatly. The next day, the parents called, and said, "You're not going to believe this but Jake slept through the night for the first time in years." Months later he was still sleeping well. I often share that case in my resilience classes. Once a football player came up to me after class and said that he tried this approach in a simplified way with his nephew who was experiencing similar nightmares. He simply had his nephew draw and describe the nightmare, and then draw and describe a different dream. He drew the pictures at Figure 11.6 and Figure 11.7. Notice the change in emotional tone and the fact that the weapon is dropped in the revised dream. Seeing these two cases, participants will often try this with their children, usually with the outcome that the nightmares end or lessen. For example, a police officer's boy was having nightmares after he overheard the parents discuss a homicide on the same night that the boy saw a frightened neighbor run into their home after being assaulted. The nightmares abated when the boy drew a "before" and "after" picture of his dream. The quality of the art is unimportant. What matters is only that it represents one's authentic thoughts, feelings, and sensations.

6. *Expect changes in dream content.* As we bring memory material into the light of day, we allow the brain's natural healing process to "reboot," or start again. You might now dream of more positive outcomes. Dreams of the deceased might include assurances that they are now well off or opportunities to say good-bye. Dreams might begin to shift in focus to everyday concerns. King and Sheehan have written:[7]

> Dreams of growth and understanding excite both the survivor and the therapist. In them, the dreamer behaves or feels differently, sees things from a different point of view, attends to some element of the situation that she has ignored in the past, sees new possibilities emerging. The affective tone of the dreams becomes more positive. The dreamer may come to realize for the first time that she did the best she could at the time of the (traumatic event), or that she had no viable options. She may see more clearly the role of significant others, then and now.

Figure 11.1
JAKE'S DREAM OF CHUCKY

Figure 11.2
JAKE'S EMOTIONS

Figure 11.3
JAKE'S SENSATIONS

Figure 11.4
JAKE'S MODIFIED DREAM

Figure 11.5
JAKE'S NEW REACTIONS

Figure 11.6
A NEPHEW'S NIGHTMARE

Figure 11.7
THE MODIFIED DREAM

PART V

KEY ATTITUDES ABOUT SELF & CIRCUMSTANCES

Chapter 12

Self-Esteem

What is a weed? A plant whose virtues have not yet been discovered.
Ralph Waldo Emerson

A father once watched his son play a musical piece from memory at a piano recital. The boy played fine until he reached a certain point in the music. And then he was stuck. So calmly he started over, with a look more of curiosity than frustration, but achieved the same results. This happened several times. Each time he played well until he reached that particular point. The father, feeling mortified, wanted to rescue the boy from embarrassment. However, the son persisted, calmly and fully engaged. Eventually the boy worked his way through that difficult point and finished the piece. A secure sense of self had enabled the boy to calmly persist, without undue arousal or self-consciousness, and eventually succeed.[1]

This part of the book begins our exploration of the strengths of positive psychology. Self-esteem makes a fitting starting point because it is so central to resilience. There is general agreement that wholesome self-esteem is linked to optimal mental health and performance For example, the psychologist Abraham Maslow noted that healthy self-esteem is needed to be truly successful and productive. Research bears this out.

In functioning adults, self-esteem is correlated, strongly in most cases, with resilience and several related psychological and physical conditions as Table 12.1 indicates:

Table 12.1
CORRELATES OF SELF-ESTEEM (Brown & Schiraldi, 2003)

Resilience	.63
Happiness	.61
Optimism	.68
Humility	.51
Anxiety	-.80
Depression	-.64
Bodily Symptoms	-.33

Notice the particularly strong inverse correlation between self-esteem and anxiety. Notice as well that the higher self-esteem is, the less likely one is to experience bodily symptoms, even in a generally young and healthy population.

Other research indicates that self-esteem:
- *Is linked to life satisfaction.* In a study of 31 countries around the world, self-esteem was the strongest predictor of life satisfaction in both genders—surpassing satisfaction with finances, family, or friends as predictors. This was

true even in countries where individualism is discouraged, such as Korea and Singapore (Diener & Diener, 1995). In fact, in a large study of Chinese adults (Zhang, 2005), self-esteem was the strongest predictor of satisfaction, surpassing even collective esteem (the degree to which one values group membership). In war-ravaged Korean women, self-esteem was also the strongest predictor of resilience (Lee, 2002).

- *Protects against the development of depression in highly stressful times* (e.g., Hobfall & London, 1986; Hobfoll & Walfisch, 1986).
- *Predicts more persistence and active, problem-solving coping in the face of setbacks* (see review in Barker, 2007; Dumont & Provost, 1999).
- *Motivates one to pursue goals* (Harter, 1986 & 1999), perhaps more than anything else (Gallup survey, 1992).
- *Is related to competent functioning in children living in extremely stressful environments* (e.g., Cicchetti et al., 1993).[2]

Conversely, people with low self-esteem were more likely to experience:

- *Symptoms of PTSD, anxiety, and depression following the World Trade Center Disaster* (Boscarino & Adams, 2008; Boscarino, Adams & Figley, 2005). Lacking the secure anchor of self-esteem, one who confronts overwhelming stress will likely feel more vulnerable and be more likely to freeze, raising the risk of PTSD and other mental disorders.[3]
- *Worse mental and physical health and drug use later in life.*[4]
- *Suicidal ideation following stressful life events* (Wilburn & Smith, 2005).
- *Feeling worse about failure,* experiencing more shame and guilt than those with greater self-esteem (Brown & Dutton, 1995). Shame proneness (i.e., feeling embarrassed by mistakes, wanting to hide, can't stand yourself) is also associated with dissociation (Talbot, Talbot, & Tu, 2004).
- *Greater arousal under stress.* For example, those low in self-esteem secreted six times more cortisol when challenged (theoretically putting one at risk for dissociation[5] and a range of harmful medical diseases (Kirschbaum et al., 1995; see also Martens, Greenbert, & Allen 2008).

These findings make sense. Those with a positive sense of self are less likely to feel threatened by stressful challenges. Already secure in their inner worth, they don't feel they have to prove their worth and don't feel that their inner worth is compromised by imperfect performance or poor treatment. Undistracted by self-doubts, they can focus on performing at their best and enjoying the process—even though the results might be disappointing.

Key Concepts[6]

How we define self-esteem is critical. Self-esteem is a *realistic, appreciative* opinion of oneself. *Realistic* suggests that we are truthfully aware of our strengths and weaknesses. *Appreciative* implies that we have an overall positive regard or feeling about self—a quiet gladness, despite being imperfect.

Self-esteem does not equal perfection. If it did, no one would have it. Often, people who are neurotically driven for perfection are trying to compensate for their lack of inner security. Self-esteem is not omnipotence or narcissism—the false security that says one is more worthwhile and capable than others and should be the ruler. A brittle sense of worth might lead one to overcompensate by having feelings of grandiosity or entitlement. It has been observed that criminals and bullies appear to think themselves superior to others. However, a large study of ten- and eleven-year-olds suggests that this is not the case: The most aggressive children felt left out and bullied, had a negative self-image, and did not enjoy themselves (Sprott & Doob, 2000).[7] This is hardly the picture of one with stable self-esteem. To be mortal is to be imperfect. We can calmly accept that and enjoy progressing, or we can fight this reality by becoming boastful, conceited, or overly competitive—fighting to prove our worth.

Wholesome self-esteem partners with wholesome humility. Humility recognizes that all people have worth, unique strengths, different viewpoints shaped by their life experience, and something valuable to contribute. To be humble is to recognize that we can learn from everyone, that there will always be people who are more advanced than we are in certain areas. Like self-esteem, humility is grounded in truth. It recognizes and celebrates the strengths in self (without arrogance or boasting) *and* others—along with our limitations. Humility readies us to learn from, and cooperate with, others.

Finally, self-esteem is not selfishness. The selfish person cares only for self. The other extreme is to care only for others. Wholesome self-esteem has an enlightened "both focus," a healthy regard and respect for self and others. Inner security frees one to be more conscious of others.

The Three Pillars of Self-Esteem

Self-esteem rests upon three pillars, or building blocks. The first is unconditional worth *as a person*. While others might have more *social* or *market* worth than you or I, the dignity of *human* worth comes with birth. Social and market worth might result from externals, such as appearance, health status, education, acquired skills, the house we live in, the car we drive, the uniform we wear, or the group we belong to.[8] Such worth can fluctuate with the stock market, age, popularity, performance, promotions, firings, awards, or the way others treat or label us. By contrast, worth as a person is unchanging and anchored in something deeper—the recognition of who we are at the core. Each person, at birth, comes with a set of capacities—all the attributes and potentialities needed to live well. Thus, each person has the capacity to love, learn, sacrifice, enjoy, and contribute. While others might be more advanced in certain areas (e.g., math or humor), each individual possesses these attributes in embryo, capable of being grown. It is the unique mix of strengths that makes one person different from another. Inner worth already exists; it does not need to be created and it is not lost by imperfect performance or treatment. Fortunate children will learn this from the way their parents treat them. They come to understand that mistakes don't diminish their inner worth—and thus don't fear "failing." They realize that they are *worthwhile*—literally worth the time to live well and actualize their potential.

Unconditional love is the second pillar. Ponder how effective parents communicate this to a nursing infant. They non-verbally communicate unconditional love to the child through hugs, smiles, gazes, and soothing sounds. They do not say, "Well, I'll only love you if you don't mess your diapers, and by the way I only love you because you will someday represent us in Congress." Unconditional love, along with a sense of unconditional worth, becomes the secure foundation for the child's growth—the third pillar of self-esteem. Note that love from others does not *make* one worthwhile, although it might help one to *feel* worthwhile. A great task in life is to learn to love unconditionally. If you did not learn to do this from your parents you can still learn to be unconditionally loving to yourself. Doing so makes life's journey so much more enjoyable. There is no survival value whatsoever in self-hatred.

Growing, the third pillar, is the process of actualizing our strengths—coming to flower, if you will—becoming more capable, caring, and productive, and elevating both self and others. Although fruitful living does not create or increase inner worth, it definitely helps one to feel more satisfied with oneself and one's life course. So we do not grow in order to make ourselves worthwhile; we already are. Rather we enjoy growing as an expression of who we are. Growing does not mean reaching perfection. Rather it is the process of doing one's personal best and feeling the satisfaction of trying. When we see that growing *springs from* our worth and is *not a condition for* worth, we become free to grow—to do our best (which is the one thing we can control) with more joy and much less fear of failure. Core worth is the seed; love is the fertilizer.

How Is Self-Esteem Raised?[9]

Self-esteem is cultivated by practicing skills that address each of the three pillars. A sense of worth is cultivated by recognizing strengths and capacities that already exist (e.g., being raised in a dysfunctional family might cause a person to apply and recognize strengths, such as persistence and the knack for anticipating problems). Unconditional love increases by deciding each day to want and do what is best for self and others. Growing is accomplished by building upon existing strengths and capacities. Space will permit us to explore some of the many effective skills taught in my courses.

Activity: Seeing Clearly

People with self-esteem are aware of their present, unique mix of strengths and weaknesses in a way that makes them more resilient and sure of themselves. Knowing one's strengths leads to confidence and motivates one to contribute. Identifying weaker areas helps us to understand our limitations and know when to seek help or invest the energy to improve. The person with self-esteem observes strengths and weaknesses with the same non-judgmental curiosity ("Isn't that interesting: there is a strength, and here is a weakness"). This activity will help you see clearly and with appreciation how your core worth is presently being expressed. You might liken people to unique portraits in various stages of completion. In one person, certain areas might shine more brightly; different areas might shine more brightly in another's. Or perhaps in another person's portrait no particular areas stand out, as in the case of a person who is versatile and balanced overall, but not necessarily outstanding in any one area. We view the portrait with pleasure, relishing the process of completing the painting. Those areas that are incomplete are viewed as those with the greatest potential for development.

112

Directions

1. Following is a list of personality traits that describe human beings. Rate yourself on each, from 0-10. A rating of "0" means a complete and total absence of this trait (i.e., you *never* demonstrate it in the least degree). A "10" means that this trait is completely developed, and that you demonstrate it as well as a human being possibly could. Try to be as fair and accurate as you can in your ratings. Neither inflate nor deflate your ratings. Don't worry if you rate yourself higher on some items and lower on others. This is normal. This is not a competition against others. High ratings do not mean more worth—worth as a person is already a given and is equal in all. We are just noticing unique ways in which worth is presently *expressed*. All of the benefit comes from being objective. Avoid all-or-none thinking and overgeneralizing.

Circle the appropriate rating:

	COMPLETELY LACKING										**COMPLETELY DEVELOPED**
Intelligence/IQ	0	1	2	3	4	5	6	7	8	9	10
Character (ethics, honesty, morality, fairness, etc.)	0	1	2	3	4	5	6	7	8	9	10
Creativity/Problem Solving	0	1	2	3	4	5	6	7	8	9	10
Judgment/Wisdom	0	1	2	3	4	5	6	7	8	9	10
Kindness/ Compassion	0	1	2	3	4	5	6	7	8	9	10

	0	1	2	3	4	5	6	7	8	9	10
Humor (initiating or appreciating)											

	0	1	2	3	4	5	6	7	8	9	10
Respect/Regard for Others											

	0	1	2	3	4	5	6	7	8	9	10
Self-Regard											

	0	1	2	3	4	5	6	7	8	9	10
Potential for Growth, Improvement, Change											

2. List five additional traits that describe the way you contribute to the well-being of yourself and/or others. This will not be difficult if you consider the many attributes that describe human beings, including: determination, persistence, loyalty, cheer/playfulness, thrift, generosity, gentleness, appreciation, gratitude, tact, reverence for human dignity, patience, industry, self-control, prudence, order/organization, sincerity, warmth, justice, cleanliness, tranquility, chastity, acceptance, steadiness, courage, sensitivity, commitment, composure, enthusiasm, courtesy, dependability, and humility.

    The standard is not that you possess these attributes perfectly, only that you possess them in some measure. Then rate the degree of development of these traits as you did in the first step.

	0	1	2	3	4	5	6	7	8	9	10
A. _____											

	0	1	2	3	4	5	6	7	8	9	10
B. _____											

114

C. _____

| 0 | 1 | 2 | 3 | 4 | 5 | 6 | 7 | 8 | 9 | 10 |

D. _____

| 0 | 1 | 2 | 3 | 4 | 5 | 6 | 7 | 8 | 9 | 10 |

E. _____

| 0 | 1 | 2 | 3 | 4 | 5 | 6 | 7 | 8 | 9 | 10 |

3. Consider what you have just done. Because humans are so complex and diverse, your pattern in completing this exercise is undoubtedly different from anyone else's. You were probably higher in some areas, lower in others. You probably also noticed an absence of zeros or tens, since such extremes rarely, if ever, exist. This activity reveals a complex and unique personal portrait of attributes at various stages of development. Emerging from this composite is a more certain awareness of core worth. The idea of numerical ratings is not to invite comparisons with others, but to present an image of wholeness and possibilities—and a recognition and appreciation for one's unique mix of strengths. Even a fortunate child can learn to do this with joy, as Linda and Richard Eyre (1980, p.149-150) relate:[10]

> A group of children were dancing, and the teacher was showing them how to skip. I was sitting at the side, observing. There were about ten children, four of whom just could not grasp the technique or coordination of skipping. It intrigued me that three of the four looked dejected, embarrassed, and upset because they couldn't do it. Each of the three, in his own way, stopped trying: one cried, one walked out, and one started acting silly and boisterous to distract attention from his failure. The fourth little boy showed absolutely no embarrassment or concern or self-consciousness for not being able to skip. He kept watching, kept trying, kept failing, kept watching, kept trying. When the exercise was over, I asked him some questions:
> "Do you like to skip?"
> "Yes, but I can't do it very good."
> "Well, did you wish they'd stop skipping and do something you were better at?"
> "No, because I want to learn how."
> 'Do you feel bad because you can't skip?"
> "No."
> "Why not?"
> "Because I'm better at other things."
> "Like what?"
> "Mommy says I'm good at painting pictures."

115

"I see."

"And I'm 'specially good at keeping my baby brother happy."

"I see, Jimmy. Thanks for answering my questions."

"That's all right. Don't worry, someday I'm going to be good at skipping, too."

An amazing interchange for a four-year-old. But the principle behind it is not particularly amazing—it's quite natural. A person who is secure in the knowledge that he is good at certain things can much more easily accept the things he is not good at.

Please respond to the following questions:

A. As you ponder your responses to steps 1 and 2, which attribute(s) do you feel best about?
B. Let's consider the self-as-a-painting analogy. If an impartial observer were to consider the entire portrait, where would "the light shine brightest?" In other words, if a person were to take the time to see you as you really are at present, what areas would likely be most appreciated or enjoyed?
C. Which attributes or strengths could you enjoy applying more in your life?
D. From this activity, I learned that.....

Activity: The Inner Dialogue of Self-Esteem

People with self-esteem talk to themselves differently compared to those who dislike themselves. In chapter 7 you learned to eliminate negative, self-defeating self-talk that undermines self-esteem. Now you will practice the inner dialogue typical in those with sound self-esteem. You might think of this as laying down new neural pathways or installing new software in the brain. Research with athletes has demonstrated that mentally rehearsing in detail can be as effective as actual practice. In this activity you will mentally rehearse thoughts that affirm core worth, enhance security, and motivate growth.

Directions

Following is a list of statements representing the inner dialogue of self-esteem. Each separate statement will be focused on in turn, as follows:

1. Sit in a quiet place, well supported in a chair where you will be comfortable for about twenty minutes.
2. Close your eyes if that is comfortable. Take two calming breaths, and relax your body as deeply and as completely as possible. Prepare yourself for, and expect, a pleasant experience.
3. Open your eyes long enough to read the first statement. Then close your eyes and *concentrate* on that statement. Repeat it to yourself three times slowly, allowing yourself to feel as though that statement were essentially accurate. You might wish to imagine yourself in a situation actually thinking and believing that statement. Use all your senses to experience the situation.

4. Don't worry if a statement doesn't seem to apply to you yet. Just think of this as patient practice in creating a new mental habit. Don't allow negative or pessimistic thoughts to distract you or undermine your progress. Accept whatever actually happens, without demanding perfection. If a statement still does not feel right, bypass it and return later to it. Or modify it so that it does feel right, keeping it positive though.
5. Repeat step three for each statement listed below. The entire exercise will take about twenty minutes.
6. Repeat this activity daily for at least three days.
7. Each day, after doing this activity, notice how you feel. Many notice that with practice, the thoughts begin to feel more and more comfortable, becoming as it were trusted friends. Thoughts that do not become comfortable initially will likely become so upon returning to them at program's end.

The Thoughts of Self-Esteem

1. I think well of myself. This is good.
2. I accept myself because I realize that I am more than my current skill levels, shortcomings, or any other externals.
3. Criticism is an external. I examine it for ways to improve, without concluding that the criticism makes me less worthwhile as a person.
4. I can criticize my own behavior without questioning my worth as a human being.
5. I notice and enjoy each sign of achievement or progress, no matter how insignificant it may seem to me or others.
6. I enjoy the achievements and progress that others make, without concluding they are more valuable than I am as a person.
7. I am generally capable of living well, and of applying the time, effort, patience, training, and assistance needed to do so.
8. I expect others to like and respect me. If they don't, that's okay.
9. I can usually earn people's trust and affection through sincere and respectful treatment. If not, that's okay.
10. I generally show sound judgment in relationships and work.
11. I often constructively influence others by my well-reasoned viewpoints, which I offer and explain effectively.
12. I like to help others enjoy themselves.
13. I enjoy new challenges and don't get upset when things don't go well right off the bat.
14. The work I do is generally good quality, and I expect to do many worthwhile things in the future.
15. I am aware of my strengths and respect them.
16. I can laugh at some of the ridiculous things I do sometimes.
17. I can make a difference in people's lives by what I contribute.
18. I enjoy making others feel happier and glad for time we shared.
19. I consider myself a worthwhile person.
20. I like being a one-of-a-kind portrait. I'm glad to be unique.
22. I like myself without comparison to others.
23. I feel stable and secure inside because I rightly regard my core worth.

Activity: Acknowledging Strengths

This especially effective activity fosters a realistic appreciation of one's strengths. It is based on the research of three Canadians,[11] whose method enhanced the self-esteem of subjects in just a few weeks.

To warm-up, consider the strengths below and circle each one that applies to you. Circle one if you sometimes are, or have ever been, reasonably:

Accepting, tolerant of others
Adventurous
Brave, courageous
Cheerful, mirthful, good humored
Clean
Committed
Complimentary
Composed
Confident, self-assured
Cooperative
Courteous
Creative in problem solving, imaginative
Curious, interested
Dependable, responsible, reliable

Determined, persistent, resolved
Disciplined
Encouraging
Energetic
Ethical, moral, honest
Enthusiastic, spirited
Flexible
Forgiving
Generous
Gentle
Grateful, appreciative
Graceful, dignified
Handy
Humble, modest
Industrious
Introspective

Intuitive, trusting one's own instincts
Just, fair
Kind, compassionate
Loving
Loyal
Open minded
Optimistic
Orderly, neat
Organized
Patient
Persuasive
Playful
Prudent, wise
Punctual
Responsive to beauty or nature
Rational, reasonable, logical

Respectful
Reverent
Self-accepting
Self-controlled, able to regulate emotions
Spontaneous
Tactful
Thrift
Trusting
Trustworthy
Sensitive
Sincere
Steady, consistent
Tactful, sensitive
Tranquil, serene, peaceful
Warm, friendly
Wise in judgment, sees what is important

Check the words that describe what you are sometimes reasonably good at:

_____socializer
_____listener
_____cook
_____athlete
_____cleaner
_____worker
_____friend
_____musician or singer
_____learner
_____leader or coach
_____story teller

_____decision maker
_____counselor
_____helper
_____"cheerleader," supporter
_____planner
_____follower
_____mistake corrector
_____smiler
_____debater
_____mediator
_____family member

_____letter writer
_____thinker
_____requester
_____example
_____mate
_____taker of criticism
_____risk taker
_____enjoyer of hobbies
_____financial manager
_____organizer

118

Perfection was not required to circle these items, since *nobody* does any of these all of the time or perfectly. However, if you circled a few of these and have managed to maintain reasonable sanity in a very complex world, give yourself a pat on the back. Remember, this was just a warm-up. The exercise that follows has been found to be very effective in building self-esteem.

Directions

1. In the space following, write ten positive statements about yourself that are meaningful and realistic/true. You may develop the statements from the list on the preceding pages, generate your own statements, or do both. Examples might be: "I am a loyal, responsible member of my_____ (family, team, unit, etc.)"; "I am clean, orderly, etc."; "I am a concerned listener." If you mention a role that you perform well, try to add specific personal characteristics that explain why. For example, instead of saying that one is a good football player, one might add that he sizes up situations quickly and reacts decisively. Roles can change (e.g., after an injury or with age), but character and personality traits can be expressed across many different roles.
2. Find a place to relax undisturbed for 15-20 minutes. Meditate upon one statement and the evidences for its accuracy for a minute or two. Repeat this for each statement.
3. Repeat this exercise every day for seven days. Each day, add an additional statement.
4. Several times each day, look at an item on the list, and for about two minutes meditate on the evidences for its accuracy.

Ten Positive Statements

1.

2.

3.

4.

5.

6.

7.

8.

9.

10.

<u>Additional Statements</u>

1.

2.

3.

4.

5.

6.

7.

If you prefer, you can write the statements on index cards and carry them with you. Some find cards easier to refer to during the day.

Notice how you feel after practicing this skill, which disputes distortions such as "I am no good" or "I have no strengths" by substituting appreciative thoughts and feelings. Upon completing this activity, individuals will often say things, such as:

- Hey! I am not so bad after all.
- I got better with practice. I didn't believe the statements at first. Then I found myself smiling on the way to work.
- I feel <u>motivated</u> to act on them.
- I felt peaceful and calm.
- I learned I have a lot more good than I give myself credit for.

Activity: Viewing Self with Love

U.S. Army Chaplain N. Alden Brown taught this very powerful way to non-verbally counter feelings associated with long-held negative thoughts. In it you will look kindly into a mirror, and view the core self, perhaps differently than you ever have before.

Do you ever notice what you notice when you look into a mirror? Do you immediately focus on the externals—clothes, hair, wrinkles, blemishes? Do you notice imperfections, perhaps, in a harsh, judgmental way? Or do you first experience your core self with a pleasant feeling?

Directions

1. Over the next four days, seek out a mirror several times throughout the course of each day.
2. Look into your eyes in the mirror with the eyes of love. You might first notice as you look that there is stress in and around the eyes. Look with real understanding and emotion. Try to understand what's behind the stress and let it subside. As you look deeply with love you will notice a change in your eyes and in your entire countenance.
3. Repeat this exercise often. You can use the car mirror or any other mirror.

Over time, this simple yet profound exercise allows a very wholesome and good feeling to take root and grow. As you look into your eyes and see the core self kindly, appearances and externals begin to assume their correct (i.e., secondary) importance. Instead of dreading mirrors, they might come to remind you to experience an appreciative feeling for the core self, a feeling that provides the secure foundation for optimal performance and growth.

In addition, when you do need to check out your appearance in the mirror, focus on what is right, rather than what is wrong. Consider how remarkable it is that the body performs so well so much of the time. Notice attractive features and appreciate steadily performing organs (the amazing heart, eyes, ears, lungs, kidneys, etc.).

Also, notice and appreciate any accomplishments, no matter how small or where they occur. Give back-pats for effective efforts ("Good job; Well done; Wow, I accomplished a lot"), rather than dwelling on what went wrong. Encouragement is generally more motivating than harsh criticism. It is not immodest to realistically recognize and enjoy productive efforts—we would wish loved ones and friends to do this. Humility is preserved as we recognize that others could likewise succeed with similar effort.

Growing

Much about growing—developing our strengths and potentials in a way that elevates self and others, and makes life more satisfying and productive—will be addressed in ensuing chapters. Growing strengths also makes us more resistant to breaking under stress, just as tempering glass makes it more resistant to shattering from a blow.

Chapter 13

Realistic Optimism

"Where there is life there is hope."

Strengthening realistic optimism is the next logical step in resilience training since optimism might be the second strongest predictor of resilience, anchoring many of its other strengths. Optimism is the way we choose to think about life—ourselves, our future, our past, our present, and adversity. Optimism is an attitude that says:

- I'll improve upon my past.
- I persist—I won't let adversity defeat me.
- If I do my part, things will turn out as favorably as possible.
- If things turn out badly, I can still find something to enjoy. (I think of the WWII concentration camp survivor, Viktor Frankl, who marveled at the beauty of the sunset through the barbed wire.)

Optimism motivates us to take constructive action. However, it is important to distinguish between realistic and unrealistic optimism. Realistic optimism recognizes the importance of personal effort: we hope for a good outcome and actively work for it. If one approach doesn't work, we flexibly choose another. While we expect that good will generally prevail, we accept times when nothing more can be done.

Unrealistic optimism blindly assumes that all will be well, without our active engagement, or regardless of circumstances. Unrealistic optimism also assumes that we are more capable than we are. This false security and overconfidence can leave us unprepared and disappointed. Thus, people with unrealistic optimism might fail to take care of their health, or might fail professionally because they don't sufficiently train.

Now let's translate these ideas into learnable skills.

Explanatory (or Attribution) Style

Explanatory style refers to the story we tell ourselves about bad events. If you ask a person why a bad event happened and what it means, he will explain how he thinks about himself, his life generally, and his future.

Decades of research indicate that an optimistic explanatory style conveys numerous benefits related to resilience. Optimists fare better than pessimists in the following realms:

- *Psychological.* Optimists suffer less depression, anxiety, and eating disorders. They are more confident and resilient, cope better with stress, and are more satisfied with relationships.
- *Medical.* Optimists have fewer medical symptoms (including colds) and live longer.
- *Performance.* Optimists perform better than pessimists professionally, academically, and athletically; they are better able to succeed in high-stress environments. They are more likely to persist, anticipate bad and good outcomes and plan accordingly, and not waste time on activities that bear no fruit.

Pessimists will attribute a bad event to something that is *personal* (a flaw at the core), *pervasive* (reflecting a consistent pattern in all areas of their life), and *permanent* (unchangeable). Optimists attribute a bad event to causes that are *external* to their core self, *specific* (the bad outcome only describes a limited area of one's life), and *impermanent* (temporary, changeable). Here is how this works. Let's say that two co-workers fail the promotion test at their workplace (this could also work for a sub-par performance or unfortunate event[1]). The thoughts of the pessimist are listed on the left; the optimist's thoughts are on the right.

PESSIMIST	OPTIMIST
Personal—*condemns and entirely blames self; attributes outcome to personal flaws at the core* • It's totally due to something about me. • Something's wrong with me. • I'm so disorganized, confused: I can't catch on here. • I'm incompetent; an idiot.	**External**—*sees whole picture: allows for influence of other people or difficult circumstances; no self-condemnation for poor performance; focuses on improving performance* • I sincerely tried my best, but that situation was beyond my best efforts—it was really a difficult *test*. And I was really tired from working late. • I didn't perform well. Next time I'll prepare better by being more rested and studying more. • Sometimes *that* happens—just one of those things.
Pervasive—*consistent pattern in all areas* • I mess up in *all* aspects of my life. • My *whole* life stinks. • I can't do *anything* right. • I fail in lots of different situations.	**Specific**—*limited to this situation; local* • I do other things well, like the way I treat the team members. • I had a bad day—not up to par. That doesn't mean all areas of my life are off. • I do mess up sometimes. I do well in lots of ways, too. • All in all, I'm doing pretty well.
Permanent—*unchangeable* • I'm never going to improve. • I'll always be an idiot. • I'll never get promoted. • Things won't get better; I'm doomed. I might as well give up.	**Impermanent**—*temporary, fleeting, changeable* • I am capable of learning and improving. • This isn't a signpost for the rest of my life. • My disappointment won't last long. Tomorrow will likely be better. • I'm enthusiastic about the future.

You might ask yourself which explanatory style is more likely to motivate you to feel and function at your best. The optimist's thoughts are realistic and adaptive. The pessimist's are more likely to lead to feelings of passivity and helplessness.[2]

124

Figure 13.1
BLANK EXPLANATORY STYLE SHEET

Bad Situation (Describe something that happened or could happen):

_____

PESSIMISTIC THOUGHTS	OPTIMISTIC THOUGHTS
Personal—*condemns and entirely blames self; attributes outcome to personal flaws at the core*	**External**—*sees whole picture: allows for influence of other people or difficult circumstances; no self-condemnation for poor performance; focuses on improving performance*
Pervasive—*consistent pattern in all areas*	**Specific**—*limited to this situation; local*
Permanent—*unchangeable*	**Impermanent**—*temporary, fleeting, changeable*

Activity: Explanatory Style

This activity works well in a group of two or three, but can also be done individually.

1. *Generate a list of bad situations that have happened or could happen.* (e.g., You might finish this sentence stem: "The worst thing about my job is......")
2. *Selecting one bad situation, complete the blank explanatory style sheet* (Figure 13.1), filling in as many thoughts as you can for what a pessimist would think, and then what an optimist would think.
3. *Once the blank form is completed, play the devil's advocate game*: Read or have someone read each of the pessimistic thoughts, one at a time. Try to respond to each with a more optimistic thought. For instance, if you hear "I failed because I'm stupid," you might reply, "I failed because I used the wrong strategy (or didn't try hard enough, or because the problem was unsolvable)."

Activities: Strengthen Optimistic Beliefs

Optimistic thoughts can be reinforced by practicing the following:

1. *Read books that reveal the optimistic thinking of resilient survivors.* Excellent examples are the autobiographies of Arthur Ashe (the tennis star who contracted AIDS through a blood transfusion for heart surgery) and WWII survivors Viktor Frankl and Irene Opdyke (see Appendix 9). Put such books in living areas at home or work and encourage others to read them.
2. *Collect and ponder reflections regarding optimism,* such as those at the end of this chapter.
3. *Complete the Optimism Questionnaire* (Appendix 8), which suggests optimistic thoughts to use during adversity. (This questionnaire also reinforces active coping behaviors, which are discussed further in chapter 27.)
4. *Use self-instruction training.* This also works well in groups of two or three but can be done individually:
   - Anticipate a difficult event that could happen to you as an individual or to your unit or team (e.g., a threat, failure, defeat, or loss).
   - Brainstorm realistic optimistic thoughts to use before, during, and after the event occurs. What could you tell yourself or your buddy? You might use the Optimism Questionnaire for ideas. For example:
     Before
       - This could be tough. If I do what seems best, things will probably turn out as well as possible.
       - The first time through is usually more difficult. Keep goals realistic.
       - I'll approach this with curiosity, not self-doubt.
       - I'll recognize if it is time to shift strategies.
     During
       - This is a difficult situation.
       - Keep calm and steady. I'll probably solve this.
       - If I try a different strategy, perhaps I'll get better results.
       - My best is all I can expect to give this challenge.

126

After (Identify thoughts for both a good and bad outcome)
  - For a good outcome
    - Good job.
    - All in all, I did pretty well.
    - I used my strengths and skills, and marshaled needed resources.
    - This gives me confidence to succeed in other areas and in the future.
  - For a bad outcome
    - It's water under the bridge; tomorrow is another day.
    - This challenge revealed both strengths and areas to improve; I'll improve with time and experience.
    - Next time, I'll try a different strategy, specifically_____.
    - Some situations are beyond control.
    - Even though I came up short, I'm still a worthwhile person.

Activity: The "At Least" Exercise

When the going gets tough, a pessimist tends to give up. This is understandable. Perhaps earlier experiences convinced her to expect the worst and believe that trying is futile. By contrast, an optimist tends to look at adversity and think:
- There could be a silver lining in this cloud—a hidden benefit, something that is right, something that can lead to a new chapter in life.
- It could be worse. I could have died. I still have resources left to use. I appreciate resources that have gotten me this far in life.
- Others have faced similar challenges, or worse, and survived. So will I.

The "At Least" exercise stimulates a constructive shift in the way we view adversity. Like a military inventory, it helps us appreciate what's left to work with. It provokes us to ask how well we can manage despite what happened. It stimulates curiosity about future possibilities. The instructions are to simply identify an adversity and complete the sentence stem, "At least....." Write down as many completions to this stem as you can. Let the thoughts flow without inhibitions of any sort. Put it aside and come back to it after sleeping on it to add additional thoughts. When finished, you might ask others to contribute their thoughts.
Examples of how resilient survivors think are:
- A Vietnam veteran said, "I lost a leg, but at least I didn't lose an eye."[3]
- A survivor of multiple surgeries, which left his face scarred and missing bones, thinks, "Everyone has handicaps. I least I didn't die."[4]
- Survivors pride is reflected in:
  - "At least I realized I can survive almost anything."
  - "At least I realized what's most important in life."
  - "At least I still have my goals, my faith, and my sense of humor."
- After a crippling accident, a survivor reflects, "At least I can still see and hear; at least I can play (or enjoy) music; at least I can find new things to enjoy."

- One who loses a loved one thinks, "At least there still are people who love me and whom I can love."
- Humor is encouraged:
  - "At least with chemotherapy, you don't have bad hair days."
  - "At least I don't have to see that nutty boss (who fired me) anymore."

Activity: The Best Possible Future Self

While writing about past traumas for up to thirty minutes on each of four days raised mood and reduced health visits, writing for the same amount of time about creating one's hoped-for future also achieves these results. [5]

Can you imagine describing a bright future, one in which you have worked hard, overcome obstacles, and achieved the goals you most desire? Could you see yourself open to the idea of a better future? The process of describing this type of future life helps to sharpen goals (and reminds us what we are really working for), and motivates and empowers us to achieve these goals. This activity involves writing continuously for twenty to thirty minutes on each of four consecutive days. Here are the instructions:[6]

1. *Imagine your life in the future.* Imagine that everything has gone ideally, as well as it possibly could, and you've realized all your dreams. You have worked hard, overcome obstacles, and achieved your goals in all areas of your life—professional and personal. You might consider, for example, goals in the following areas: professional/educational, relationships, recreation/leisure, meaningful causes, spiritual/ethical, and health. Think about goals being reached at various points in your life, such as ten, five and one years. Now describe this life in writing. Add details such as what you see and feel.
2. *In writing, describe what you will have specifically done to achieve these goals.*[7] How specifically will you have overcome at least one major obstacle?
3. *Along the way:*
   - Notice and replace pessimistic thoughts, such as "I can't do it," or "This good thing will never happen."
   - Pay attention for new insights or directions. (e.g., "Perhaps I can be content with less, with excellence rather than perfection, or with something altogether different, such as greater inner peace. Perhaps a new strategy could work better than my old ways. Perhaps I better appreciate how my strengths and strategies have gotten me this far. Perhaps I can accept what I realistically can't control. Perhaps I see myself forgiving old wounds. Perhaps I see how giving myself kind, wise advice or encouragement could benefit me.")

Activity: Create a Hope Kit

Hope is learned. Those with hope are better adjusted and cope better with adversity. If it was dimmed, hope can be re-ignited. You might create a collection or an album of things that remind you of hope: photos of loved ones, mementos, inspiring quotes, a record of things you've accomplished and plan to accomplish (goals/dreams), and how and when you will achieve your goals. Keep your hope kit accessible and refer to it regularly.[8] You might also include reminders of hopeful thinking—thoughts such as:

- The best is yet to come.
- I expect good outcomes generally.
- I can and I will.
- There are many ways out of a jam—including how I change the situation and/or me.
- I'll figure out a way to solve this.
- I have what I need to improve.
- The future is bright. I expect to achieve what is most important to me.
- I'll be realistic, knowing what I can and can't control. I know when to keep plugging and when to accept the situation.
- Even when I can't control the outcome I have many ways to lift my spirits (e.g., actively record my thoughts and feelings in a journal, exercise, distract, see friends).
- Things won't stay this bad forever.
- I'm wiser; I've learned from bad experiences in my life and am better prepared for the future.
- Even from future bad experiences, I'll learn lessons that will help me succeed later.
- I look ahead, anticipate roadblocks, and problem solve.
- I look ahead, anticipate pleasant times, and see what is required of me to make them happen.
- I will grow from every experience.

Activity: Counter Developmental Issues

Childhood antecedents of pessimism include a harsh environment (e.g., divorce, violence, trauma), lower self-esteem, and fewer emotional skills. Knowledge of these antecedents suggest useful countermeasures (Snyder & Lopez, 2007):
- Minimize television or other forms of entertainment that encourage passivity, violence, and other negative themes. Optimists watch less television than pessimists.
- Seek professional help for lingering symptoms of trauma, depression, or grief that have not subsided with time.
- Actively work to acquire self-esteem skills and greater emotional intelligence (we'll explore many skills for the latter in subsequent chapters).

Reflections to Ponder

- It is a peculiarity of man that he can only live by looking to the future...and this is his salvation in the most difficult moments of his existence, although he sometimes has to force his mind to the task. (Viktor Frankl)
- Perpetual optimism is a force multiplier...we can change things here, we can achieve awesome goals, we can be the best. (General Colin Powell)

- We are troubled on every side, yet not distressed; we are perplexed, but not in despair. (2 Cor 4:8)
- Freedom is nothing else but a chance to be better, whereas enslavement is a certainty of the worst. (Albert Camus)
- The optimist sees opportunity in every danger; the pessimist sees danger in every opportunity. (Winston Churchill)

PART VI

BROADEN AND BUILD:

THE PSYCHOLOGY OF HAPPINESS

Chapter 14

Happiness Basics

We all live with the objective of being happy; our lives are all different and yet the same.
Anne Frank

On average, happier people are more resilient people. Happiness has been recognized by thinkers from Aristotle to Freud and William James as the ultimate goal and motivation of life. Once largely ignored by researchers, happiness has garnered considerable attention in recent years; its centrality to health and performance has been firmly established. In this part of the book we will explore what the research shows about happiness and how to increase it.

A basic premise is that happiness is largely learned, although the underlying skills often take effort and persistence. As the beloved comedian George Burns (1984) once observed, most of the things that make people happy don't fall into our laps. We "have to work at them a little." The good news is that most people say they are generally happy most of the time, even those with a mental illness.

What Is Happiness?

Happiness is:
- Inwardly feeling positive emotions on a fairly regular basis—such as contentment, joy, inner peace, gratitude, calm, serenity, social harmony, vigor, awe, hope, enthusiasm, love, interest, compassion, curiosity, and amusement.
- The overall feeling of satisfaction with one's life and oneself—that these are worthwhile and meaningful.

So happiness is not merely a fleeting feeling, as in "I'm so happy that I got everything I wanted for my birthday." Rather it is a deeper, more enduring overall sense of satisfaction, a fairly consistent positive mood, and the ability to enjoy life's moments. Happiness is an inner condition that can exist even amidst outer turmoil.

Happiness is measured by standardized self-report scales. However, it can also be effectively measured by asking a simple question, such as, "Overall, all things considered, how happy would you say you are?" Responses range from one (extremely unhappy) to seven (extremely happy).

Why Is Happiness Important?

Happiness is what most people say they most want for themselves and their children. Its pursuit was recognized as an unalienable right by the framers of the Declaration of Independence. It turns out that happiness is also very good medicine.

Is there one word that represents sound mental health and the opposite of mental illness and stress? *Happiness* might be that word. As Table 14.1 shows, happiness correlates strongly and directly with resilience and other indicators of mental health.

Happiness correlates as strongly, but inversely, with numerous indicators of mental problems and stress.

Table 14.1
CORRELATES OF HAPPINESS[1]

Happiness correlates strongly... (r's = .5-.8)	
...and positively with:	**...and negatively with:**
Resilience Self-Esteem Optimism Emotional Stability Extroversion	Anxiety Depression Hostility Neuroticism Tension Guilt Proneness Emotional Problems Social Problems Introversion Psychopathy

Furthermore, numerous studies show that happy individuals thrive and fare better in many areas of life:

- *Occupational.* Happy people are more productive, creative, flexible, and energetic at work. They earn more, are better leaders/mediators, and enjoy greater career satisfaction.
- *Social.* Happy people have more friends, less divorces, and greater satisfaction with family; they are more altruistic, give more to charity, show less aggression, and tend to make those around them feel happier.
- *Medical.* Happy people live longer,[2] suffering fewer colds and many other medical conditions.
- *Resilience.* Happy people recover better from hardship, such as depression and bereavement; they solve problems better and more quickly, cope better, and adapt better to adversity. Positive feelings also stimulate brain growth and hasten recovery from arousal.

Why are happy people more successful across so many of life's domains? Barbara Fredrickson, a professor at the University of North Carolina, has developed the Broaden and Build model, based on research findings, to explain this. Pleasant emotions expand our view of adversity, helping us see a broader range of coping options.[3] They also motivate us to act on new coping options. Applying a broader range of coping options builds new neural pathways in the brain—and a larger coping repertoire for future adversity. The mechanism is suggested by brain biochemistry. Pleasant emotions cause the brain to secrete neurotransmitters such as dopamine and opioids. These chemicals foster the tendency to approach and solve problems (rather than avoid them), and reinforce or reward coping efforts with more positive feelings. An upward spiral is now created whereby positive emotions lead to more effective coping, which increases satisfaction levels and the openness to tackle more problems.

Thus, happiness researcher Sonja Lyubomirsky and her colleagues (2008) have concluded that feeling happier makes people more productive, likable, energetic, healthy, friendly, helpful, resilient, and creative.

Questions About Happiness

What Kinds of People Are Happy?

There are two kinds of happy people: Those who are born with a cheerful temperament (we don't like these people very much), and those who learn to become happy.

Can We Be Happy All the Time?

In an imperfect world, perpetual happiness is an unrealistic expectation. Most would find this boring and shallow. Constant happiness does not favor optimal functioning. Down times make us go back to the drawing board, to become wiser, stronger, and more compassionate. Happy people do experience distress. However, they spend less time feeling negative emotions, and when they do they know how to bounce back.

Is Happiness in the Genes?

Yes and no. In a famous twins study, David Lykken and Auke Tellegen at Minnesota State University estimated that 50% of happiness across a population is inherited. Ten percent is governed by circumstances, and 40% is governed by intentional activity (see Figure 14.1).

Figure 14.1
HAPPINESS PIE: WHERE DOES HAPPINESS COME FROM? (Lyubomirsky, 2008)[4]

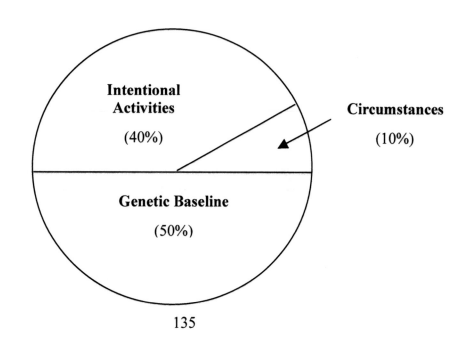

Genes within our cells establish an inherited baseline temperament that we tend to return to. Thus, while a positive event such as a promotion or winning the lottery might produce a temporary bump in happiness, people will generally return to their baseline levels of happiness within several months.

However, evidence suggests that genes are not destiny: the genetic baseline is a predisposition or starting point that can be nudged up or down, just as the genetic predisposition for weight, height, and IQ can be altered through hard work and/or environmental support. Within the cells, an epigenetic code determines gene expression—which genes are activated or left dormant. The epigenetic code is influenced by many factors—such as nutrition, exercise, learning, experience, or nurture—and it can change over the lifespan.

Richard Davidson, a University of Wisconsin-Madison researcher, has noted that happy people have more activity in the left pre-frontal cortex relative to the right pre-frontal cortex. The left to right ratio probably reflects one's natural genetic baseline. Davidson found that babies with higher activity on the left side were more resilient: they cried less and were calmer and more adventurous when their mothers left the room. Babies with more activity on the right side had more anxiety. However, ten years later there was little relationship between the cortical patterns in school children and their patterns in infancy. In other words, the cortical patterns, and probably the genetic baseline, had shifted in many children.[5]

The brain is plastic. It can be reprogrammed through learning and repeatedly practicing the habits of happiness. Like exercised muscles, neurons can be trained, strengthened, and changed in structure and function. New neural pathways can be formed that favor happiness.

What about circumstances? External conditions do not influence happiness levels that much. In the Minnesota Twins study, all externals combined accounted for only 10% of reported happiness, and no individual external condition accounted for more than 3%. External conditions include:

- Income
- Physical attractiveness[6]
- Where people live or were born
- Climate
- Age[7]
- Gender (men and women are equally happy)[8]
- Race/ethnicity
- Religious affiliation
- Marital status
- Objective physical health
- Education or IQ[9]
- Others—promotions, possessions, athletic victories, sensual pleasures (e.g., food or drink), passive entertainment (such as television watching, which is actually linked to a slight drop in mood)

At best, externals give momentary happiness. Then we tend to adapt and return to baseline happiness.

The greatest potential for increasing happiness lies with intentional activities that program the brain for happiness—things that we *regularly* (Lyubormirsky, 2008):

- *Think.* These include learning and practicing the thought patterns, attitudes, and values associated with happiness.
- *Do.* Certain activities promote happiness. These include setting goals, mindfully enjoying the moments of life, helping others, exercising, and meditating.

We might depict the relationship between genetic baseline, circumstances, and intentional activity as follows (see Figure 14.2). External events, such as getting a new car or a promotion, can give rise to an increase in happiness, which eventually returns to the genetic baseline. However, regularly and intentionally engaging in activities that promote happiness can raise happiness levels to a new baseline.

Figure 14.2
INCREASING HAPPINESS THROUGH INTENTIONAL ACTIVITY

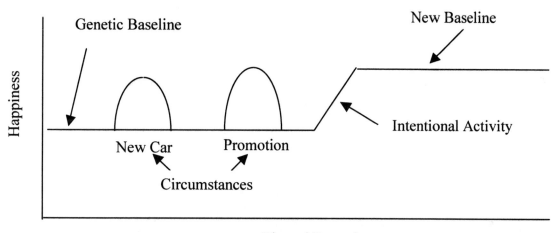

Can Happiness Be Taught?

Although they are surprisingly few in number, studies indicate that happiness skills can be learned, resulting in significant increases in happiness. A few promising studies also indicate that happiness skills improve depression and happiness scores as effectively as traditional treatments, suggesting the utility of happiness training as an adjunct to traditional psychotherapy.

Once Learned, Always Learned?

It takes consistent practice of happiness skills over time to raise the happiness baseline and maintain it. Brain plasticity can be utilized to our benefit if we repeatedly reinforce new learning pathways in the brain. However, brain plasticity can work against us, as well. With disuse, neural pathways weaken and neural connections break, a process called dendritic pruning. So consider starting a program of happiness training that you can maintain for life, much as you would develop an exercise or nutrition program. We might liken happiness skills to learning a musical instrument, a new language, or golf. Repetition and practice are required to keep our skills sharp.

Who Is Happy?

In *Gross National Happiness*, Arthur Brooks (2008) has explored the economics and culture of happiness, using data from national surveys, such as the University of Chicago's General Social Survey. The results shed interesting light on happiness:

Does Money Buy Happiness?

Yes, but not very much, and not for very long. Once people are out of economic misery, once their basic needs are met, income and wealth have little relationship to happiness. For example, in America happiness levels have stayed virtually unchanged in recent decades, despite huge increases in purchasing power and material comforts. The hedonic treadmill[10] principle states that the more money people make, the more they think they need to get along (in other words, the more we have the more we want). Materialists, those who highly value wealth and possessions, are less happy. Perhaps the pursuit of wealth distracts them from the pursuit of happiness. Perhaps they are disappointed to learn that possessions don't satisfy as much as they expected.[11]

It appears that there are more cost-effective pathways to happiness than the dogged pursuit of wealth. Perhaps we can cultivate an attitude of contentment with what we presently have; perhaps success can be redefined as what we contribute, rather than what we earn.

Do Politics Matter?

Yes, in a number of ways. People living in a democracy are happier than those who are not. The more actively people are engaged in running their government, the happier they are. For example, in Switzerland, happiness was higher in cantons in which people had the most citizen participation. In every year since the General Social Survey has been compiled, political conservatives have always been happier than liberals, irrespective of which party is on office.[12]

Does Marriage Make People Happier?

Yes and no. Married people on average are happier; also physically and mentally healthier. However, the effect of marriage is fairly small in a number of studies. It appears that happy people are more likely to marry and stay married. In other words, happiness before marriage might lead to more satisfying and enduring marriages. A large German study found that marriage gives a happiness bump that on average returns to baseline within two years. This, however, is the average. Some people maintain this happiness bump, while for others happiness drops below the pre-marriage level. Perhaps it is not the status of marriage, but how much couples actively invest in maintaining a high quality relationship that predicts happiness.[13] In several studies, married people are happier than cohabitating couples.

Expectations seem to matter. Those with the highest expectations going into marriage experience the steepest declines in happiness. A particularly lethal combination is high marital expectations (e.g., expecting the marriage or partner to be perfect) coupled with a lack of marriage skills.

What about kids? Do they make us happy? Yes, especially when they leave home. As Brooks notes, children usually come with married parents who are committed to meaning, morality, stable work, religion, and other factors that make parents with children somewhat happier overall compared to childless couples. However, controlling for these, children, especially teenagers, make happiness levels fall somewhat. Nevertheless, polls indicate that relationships with children are the greatest sources of happiness to parents, while spending time with family was the greatest source of happiness for teenagers. It appears that parenting can be stressful, but also deeply satisfying in the long run.

Pathways to Happiness

The regular practice of certain habits has been found to increase happiness levels significantly. In Eastern thought, happiness follows from inner peace, simple satisfactions, and social harmony. Happiness also follows from full engagement in meaningful activities and causes. Let's review a few principles before exploring the various happiness pathways.

1. *The brain is plastic.* Whenever we learn something new (thoughts, feelings, behaviors), the brain changes. New circuits are formed, linking neurons together. The more we rehearse the new learning, the stronger these new circuits become. The goal is to optimize brain "hardware" through:
   - Regular exercise, which has been found to increase happiness
   - Sound nutrition
   - Sufficient sleep, which is linked to happiness in numerous studies
   - Sufficient light and vitamin D
   A strong brain can be more readily programmed in productive ways.

2. *Relieving misery can facilitate happiness.* It is difficult to feel happy when one is in physical or mental misery. Remember the importance of treating sleep apnea and regulating cholesterol and thyroxine imbalances. Also remember that depression and anxiety, including PTSD, can be very effectively treated. If you seek treatment, discuss augmenting your treatment with skills that improve positive functioning, rather than simply treating the symptoms. Don't judge yourself for having symptoms. Negative judgments can cause treatment to be delayed or avoided. Simply accept symptoms as part of life, and get the treatment that will allow you to return to full functioning.

Activity

You might wish to review chapters 3 and 4 on the brain. Jot down any steps that might strengthen your brain and prepare you to etch new neural pathways of happiness. Even small steps, such as increasing sleep by fifteen minutes, reducing excessive caloric intake by fifty calories per day, adding a serving of fruits and vegetables to your daily menu, or taking a short walk, can pay large dividends.

Let's turn now in ensuing chapters to optimizing the "happiness software" of the brain—reinforcing the programming that increases happiness at both the brain and heart levels.

Chapter 15

Gratitude

He who is grateful doesn't suffer.
Buddha

The first happiness skill, gratitude, has received considerable research attention. Gratitude is more than saying "thanks." It is an attitude and genuine feelings of appreciation, awe, and wonder for all of life's good things. The expression of gratitude has been causally linked to numerous benefits:

- Greater happiness, optimism, energy, and movement toward goals
- Greater job satisfaction
- Better health (e.g., fewer headaches and colds)
- Less pain and fatigue
- Better sleep
- Feeling more connected to others
- Improvements in severe depression
- Improvements in traumatic memories (which become less troubling and intrude into awareness less frequently)
- Greater likelihood of exercising
- Less materialism and envy

Why is gratitude so beneficial? Gratitude:

- *Counters the tendency to dwell on problems.* Even during adversity, we are less inclined to think, "My whole life stinks." We are more likely to see what is around us to enjoy. Seeing life in a positive way motivates us do what it takes to keep it enjoyable and to persist during adversity.
- *Builds happiness inertia.* The more we practice gratitude, the more we find to enjoy, the longer we prolong enjoyment, and the more optimistic we become about enjoying the future.
- *Causes physical changes.* Gratitude is thought to raise levels of dopamine and serotonin, two key neurotransmitters in the brain related to mood and motivation. Appreciation also increases heart coherence.
- *Increases a sense of trust, appreciation, and connection with others* as we realize how much they have done for us. Cynicism declines as we appreciate the goodness in others and the world. Appreciating others makes us less self-centered and more likeable.
- *Decreases materialism.* We become less attached to money and more willing to part with possessions as we realize that much of what we are grateful for does not require ownership. Envy also decreases as contentment with what we have increases.

How Is Gratitude Cultivated?

Two basic approaches have been tested in the research. They are:

1. *Keep a gratitude journal.* Each night list up to five things you are grateful for over the previous twenty-four hours. Briefly describe in writing why you appreciate each—what it means, how it makes you feel, and why it happened. Do this for about five minutes each night over a two-week period. Alternatively, pick one night a week, say a Sunday, and list five things you are thankful for over the past week. Keep this up for six to ten weeks or longer. Spreading out the journal writing might keep the process fresher. This seems to work as well or better as writing more frequently. Experiment and see what works better for you. The following tips can help:

   - Note anything that makes you happier or enriches your life, big or small, including:
     - What went well
     - Funny or pleasant moments (such as hobbies, movies, time with loved ones, meals, conversation, sleep)
     - Accomplishments (yours and others)
     - What you have
     - A scene in nature, beautiful surroundings
     - Pleasures that don't cost money (such as the simple pleasure of studying a simple leaf or blade of grass)
     - Things you learned
     - Liberating or inspiring principles
     - Things in progress: goals, opportunities, possibilities to anticipate
     - New things you tried
     - Acts of kindness—benefits provided by others, nature, or Providence
     - Being reminded that you matter
     - Pride in surviving
     - Conveniences (e.g., heat, running water, lighting, appliances, restaurants)
     - A country that works (economic, political, and religious freedom; laws, police, firefighters, and armed forces for protection; roads; schools)
     - Strengths in yourself and others
     - Art and inventions
     - Medical care, insurance
     - Employment
     - The capacity to feel peace, contentment, humor, enjoyment, compassion, relaxation, and so forth.
   - Spend some time savoring the moment. Don't just write analytically with emotional detachment. It is important to really feel the experience. Describe and re-experience it in detail. Consider the goodness of nature, God, or people. Think of what each means to you. Consider what you, others, or God did to make the moment turn out well.

- For variety, try:
  - Adding photos or other mementos
  - Keeping a gratitude journal in conjunction with practicing heart coherence
  - Being alert during the day to the details of enjoyable moments, such as the colors and sounds in nature and the flavors and aromas of food
  - Listing things you are grateful for by categories, such as nature, self (appearance, accomplishments, strengths, and health—including parts of the body that are working), the goodness of others (strengths, examples, kindnesses, a child's innocence), relationships that matter (friendship, loved ones, pets), comforts and conveniences, needs met, spiritual resources, entertainment and recreation, and so forth

2. *Write a gratitude letter to someone who has touched your life for the better, especially if you have never properly thanked that person.* Read it aloud in the person's presence. This tends to give a greater burst of happiness than journal writing, although the happiness boost from journal writing lasts several months longer. This activity makes the other person feel grateful and good, which increases your own happiness.

Other ways to practice gratitude include:

1. *Complete this sentence stem: "Something I already have that I feel grateful for is..."* Write fairly quickly, and list as many things as you can. Then go back to savor the items on the list. You might wish to write about them in your gratitude journal.

2. *Express gratitude to others frequently.* Tell soldiers, waitresses, or people working in businesses, "Thanks for your service." Be genuine and specific ("I really appreciated the way you..."). If service is especially good, tell the supervisor. This will make three people feel good: (1) To feel appreciated brings joy and motivates others to keep trying their best. (2) Leaders appreciate hearing that their workers are doing a good job. (3) We feel good when we make others feel good (mirror neurons activate the same areas of our brain that are activated in the other person). Teachers might especially appreciate this story. Mark Medoff, the creator of "Children of a Lesser God," returned to his school. He introduced himself to a favorite teacher as a student of hers from many years before. She cocked her head, hoping the angle might jog her memory. He wanted to deliver a perfectly worded message. Instead, all he could say was, "I wanted you to know you were important to me." Here in the hallway, this lovely, dignified lady begins to weep. She encircles him in her arms, and whispers, "Thank you!" before disappearing back into her classroom. Gratitude lifted the spirits of two people that day. The ripple effect undoubtedly benefited the students that day, as well.[1] Remember to thank loved ones often. It strengthens bonds.

3. *Share gratitude experiences with loved ones at the end of the day.* It is pleasant to hear about what went well and what has been working. By making time together more enjoyable, this process can strengthen relationships. This is an enjoyable way to tuck children into bed, which also helps them to cultivate the habit of gratitude. One young child looked forward to this event, calling out to his parents, "Come in for gratitude." You might also ask children how they might thank someone for giving them a gift. They might come up with ideas, such as "I

would smile and look them in they eye," or (if it's not something they like) "I really appreciate all the effort you put into selecting that gift."

4. *For a short while, give up something that you take for granted* to realize the value of little things. [2] I think of a WWII POW who told me that the deprivation of his prison experience caused him to appreciate a simple piece of chocolate immeasurably. Others told me how being a POW made them cherish freedom even more. Those who "fast" from television often discover greater pleasure in other areas of life.

5. *Increase everyday joy and gratitude*:
   • When "stuck" in a line, in traffic, or in a difficult situation, stop, take a breath, and look around. Notice something to enjoy in your surroundings (such as a face, a smile, a picture on the wall, or clouds).
   • Think of something you appreciate and place that feeling in your heart.
   • At the end of the day, sit comfortably, close your eyes, and breathe abdominally. Let your mind become quiet. Feel warmth in your heart, and let a golden light spread to your head. Ponder what you are grateful for.

6. *Fill out a gratitude reflection sheet if you prefer structure* (See Figure 15.1). List a few items each day. Then indicate how each has benefited you, and how your life without it would be less rich. One physician, for example, wrote that he was grateful for his wife, whose unconditional, constant love made him feel secure and less cynical. Without her, he might have become more "successful" in a cutthroat, materialistic sort of way.

Figure 15.1
GRATITUDE REFLECTION SHEET

I'm grateful for....	How this has enriched my life...	How life without this would be different...

7. *Try Grateful Reminiscing.* The concentration camp survivor Viktor Frankl imagined the face of his beloved wife to preserve his sanity during his imprisonment. Resilient people often reminisce to help them through difficult times. Recalling pleasant past events in great detail has been found to elevate mood, self-esteem, and positive feelings towards others, the past, and the future—while diminishing the distress of troubling memories.[3] Start by making a list of good memories, from your childhood to the more recent past. Consider especially warm, nostalgic times with people who mattered to you, significant accomplishments, unmerited favors, simple pleasures, and enjoyable moments in nature. For ten to twenty minutes, relax, close your eyes, breathe abdominally, and then immerse yourself in one pleasant memory. Recall as many details of the

memory as you can—sensations (what you saw, heard, smelled, tasted, and felt with your body), emotions (notice where you feel these in your body, too), and thoughts. Imagine that you are reliving the experience, with all the sensations, feelings, and thoughts. Recall the expression on your face, and let your face experience that expression again. If a negative thought intrudes, such as about something unpleasant that happened later, tell yourself that you won't let this ruin your experience, and go back to focusing on the pleasant memory.[4] Do this every few days for a variety of memories. When you finish reliving a memory, you might record the details of the memory in writing. This can help to solidify and reinforce the memory. A written record of happy memories can be a great resource for stressful times. You might find it helpful to refer to reminders of your experience, such as photos or other mementos. You might wish to place these with your written record. If you find that writing becomes too analytical and dampens the emotional experience, then omit the writing instructions.

Gratitude in Adversity

Resilient people have many tools in their coping toolkit to help them deal with the inevitable adversities of life. Could gratitude be one such tool? Gratitude can change our perspective in a way that lifts our spirits and helps us through difficult times. Adversity, if we are not completely overwhelmed or do not stop trying to cope, requires us to use and strengthen the most cherished human virtues, such as persistence, determination, hope in the future, and compassion for others' pain—in a way that the easy life might not. If we can view hardship this way, we will not give in to bitterness or despair easily. Often growth is not obvious until well after hardship has been survived.[5] Here are several examples of people who used gratitude to cope with adversity:

- In WWII, Corrie ten Boom (1971) and her sister were imprisoned in a concentration camp for helping Jews in Holland. Corrie's sister used gratitude to reframe the imprisonment, choosing to be grateful that she and her sister were incarcerated together. She even expressed gratitude for the fleas, which kept the Nazi guards away from their building.
- Shipwrecked and isolated on an island, Robinson Crusoe seemed singled out to suffer miserably and was probably asking, "Why me?" Yet he was also singled out to be spared from death. He had no clothes yet he was marooned in a hot climate. He concluded: "Upon the whole, here was an undoubted testimony that there was scarce any condition in the world so miserable but there was something negative or something positive to be thankful for in it; and let this stand as a direction from the experience of the most miserable of all conditions in this world: that we may always find in it something to comfort ourselves from, and to set, in the description of good and evil, on the credit side of the account."[6] This perspective allowed him to persist and live. In real life, the gracious tennis star Arthur Ashe (1993, p.326) was dying from AIDS, innocently contracted from a blood transfusion during heart surgery. He said, "If I ask 'Why me?' as I am assaulted by heart disease and AIDS, I must ask 'Why me?' about my blessings, and question my right to enjoy them."
- In the third year of incarceration for being a pacifist, Rosa Luxemburg wrote in a 1917 letter to her friend:[7] "Do you know where I am, where I am writing this letter

145

from? I've taken a small table outside and am sitting hidden between green bushes. To my right are ornamental yellow currants, which smell like clove, to the left a privet, and before me the white leaves of a large, earnest, and tired silver poplar are rustling...How beautiful it is, how happy I am, I can almost feel the mood of approaching Midsummer—the full, lush ripeness of summer and the intoxication of life itself." Finding meaning in her suffering and absorption in life's beauties gave her inner joy.

- The Chinese master Chin Kung taught:[8]
  - "Be grateful to those who have hurt or harmed you, for they have reinforced your determination."
  - "Be grateful to those who have deceived you, for they have deepened your insight."
  - "Be grateful to those who have abandoned you, for they have taught you to be independent."
  - "Be grateful to those who have made you stumble, for they have strengthened your ability."

Think of your life as a card game. Your hand has many, many cards, some of which seem less favorable. Gratitude helps us to recognize the good cards that have been dealt, and the opportunities remaining to play your hand well. The challenge is to enjoy the game despite the hand we've been dealt.

Grateful Processing of Troubling Memories

Processing troubling memories can help to neutralize them. As we saw in chapter 10, writing down the facts, thoughts, and feelings surrounding a distressing event from the past can be very helpful. Cognitive restructuring can also be helpful. Another approach is to gratefully process troubling memories, as follows:

1. *Identify a difficult experience,* one perhaps where you disappointed yourself, lost a loved one or an opportunity, or were hurt by another or unfairness.
2. *Ponder the positive consequences that have resulted even from this bad situation.* Are there actually some benefits that resulted from that bad experience?
   - In what good ways have you grown?
     - Has adversity caused you to commit or recommit to cherished values, such as integrity? (e.g., "Because I hurt someone, I realized that certain behaviors are no longer an option.")
     - Has a difficult time helped you to realize what's most important, what is still left that you cherish, such as loved ones or faith?
     - Have you become wiser, reordered your priorities, or gained insight?
     - Have you committed to a cherished cause? (e.g., Many people who survive trauma become seasoned resources for others.)
   - What did you actually do in a positive sense? (e.g., "I froze initially, but then I performed quite well. Since then, I have...")
   - Did you discover inner strengths? For example, survivors' pride is realizing that you survived adversity, are stronger than you thought, persist through

146

difficulty, or have the capacity to help others in difficulty. How has adversity better equipped you to face future challenges?

- What good has occurred since? What opportunities have opened up?
- What opportunities still exist for a more satisfying life? How might you still change for the better?

3. *Describe the event in writing and what you found in it to be grateful for.* For example, a colleague in the Peace Corps was traveling on a bus in a third world country with his only valuable possession, an expensive camera. He remembers regaining consciousness on the side of the road, having been poisoned by the lady sitting next to him in the bus. He related that he was actually grateful for the experience—first to be alive, and second to realize that he could still be happy even when stripped of his possessions.

4. *Notice that in doing this exercise we are not calling a bad event good.* Nor are we minimizing or ignoring the pain. For some experiences, it might be premature to do this activity without first processing strong negative emotions such as guilt, shame, anger, regret, and grief.[9] However, this activity broadens our perspective of negative situations in life, lessens preoccupation with negative thoughts and feelings, and brings greater healing to troubling memories.

Create a Gratitude Skit

I am grateful for my honor students, who created this useful, and often-hilarious activity. Give a small group a card with a difficult situation on it, or have them identify their own. Ask the group to act it out, and then act out somehow figuring a way to get past the situation. For example, you see your best friend dating your significant other, and say, "I'm grateful for a pre-nup." You have a car accident and embrace the offender, who becomes a new friend. Groups often come up with creative ways to construe benefits in tragedy. Surrounding the negative event with humor helps to soften its impact.

Gratitude Activities

Reviewing this chapter, pick one or more gratitude activities to try. You might pick, for example, one structured and one unstructured activity:

- *Structured*: Gratitude journal, gratitude letter, gratitude list, grateful reflection sheet, grateful reminiscing, grateful processing of a troubling memory, and gratitude skit.
- *Unstructured*: Express gratitude spontaneously to others, talk about what you're grateful for with others, give up something you take for granted, and be on the watch for things you are grateful for and savor them during the day or in imagery.

Gratitude Reflections to Ponder

- When you arise in the morning give thanks for the food and for the joy of living. If you see no reason for giving thanks, the fault lies only in yourself. (Tecumseh, Shawnee Warrior)

- Let us rise up and be thankful, for if we didn't learn a lot today, at least we learned a little, and if we didn't learn a little, at least we didn't get sick, and if we got sick, at least we didn't die; so, let us all be thankful. (Buddha)
- If you haven't got all the things you want, be grateful for the things you don't have that you don't want. (Anonymous)
- Happiness is not about getting what you want, but about appreciating what you have. (Gilda Radner, comedian)
- The pessimist looks at a glass of water and wonders why it isn't full, why everyone else has more water, and why it isn't wine. The grateful optimist thinks, "See how beautiful and clear the water is." (Anonymous)
- Unless we are grateful for what we have, we'll never be happy with more. (David Rich)
- [Noticing the beautiful things in others] fostered a beautiful spirit of love, understanding, and sharing. (Mother Teresa)
- A grateful heart is a happy heart, and a grateful heart is a generous heart. (Chieko Okazaki)
- God gave us memories, so that we might have June roses in the December of our lives. (James Barrie, Scottish poet)
- He is a wise man who does not grieve for the things which he has not, but rejoices for those which he has. (Epictetus)

Chapter 16

Altruism

Whatever joy there is in the world, all comes from desiring others to be happy.
Shantideva

The dictionary defines altruism as unselfish concern for the welfare of others; selflessness; kindness, benevolence. Altruism aims to benefit others without concern for our own gain. It is giving another a leg up.

In the famous Harvard men's study, George Vaillant, M.D., (1977) found that an altruistic disposition in college was among five predictors of medical, psychological, social, and occupational success decades later. Altruistic activities boost happiness more than recreational or passive activities, irrespective of the age of those studied. Happiness researcher Sonja Lyubomirsky (2008) summarizes that altruism promotes good will, cooperation, interpersonal connections, and mutuality, while distracting us from our own cares. Through mirror neurons, the lift that we give others in selfless service is reflected in our own brains. Kindness changes the way we see others and ourselves. We begin to see the person served as one who matters. We see ourselves as more capable, useful, and strong, and our lives as more meaningful. Others like and appreciate altruistic people. Unlike sensual pleasures, the satisfactions from altruism seem to grow over time (as long as we don't overextend), benefiting the giver along with the receiver. Interestingly, those who say they are the happiest in both their jobs and their lives include those in altruistic professions—such as clergy, firefighters, and special education teachers. Those with higher status jobs, such as lawyers and bankers, score lower in life and job satisfaction.[1]

Altruism can inspire others to be kinder and less cynical. For example, one youth decided to become an emergency medical technician after being impressed by the bravery of emergency workers during Hurricane Katrina. Psychologist Jackie Lapidus interrupted her private practice to donate five days to work with Pentagon survivors after 9/11. As a result, she said, "I'm less cynical because I have witnessed so many acts of kindness and courage."[2] Regarding WWII, Viktor Frankl observed, "We who lived in concentration camps can remember the men who walked through the huts comforting others, giving away their last piece of bread. They may have been few in number, but they offer sufficient proof that everything can be taken away from a man but one thing: the last of the human freedoms—to choose one's attitude in any given set of circumstances, to choose one's own way." A POW in the brutal Japanese prison camps of WWII told me that he was inspired by a leader who took beatings from his captors in order to spare his men from being beaten. Other POWs wept as they recounted tales of selfless comrades who gave them their own food to save them from death. In a squalid prison in North Vietnam, one sick prisoner inadvertently threw up his dentures into the "toilet." A comrade thrust his arm up to his shoulder in excrement until he retrieved the dentures, prompting Larry Chesley (1973) to say that it was an honor to live with such men.

Altruism might be cultivated in two ways:

Kindness Day

Sonja Lyubomirsky (2008) found that doing five kind acts on one day for each of six weeks boosted happiness. Concentrating the acts on one day boosted happiness more than spreading out the acts. To try this, designate one day a week as your kindness day, and plan to do five altruistic acts. Do them with heart—freely, cheerfully, and without expectation of personal rewards. If you can, try to interact with the people you help—talk, look into their eyes. Do not judge them negatively for needing help.3 Do not try to do so much that it overwhelms you and takes the joy out of giving. If it becomes drudgery, it's OK to take a break. To prime the pump, you might consider doing some of the following:

- Volunteer (at a nursing home, a soup kitchen, homeless shelter, blood drive, school, orphanage, children's team, Big Brothers, or other good cause)
- Help a child with homework; tutor
- Help a neighbor without being asked (take in the trash can, mow the lawn, shovel the walk of snow, sweep the sidewalk, take a meal to the sick, share vegetables from the garden)
- Buy or provide a meal for the homeless
- Give a larger tip
- Bring a meal to a shut-in, just visit, or take a walk with her/him
- Send an "I'm thinking of you" note or get well card to someone in your address book
- Send a thank you note to a new teacher, custodian, principal, or someone else who makes a difference
- Teach someone or a group a skill or share knowledge without asking for compensation

- Give a smile, a handshake, a hug, or a simple hello
- Welcome new neighbors with a plate of cookies
- Drive an elderly person to an appointment /errand
- Donate to charity
- Give a massage
- Pick up litter
- Babysit
- Let someone in line
- Pay for someone behind you at the toll booth or fast food drive through
- Buy dessert for someone at another table
- Do something unexpected for a family member (cook a meal, do a chore without being asked, be patient, listen, compliment, share a possession, give the gift of time)
- Bring a treat for someone's pet
- Host an unexpected birthday party
- Befriend someone who isn't popular
- Others (consider neighbors, friends, family, strangers, colleagues):

_____

Guerrilla Kindness

Whereas a kindness day is pre-planned, this less structured approach to altruism involves random acts of kindness. A reporter once asked Mother Teresa how he could help her serve the poorest of the poor. She said simply, "Come and see." In other words, kindness does not usually take elaborate planning, training, or effort. Often we simply see what needs doing, and then we do it. All we need to bring is ourselves and our willingness to help. We see that we can each uplift and contribute in our own unique way.

Ask yourself which is more satisfying—doing a kind deed or buying something? Doing good or making money? As the song says, a dollar bill doesn't kiss you back—but kindness lights up the brain.

A Story of Kindness

A newspaper story some years ago reported this story of altruism and gratitude, as related by Thomas S. Monson:[1]

> The District of Columbia police auctioned off about 100 unclaimed bicycles Friday. "One dollar," said an 11-year-old boy as the bidding opened on the first bike. The bidding, however, went much higher. "One dollar," the boy repeated hopefully each time another bike came up.
>
> The auctioneer, who had been auctioning stolen or lost bikes for 43 years, noticed that the boy's hopes seemed to soar higher whenever a racer-type bicycle was put up.
>
> Then there was just one racer left. The bidding went to eight dollars. "Sold to that boy over there for nine dollars!" said the auctioneer. He took eight dollars from his own pocket and asked the boy for his dollar. The youngster turned it over in pennies, nickels, dimes, and quarters—took his bike, and started to leave. But he went only a few feet. Carefully parking his new possession, he went back, gratefully threw his arms around the auctioneer's neck, and cried.

Reflections

- When I was young, I admired clever people. Now that I am old, I admire kind people. (Abraham Joshua Heschel)
- Sometimes our light goes out but is blown into a flame by another human being. Each of us owes deepest thanks to those who have rekindled this light. (Albert Schweitzer)
- Kind words produce their own image in men's souls; and a beautiful image it is. They soothe and quiet and comfort the hearer. They shame him out of his sour, morose, unkind feelings. We have not yet begun to use kind words in such abundance as they ought to be used. (Blaise Pascal)
- Let no one ever come to you without leaving better and happier. Be the living expression of God's kindness: kindness in your face, kindness in your eyes, kindness in your smile. (Mother Teresa)
- If you can't feed a hundred people, then feed just one. (Mother Teresa)
- If you want others to be happy, practice compassion. If you want to be happy, practice compassion. (Dalai Lama)
- Never get tired of doing little things for others. Sometimes, those little things occupy

the biggest part of their hearts. (Unknown)
- Kindness in words creates confidence. (Lao-Tzu)
- Whosoever will [selfishly] save his life shall lose it: but whosoever will [selflessly] lose his life...the same shall save it. (Jesus, Luke 9:24)

Chapter 17

Humor

My psychiatrist told me I was insane. I told him I wanted another opinion. "Okay," he said, "You're ugly, too."

I once liked clever people. Now I like good people.
Solomon Freehof

A sense of humor is a vital asset of resilient people—one, it is generally agreed, that is necessary for optimal mental and social health. A wholesome sense of humor both springs from, and helps to maintain, a happy disposition. There's a Jewish tradition that before kicking Adam and Eve out of the Garden of Eden God gave them a sense of humor to get them through life with grace and composure. In this chapter we'll explore what humor is, its potential benefits, when it is not beneficial, and how to grow a healthy sense of humor.

What is humor?

The word *humor* derives from the Latin word for moisture. Indeed, humor can moisten, or lubricate, life. Humor is a rather complex, but learnable, skill that is most effectively used alongside the other skills in this book.

Specifically, humor is the propensity to amuse and be amused (Franzini, 2002), the ability to see the comical and find pleasure in any situation. Bigger than joking, humor is a way of looking at life with clarity, acceptance, playfulness, and optimism. Humor says, "I may not be great, but I'm a darn sight better than *some* might think!" Loretta LaRoche of Boston's Deaconness Hospital describes humor as "the ability to feel inner joy, peace, and harmony within yourself and your surroundings—to discover that we are all part of a divine comedy."[1]

Humor takes a familiar situation and juxtaposes two different ways of looking at it, such that one is amusing. In other words, it presents the situation in a new light—a lighter, less serious,[2] and safer one. The goal of humor is fun.

You might begin your exploration of humor by taking the not-so-serious humor checkup on the next page. This will give you a feel for the dimensions of wholesome humor and where you stand with regard to them.

How's My Sense of Humor?

Rate yourself from one to seven, according to the chart below. Be as honest and objective as you can. Higher ratings indicate present strengths. Lower ratings indicate areas for potential improvement.

Totally disagree	Moderately disagree	Slightly disagree	Neither agree nor disagree	Slightly agree	Moderately agree	Totally agree
1	2	3	4	5	6	7

_____ I'm usually in a cheerful mood and take joy in being alive (joie de vivre).
_____ I am playful.
_____ I'm usually composed and not overly serious.
_____ I'm inclined to see the funny side of things.
_____ I find the comical, incongruous, ridiculous, absurd, ironic, unexpected, or bizarre in everyday situations—and take pleasure in them.
_____ I enjoy a good laugh.
_____ I can usually think of something to say or do to make others laugh.
_____ I appreciate and enjoy a funny joke, story, or situation.
_____ When I hear a joke, I am quick to "get it."
_____ I enjoy telling jokes or amusing stories that make others laugh, and do so often.
_____ I remember jokes.
_____ Although I can be serious, I am also ready to be mirthful.
_____ I like to play with ideas and words.
_____ I smile easily—the kind of warm smile where my eyes twinkle.
_____ I usually find humor in even serious situations.
_____ I express humor in words—written or spoken.
_____ I often come up with ways of viewing situations in ways that others find funny.
_____ I interact playfully with others (pleasant banter, sharing amusing stories, etc.).
_____ I am a master of physical humor—making funny facial gestures or silly movements.
_____ I look forward to a new day. I don't want to miss the fun.[3]
_____ I seek out things that make me laugh (e.g., funny movies, television programs, cards, cartoons).
_____ Even during adversity, I can usually find something funny.
_____ Even during adversity, I produce humor to lift others' spirits (e.g., commenting on the ludicrous, bantering, saying something funny, refusing to be too troubled).
_____ My humor tends to reduce tension and draw me closer to others.
_____ I find it easy, and usually enjoyable, to laugh at my own weaknesses.
_____ I enjoy the company of capable people who enjoy life.
_____ My humor is kind: it does not put me or others down because of mistakes or flaws, and it does not offend others.
_____ I don't use humor to avoid problem or hide my feelings.
_____ When my mood begins to slip, I often use humor to lift it.
_____ I am comfortable being playful.

154

The Varieties of Humor

Humor comes in many guises, including:
- Good natured teasing or ribbing
- Banter, repartee
- Wit
- Wisecracks
- Slips of the tongue (e.g., former quarterback Joe Theismann commented, "A genius is a guy like Norman Einstein.")
- Malapropisms (Think of Yogi Berra's "This restaurant is so busy that no one comes here anymore" or Archie Bunker's "last will and testicle.")
- Blunders, bloopers, accidents
- Slapstick
- Horseplay
- Sarcasm (which usually intends to hurt or mock an individual)
- Satire, parody, and burlesque
- Irony (getting the opposite of what you expected)
- Jokes or story telling
- Gallows or dark humor (defiantly laughing at our darkest threats)
- Puns or other word play
- Practical jokes or pranks
- Endearing nicknames
- Comical slang or acronyms

The Four Humor Styles

Humor is a double-edged sword. It can be used to build bridges or fences. Humor researcher Rod A. Martin, Ph.D., (2007) has described four ways in which people use humor:[4]

1. *Affiliative humor* draws people together through telling funny stories or jokes, or by funny comments that amuse others and reduce social tension. Affiliative humor laughs at our common lot in life. It conveys the feeling that we are all in the same boat. It promotes warm laughter at our shared silliness and pokes fun at something that anyone might do. For example, Mother Teresa said with a smile to her Missionaries of Charity, "Keep smiling, and anyone who doesn't smile, make her smile." Carlos Mencia said, "God has a sense of humor. If you don't believe me, tomorrow go to Wal-mart and just look at people." Affiliative humor usually has a good-natured rather than a hostile tone. This humor style makes someone safe and fun to be around. People with this humor style can also laugh at themselves in a good-natured, accepting way. As a fifth-grader, I was once annoyed at my favorite teacher. I drew a picture of her with measles and frizzy hair and was just putting the finishing touches on the caption, "This is Mrs. Mulholland. She has the measles." I was so engrossed in the project that I didn't notice that she had walked up to my desk and saw the drawing. Horrified, I looked up to see her throw back her head and laugh,

155

"Oh, Glenn, is that what I really look like!" That cemented my adoration of her. Occasionally, affiliative humor can bind group members together by poking good-natured fun at someone who is outside of the group.

2. *Self-enhancing humor* is used when one is alone. This style enables one to be amused by incongruities, and to cope with adversity. Perhaps you think of something funny when you are down. Perhaps you show amused tolerance for life's absurdities or think of something to cheer yourself up when stressed.

3. *Aggressive humor* puts others down in a way that hurts, offends, or embarrasses. There is an element of hostility in this style, which derides, criticizes, ridicules and/or manipulates. Much sarcasm, teasing, and derisive nicknames are of this humor style. People in power might use this style to elevate themselves at the expense of others or to reinforce social norms, such as a boss who ridicules a subordinate. Telling an embarrassing story of a co-worker in order to exclude that person exemplifies this style. If someone is offended or doesn't enjoy an attempt at humor, there is a good chance that it is aggressive. Rodney Dangerfield once quipped, "I haven't spoken to my wife in sixty years. I didn't want to interrupt her." If she was not amused, this would be aggressive humor. If you have to say "just kidding" when challenged, you might be using aggressive humor.

4. *Self-defeating humor* puts oneself down in a habitually disparaging way. In this style, you make yourself the butt of the jokes in order to amuse others. Whereas affiliative humor might be used to poke fun at ourselves in a light-hearted, accepting way, self-defeating humor reveals a deeper self-dislike. For example, Ronnie Shakes said, "I always wanted to be the last guy on earth, just to see if all those women were lying to me." The prince of self-defeating humor was Rodney Dangerfield ("I told my psychiatrist that everyone hates me. He said I was being ridiculous—everyone hasn't met me yet."). While some comedians make a living with this humor style, this style usually does not wear well in real life. It can bring others down as it reminds them of their own insecurities or the negativity they are trying to rise above. For the teller, this style might reinforce negativity and the habit of trying to cover up real pain and insecurity, rather than confronting these directly. Chris Farley, for example, made people laugh at his own expense, but was deeply unhappy inside. In short, this style erodes self-respect, invites ridicule, and puts others off.

Research indicates that the first two humor styles, affiliative and self-enhancing, are associated with greater psychological well-being, self-esteem, optimism, and intimacy, and less depression and anxiety. Aggressive and self-defeating humor, which men are more likely than women to use, correlate with each other, and are associated with poorer mental health, less relationship satisfaction, and less happiness (Martin, 2007).

Developmentally, aggressive and self-defeating humor spring from insecurity and dislike of people, whereas affiliative and self-enhancing styles express inner emotional security and liking. Often, people develop humor as a way to deal with pain—their own or others. Art Buchwald said. "When you make bullies laugh, they don't beat on you." A number of skilled comedians first learned their trade by trying to lift depressed family members through humor.

The Beneficial Functions of Humor

The judicious use of humor has many potential benefits both for ourselves and for those around us. Humor can:

- *Improve cognitive abilities.* Consistent with the broaden and build model, watching comedy clips has been found to improve memory, problem solving, and executive function.

- *Help us cope with adversity.* Humor enables us to rise above and survive even the most dire situations. If only for a moment, humor shrinks the pain and infuses adversity with pleasure—reminding us that we still have inner resources and the hope of triumphing. Some of the most profound examples of comic relief have been found in life's darkest moments. Viktor Frankl (1992) reported that in the WWII concentration camps, at least one joke was told each day. He and a comrade joked about the ways that camp life lessons could be applied in the outside world, one time saying that when they were free and attending a formal dinner party, they would ask the hostess to ladle the soup from the bottom. He even laughed with relief and gratitude when he arrived at a new concentration camp that didn't have a chimney.[5]

  Historically, war prisoners have diminished the fearfulness of even the cruelest prison guards by giving them mocking nicknames or burlesquing them. About being imprisoned for many years in North Vietnam, Larry Chesley writes (1973, p.78-9):[6]

  > [O]ne of the most significant things that helped us hang on over there was a sense of humor, being able to laugh at each other and ourselves. Towards the end, when we had a little less restriction on our movements, we used to watch one prisoner ride his "motorcycle" around the camp. He would polish it and wash it—he even had a helmet made out of something or other. He had the high handlebars, and he would kick-start the bike and make all the appropriate noises as he rode it around. Of course all of this was imaginary, but he really entertained the other prisoners. The Vietnamese authorities didn't know what to make of him. He had them all flustered. They probably thought he was crazy. One day the camp commander told him he was not allowed to ride his motorcycle any more because there wasn't room in the yard; and besides, the other prisoners didn't have a motorcycle.

  > We had some riotous times laughing at some of the silly little things that happened. I think I may have laughed harder in prison than I have ever laughed at anything in my life. We put on some skits and some commercials that were really hilarious. Often we would be poking fun at another roommate, but we all got our turn and everyone seemed to take it in good spirit. We put on musicals such as "South Pacific" and "The Sound of Music," with costumes, "girlies," and everything.

  Some evidence indicates that the greatest benefits from humor (such as reducing stress and lifting the mood) occurs in those who actively create it amidst adversity, such as through joke or story telling, Once we learn to laugh and lift our own mood in the most dire circumstances, we realize that nothing can defeat us inwardly.

- *Reveal truth.* When we can acknowledge our weaknesses and laugh at ourselves, we create a fertile climate for growth. As author Mary Ellen Edmunds notes (1999, p.135), humor keep us from being "too pretentious, too perfect, or too isolated or insulated from others. It's a kind of honesty in looking at ourselves and all that surrounds us. Humor for me is often two parts love and three parts courage." Likewise, noting the comical in others can help us to avoid similar follies.

- *Be an act of service.* Laughter is contagious. When we laugh or smile, areas in the brain linked to pleasure become active, lifting our own mood. However, mirror neurons in others' brains activate the same brain circuits, thereby lifting their mood at the same time as we lift our own. Concerned leaders who strive to make the workplace enjoyable increase motivation, morale, and productivity in workers. Teachers who judiciously use humor make learning more fun, while parents who make the home environment more fun lift the spirits of family members. If "management" fails to create an enjoyable environment, then individuals can find ways to make their own fun.

- *Be a social lubricant.* Imagine a roomful of people laughing together over shared suffering. We tend to think that the one making us laugh understands us. We feel that we are not alone—but are more connected and comfortable. We tend to like and want to be around people who are fun. People who have a sense of humor are perceived as more likeable, attractive, effective on the job, confidant, friendly, pleasant, positive, warm, open, creative, and intelligent. Humor can also defuse conflict. When Soviet and American negotiators were deadlocked during the Cuban missile crisis, a Russian said, "What is the difference between capitalism and communism? In capitalism, man exploits man. In communism, it's the other way around." Humor relaxed the mood and enabled the talks to continue (Klein, 1989, p.9). And couples often cite appropriate humor as a factor that helps marriages endure.

- *Improve health.* While laughter might exercise the heart, improve circulation, and reduce stress hormones, the best evidence suggests that laughter improves immune function and decreases pain.

Humor Guidelines and Principles

1. *Try noticing the joyful in life before trying to be funny.* A colleague, a distinguished professor with a young-at-heart marriage, said, "Janet will come home from a walk and say, 'Did you see that moon (or leaves)?' Or she'll purr when I share something with her. In turn I try to give nourishment or compliments at every honest opportunity."

2. *Then just chuckle at the incongruous, comical, amusing, ludicrous, or absurd.* Will Rogers used to say, "I don't make jokes. I just watch the government and report the facts." If you can then make others laugh, that's icing on the cake.

3. *Be kind and affectionate.* Ensure that humor builds bonds, and does not make others uncomfortable. Teasing, even when offered in a good-natured way, is usually more upsetting than the teaser realizes.[7] Be especially cautious about humor that:

   - Demeans or excludes—including sarcasm, hateful/aggressive humor, humor intended to dominate or demean, merciless teasing, and laughing at outsiders[8]
   - Disrupts serious conversations or attempts to resolve problems
   - Invalidates another person's views

- Is off color or offensive

Be especially cautious with humor directed at the insecure, anxious, depressed, guilty, or overly serious. If you are uncertain as to how humor is being received, ask. You might say, for instance, "I was just trying to lighten things up. Was that OK?" Then listen to the other person's response.

4. *Be yourself.* You needn't force humor or use a humor style you are not comfortable with. There is no one-humor-size-fits-all. Some find real-life stories most amusing. Some prefer jokes or slapstick. Some make up their own humor and give it away, while others respond to and appreciate humor. Some smile, while others roar with laughter. Some might only be funny around close friends, but not in large groups—and that's OK. Discover what you find funny. Everyone has different tastes. Often you don't have to try to be funny. Just notice and enjoy life's incongruities. Be mindful of hidden truths. See through pretense. Behold the ridiculous. Ask yourself what's comical. Be willing to say what others are thinking.

5. *Be serious and sober, too.* Not every moment needs to be turned into a joke. Some humor experts counsel people not to take themselves seriously. However, if you don't take yourself seriously, no one else will. No one wants to *be* a joke. Those who are always clowning around are often perceived as less conscientious, insensitive, and avoidant. Individual worth, meaning and purpose, commitment, human suffering—these are serious concepts. Take them seriously, just not *too* seriously and not too often. Paradoxically, those who are secure in their own self-worth and the direction that their lives are taking can more readily laugh at themselves and the ridiculous situations they sometimes find themselves in. Be humble enough to do so. But trying to be playful in serious times can backfire. If someone is in pain and has a concern, take it seriously. Don't use humor to invalidate the pain or avoid a serious discussion of the problem. Using humor to change the topic or demean another's concerns can create resentment. As a rule, avoid making light of something that is hard to change, such as weight or an entrenched flaw. Don't expect humor to compensate for incompetence or lack of effort. Recognize that it is often possible to be cheerful and serious at the same time, but have the wisdom to discern when humor is inappropriate.

6. *Use self-effacing humor judiciously.* During his second bid for the White House, Ronald Reagan said (Klein, 1989, p.50), "Andrew Jackson was seventy-five years old and still vigorous when he left the White House. I know, because he told me." Making fun of the obvious communicated self-acceptance, but also showed that he was sharp enough to jest about it. It showed that he was a regular guy who didn't take himself too seriously, while allowing others to be more comfortable with his age.

7. *Be spontaneous.* Respond in an unplanned and playful way. Most laughter results from spontaneous conversational humor. The second greatest source of laughter results from mishaps where no one is seriously hurt. Judith Viorst relates that at a formal dinner party, the hostess came out of the kitchen carrying a beautiful roast. Unfortunately, her formal gown snagged on something, and she tripped and fell. And she not only fell, but she sprawled spread eagle, face down. The platter hit the floor and the roast skidded across it. Picking herself up, she said, "Not to worry. Fortunately, I have another roast just like this one in the kitchen." In the kitchen, she dusted off the roast and re-garnished it. Many of the guests thought it actually *was* a

different roast. This is grace under pressure, and her humor was saying, "I'm more than my mistakes. I can dance around them even under duress."

8. *Commit to finding humor.* Be on the lookout for the comical. (Why do they park in driveways and drive in parkways?)

9. *Don't be afraid of jokes.* Although jokes account for only about 11% of laughter (Martin, 2007), jokes can be a great way to share mirth. Jokes are stories that lead the listener down a certain path, but then take her in an unexpected direction at the punch line. Even professional comedians bomb with many jokes since not everyone laughs at the same things. Yet most people appreciate one's attempts to tell a joke. Joke telling is an art and a learned skill that is refined with much practice. Start with a joke you personally enjoy. Practice until you can tell it in a relaxed and confident way, believing that it will likely amuse the hearer. Especially rehearse the punch line, the most critical part. When you actually tell the joke, look like you are enjoying the process—perhaps with a twinkle in the eye, an amused look, animated gestures, and a lilt in the voice.

Activities

1. *Discover your humor preferences.* Recall what your sense of humor was like as a child. What made you laugh? How would you describe the humor of your closest relatives and friends in childhood? Did they enjoy humor? What kind? Did they initiate everyday humor? Did they initiate humor during stressful times? Who most influenced you and why? Pondering these questions will probably give you insights into the types of humor you most appreciate.

2. *Humor reminiscing.* Find a quiet place to meditate. Relax and recall three funny stories from your life that really made you laugh hard. See the picture clearly. Re-experience it. Hear yourself laugh. Feel your body laugh. Record the experience in detail in your journal. Share one with someone close to you.

3. *Be more mindful of things that make your smile.* Look around you for five blue objects. Perhaps you realize that blue objects are all around you, even if hardly noticed before. In a similar way you can find things that make you smile if you are looking for them (Klein, 1989). You might smile at a beautiful baby or a sunset, or you might find something funny. Record what you find every day for a week. Be ready to smile, laugh, and be playful.

4. *Start off the day laughing.* As we have noted, smiling and laughing activate the pleasure centers of the brain, making the mood more positive. This happens even when the laugh is forced. Try reading this paragraph aloud when you wake up in the morning:[9]

    > HA HEE HEE HEE, HA HO HA! HA HO HO HO HEE
    > HO HEE HO HEE HO HA. HA HO HEE HEE HA HA
    > HO HA HEE HO HA. HA HO HEE HEE HEE HEE, HA
    > HO HO HO HA HO HO. HA HEE HO HO!

5. *When angry, depressed, or anxious, try to find something to laugh about.* Do this consciously until it becomes automatic. Remember that you can lighten your own mood without diminishing the seriousness of a situation.

6. *Create a humor collection.* List your favorite comedy movies, cartoons, funny books, jokes, comical experiences, and cards. Keep this handy and refer to it often.

7. *Tell a joke or funny story.* Select a favorite. Practice until you can tell it well. Tell it to various groups and notice the response.

8. *Play with language.* It was when he was trapped in a boxcar that Archie Bunker decided to write his "last will and testicle." A doctor told the teenager, "You have acute vaginitis." She said with embarrassment, "Thank you." A sign reads, "Ears pierced while you wait" (McGhee, 1999, p.150). Jay Leno has shown us how to have fun with ludicrous newspaper headlines. (Go easy on the puns, though—most don't find them nearly as clever as the punster.)

9. *Exaggerate.* Laughing at the worst-case scenario makes the problem seem less serious (e.g., "I'm so old that I don't buy green bananas anymore.")

10. *Laugh at yourself.* We have to laugh at ourselves because we all do some ridiculous things at times. Be amused, knowing that flaws, weaknesses, and blunders are externals, and don't define one's core worth. And when you do, do so in an accepting way. Overdoing it can reflect low self-regard. Humor researcher Paul McGhee, Ph.D., (1999, p.203) suggests this activity. Make a list of the things you don't like about yourself. This helps you realize that flaws don't signal the end of the world. Divide the list into things that are changeable or not. Practice poking fun at the imperfections and embarrassing moments you are most sensitive about in a kind way (e.g., "My toes are so long that they get to the door two minutes before the rest of me.") Or imagine introducing yourself to a group of imperfect people, a la Alcoholics Anonymous ("I'm John, and I have protruding ears."), and they say, "Hi John," with light-hearted acceptance. Do this with the attitude that anyone who would reject me for such imperfections has a serious problem.

11. *Find humor amidst adversity.* Consider how you have responded emotionally to adversity growing up. Perhaps you got sad or anxious. Consider other options. For instance, you could stay housebound and miserable after a divorce, or you could run outside, open your arms, and yell, "Next!" (McGhee, 1999, p.233). Ask, "What would _____do in this situation?" Fill in the blank with someone who shows good humor amidst adversity. You might reframe adversity (e.g., "I'm not lost; I'm exploring"). Or you might conjure up a funny memory and superimpose it over a bad one. In Army Ranger school, my buddy and I were trying to cross a ravine in the pitch black darkness of the night. We stumbled upon a tree that had fallen across the ravine. Gingerly, we were tight-rope-walking across the tree when, like a trap door, the tree gave way when we were both midway across. We plummeted fifteen feet to the bottom of the ravine. After a short silence, I heard my buddy burst into loud laughter. When I realized that neither of us was hurt, I joined in as we both sat there in a crumpled heap laughing for several minutes. When I superimpose that comical memory over difficult memories or present situations they tend to seem less daunting. As an exercise, write down several funny memories where you or others found humor in adversity.

12. *Observe humor styles.* For several days, observe yourself and others using the four types of humor styles described before in this chapter. Record these in your journal just to get you thinking about these styles. Record the effects of the four styles on self and others.

13. *Connect with playful people.* Call or visit someone who makes you smile. Do this weekly or more.

Remember, humor is basically about being open to play and amusement.

Chapter 18

Moral Strength

No person can be truly at peace with himself if he does not live up to his moral capacity.
Norman Cousins

Resilient people are moral. They live with integrity, meaning that the way they live agrees with their highest values.[1] Moral people are happier—they possess an inner peace because they have fewer regrets, and a sense of satisfaction from striving toward moral excellence.

Peace of conscience does not require perfection. It does require that we do our best. This chapter is about cultivating moral excellence.[2] This requires a very basic form of courage, since the moral life is not necessarily the popular or easy life.

The idea that happiness is tied to goodness is ancient. Aristotle used the word *eudemonia*, or good soul, for happiness, and taught that happiness derives from virtuous living. Conversely, many writers a have described the anguish of transgressing deeply held values. For example, Ed Tick (2005) describes PTSD in veterans as a soul wound, with moral pain as the root cause. John Chaffee (1998, p.334) describes a gradual entrapment, or seduction by degrees, noting that, "immoral people are corrupted at their core, progressively ravaged by a disease of the spirit." And Jonathan Shay (2002), an expert on combat-related PTSD, notes that from moral wounds comes self-loathing, feelings of unworthiness, and loss of self-respect.

Being moral is simply being good and decent; having good character. Being moral means we choose to be good because that is what we most want. Morality seeks the common good. We realize that there is no lasting happiness in unkindness—either to ourselves or to others.

Although morality is seldom influenced in a lasting way through compulsion, most would agree that moral strengths are innate and susceptible to enlargement—just as we can nurture the potentials to play golf or do math.

Living up to our moral capacity is within everyone's grasp. Mother Teresa (1986), when asked what it's like to be a living saint, replied, "You have to be holy in the position you are in just as I have to be holy in the position [I am in]. Holiness is a simple duty for you and me. There is nothing extraordinary about being holy." To be holy, which has the same root as *whole*, means to have integrity—consistency between one's values and actions. Thus, one can be a holy teacher, garbage collector, or firefighter.

Mark Twain in his *Notebook* wrote, "No man, deep down in the privacy of his own heart, has any considerable respect for himself." It is interesting that Mark Twain suffered from depression. In contrast, resilient people strive to maintain self-respect. If it is lost, they have ways to recover it.

How to Strengthen Character

There are essentially two paths to inner peace and self-respect:

1. *Decide in advance to live morally, and then do so.* The best time to make decisions about what one will or will not do is before adversity strikes. Once a moral course has been predetermined, it is considerably easier to act with integrity when one is under duress, tired, or tempted.

2. *Have a system for righting, and making peace with, the wrongs that we will inevitably make because we are imperfect mortals.* Starting anew, bouncing back from mistakes or bad choices, is a critical part of resilience. We might call this moral resilience. In many cultures and recovery groups, the steps are:

   - *Admit the wrong.* We can't change what we deny.
   - *Make amends when possible.* This is the compassionate thing to do as it is healing to the offended party and to ourselves.
   - *Acknowledge mitigating circumstances* (e.g., "I was fatigued, I made a decision under pressure, I didn't have all the facts"). This is not making excuses, just increasing understanding.
   - *Acknowledge your right to pick yourself up after falling.* Worthwhile people don't lose their worth because of imperfections, nor do they forfeit their right to keep trying to improve.
   - *Reconcile with a Higher Power.* For example, ask for forgiveness—allowing God to take the pain and trusting that forgiveness will come.
   - *Forgive yourself.* Some become depressed, dispirited, and even suicidal because of an act or a pattern of transgression. They might conclude they are beyond redemption or can never again be good enough after doing *that*. Following the suggestion of Follette and Pistorello (2007), you might ask yourself, "Have I stopped valuing_____(honesty, kindness, temperance, etc.) just because I strayed from the path, or got turned around once, twice, or even for several years?"
   - *Commit to a better course of action, resolving not to repeat the mistake.* Be grateful for the wisdom mistakes teach us.

A Story of Honesty

Over the course of my career, I've been asked to write many letters of recommendation. I first invite the requesters in for rather searching interviews in order to make the letters personal. At some point I'll ask about character. I might lead with a question like, "What would distinguish you and make you valuable to your employer?" One unusually accomplished, self-motivated young woman said, with quiet self-assurance, "I'm honest." I asked her what integrity means. She said, "Doing the right thing even when you don't have to, when no one is watching." I asked her for examples. She said, "I don't take company supplies at work. When we are assigned online closed-book tests, I don't use books." "Anything else?" I asked. "When my class was assigned to attend a concert, my friends left after getting a ticket stub. I stayed for the concert knowing that I would have to say whether or not I attended." [This brought to mind the West Point honor code: A cadet does not lie, cheat, or steal.] As I was writing the letter, I called her father, a long-time friend, and asked him what he considered his daughter's greatest strength. Without hesitation, he said, "Kelly is honest." I thought, "There's a young woman who can be trusted, and who will have inner peace if she remains true to her values." It was a pleasure to recommend her truly without reservation, for she not only had intellectual intelligence, but moral intelligence as well.

Inspiring Moral Strength through Leadership

Although mandating moral behavior against one's will is not generally effective, moral strengths are innate and susceptible to encouragement, inspiration, example, self-discovery, and cultivation. Leaders (of families, units, or other groups) can create a climate that encourages moral excellence in the following ways:

1. *Lead by example.* Admiral Paul A. Yost, the eighteenth Commandant of the U.S. Coast Guard, is a man of uncompromising integrity and sincerity. One senses that within seconds of meeting him. In a reflective moment he shared that one can lead without compromising his values and that doing so never hindered his career. Coupled with excellent leadership skills, his quiet moral excellence inspired those who knew him to emulate him. In my experience, people do not respect leaders who lack integrity. They will especially resent such leaders when they suffer the consequences of following their unfortunate examples.

2. *Assign or encourage inspiring reading.* Don't underestimate the impact of good literature to fortify individuals, reminding them that integrity under duress is possible. Some examples:
   - *Days of Grace* tells the story of tennis star Arthur Ashe, who chose a life of quiet, modest integrity.
   - Joshua Chamberlain led the 20th Maine Regiment in the pivotal battle of the Civil War. His innovation on the battlefield when his unit was in dire straits and his ability to inspire his exhausted men to follow him in a triumphant bayonet charge were a direct result of the respect they had for this courageous, moral leader. At the surrender ceremony, he directed his men to salute the defeated Confederate Army in token of his deep respect for them.
   - WWII concentration camp survivor Viktor Frankl viewed the prison camp as an opportunity for moral growth. We tend to listen to someone who has survived adversity with his integrity intact, and believe more that such an accomplishment is possible. We might consider the prison camps as a metaphor for the environments of firefighters, police, military service members, and everyday citizens.

3. *Lead character training.* Dedicate time and a place. Many units assign character training to chaplains, when leaders can be even more effective. Leaders need not be perfect to conduct character training. They just need to be genuinely committed to the welfare of their people, and trying their utmost. The leader might start out with words to this effect: "I'm concerned not only for the effectiveness of our unit, but for your inner peace and well-being years from now. We're all mortal, imperfect, and in the same boat. But we can all try our best and support each other as we strive for moral excellence." I think of a leader whom I respected saying, "I'm a hypocrite. I'm not perfect, but I'm trying. I'd rather be a hypocrite than a cynic who gives up." Character training can include the following:
   - *Define morality.* Ask what it means to be a moral person. You are likely to hear responses such as: being good, being decent; possessing good character; doing what's in the best interest of self and others. Ask people to identify values that would make self, unit/family, or the world a better place—values

that if committed to would elevate humanity, self, and others. Aim for a consensus before listing a value, and then ask them to define each value. Irrespective of culture, most will readily agree on the basic moral strengths, such as:[3]

• Honesty	• Trustworthiness	• Courtesy
• Respect	• Fairness	• Self-control, temperance
• Responsibility	• Benevolence, kindness, caring	

- *Ask Socratic questions to provoke further reflection.* For example, many consider honesty to be the foundational or gateway virtue.[4] I like to ask my classes:
  - Is it *possible* to be entirely honest?[5]
  - When is it OK to tell a lie? (People usually give two answers: (1) To spare others' feelings; (2) To save face or get someone off your back. To the first we might ask, "Would someone melt if you were to respond to 'How do I look?' with 'I think other colors look better on you'? Would that person be more likely to trust your opinion in the future, especially if you couple your honestly with tact?" To the second, "Why would you let someone compromise your integrity by causing you to lie?"[6]
  - Is it in your long-term best interest to lie? Why or why not? (e.g., If I don't trust myself to be truthful, would I trust others to be?) It can be motivating to do a cost/benefits analysis. On a white board, ask people to list the advantages of being dishonest (e.g., If I get away with it, I might get promoted, gain materially, have fun beating the system). Then ask them for the disadvantages of being dishonest (e.g., worrying about covering my tracks, career derailment, loss of trust, loss of inner power/control, etc.). Finally ask rhetorically, "Is dishonesty a problem for you in terms of its costs?"
  - Is it in the long-term best interest of others to lie?
  - When people have lied to you, how did it make you feel? What did it do to trust?
  - What would be the positive consequences of my being more honest? (It works well to have people write down responses for themselves, then share those they are comfortable mentioning to the group. People share things, such as: "I won't worry about getting caught"; "I'd have a quiet satisfaction inside knowing I'm being truthful"; "I'll be happier"; "People would trust me more"; "I'd have more peace and self-respect." Hearing such thoughts can be very motivating.)

- *Ask people in your group to find and report on morality in people's lives.* For example,
  - In WWII, Chiune Sugihara was serving as the Japanese consul to Lithuania. In defiance of his government, he wrote visas that saved more than 6,000 Jews from the Nazis. In consequence, he was imprisoned by

the Russians and shunned by his government after the war. Influenced by his samurai code, which taught him to help those in need, he and his wife had decided to risk the consequences simply because it was the right thing to do. Their moral courage liberated them from fear of ridicule and rejection, notwithstanding the costs.

- March 16, 1968, is the date of the shameful My Lai massacre of the Vietnam war. Hugh Thompson, an ordinary guy, was flying his helicopter in aerial combat support of American troops. Below, he saw women, children, and elderly lying dead in an irrigation ditch, and witnessed executions of civilians by U.S. soldiers. Landing his chopper, he evacuated ten civilians to safety to prevent their murder by nearby troops and told the troops on the ground to stay put. Initially, his peers shunned him for his actions. Thirty years later he was reunited with two of the people he had saved from certain death, and finally recognized with gratitude by many. One letter stated: "The world needs so much more of the likes of you."[7]

- The Nazis kept the slender ballerina Edith Eva Eger alive at Auschwitz to entertain them while they killed her family. She forgave them to free herself from the past. She relates: "At the end I remember feeling sorry for the German officers and soldiers as I watched them flee through the open camp gates. I remember thinking to myself, 'I will have painful memories of what happened, but they will always have to live with memories of what they did.' I lost my family in Auschwitz. It was very traumatic. But I have integrated the experience, and I'm the person I am because of it."[8]

- Arthur Brooks (2008) concludes that unlimited moral freedoms are inconsistent with greater happiness. For example, General Social Survey data indicate that drugs and premarital sex are associated with less happiness.[9]

- Harris Poll created the National Happiness Index to track changes in happiness over time. In a Spring 2008 poll, those who said they were never or rarely pressured to act unethically were eleven percentage points more likely to be very happy than those who were pressured all the time or often.

- *Relate meaningful stories from personal experience.* For example, the honor code at West Point stated that a cadet does not lie, cheat or steal; we were instructed that expulsion would be the consequence for anyone who did. The story was told of a platoon leader who was ordered to have his platoon out of a certain area by a certain time. When asked by his commander if he had done this, the platoon leader lied to save face. The commander then ordered an artillery barrage on that area, resulting in needless deaths of platoon members. In my years at West Point, I never personally knew of anyone who violated the honor code. It was a great comfort to be able to take another at his word, and to know that grades were fairly earned. I once left a twenty-dollar bill on my desk for a several days, with full confidence that the bill would be there the next day.

- Ask people to read a reflection, such as, "You cannot have a moral holiday and remain moral" (Chambers, 1963, p.106), and ask if they agree. Then discuss what that reflection means to them.

The Fearless, Searching, Kind Moral Inventory

This activity is patterned after the Moral Inventory used in Alcoholics Anonymous. When a grocer inventories the shelves, he simply counts, without judging, what is there and what is not in order to see where he stands. Likewise, in the fearless, searching, kind moral inventory we simply take stock of our present moral condition. We notice strengths, lest this inventory only be an *immoral* inventory. And we notice what we need to do to grow stronger. The process is fearless, searching, and kind because there is no condemnation or denial—only the intention to grow and be happier at an appropriate pace. Here are the steps:

1. *Integrity meditation.* Integrity brings self-respect, inner peace, happiness, and trust. Sitting quietly, consider: Is there anything that disturbs your peace, damages your reputation with self, or leads others to distrust you?
2. *Take the Fearless, Searching, Kind Moral Inventory beginning on the next page.* Start by reading the definitions of the character/moral strengths. Make any adjustments to these definitions that you feel are appropriate. In the second column, rate where you presently stand. The third column helps to motivate improvement by reminding us of strengths and potentialities that already exist. The fourth column asks us to identify specific steps that bring us closer to moral excellence. For example, to increase honesty one might keep an Honesty-Dishonesty journal for a week. Each day, list:
   - Lies you hear. How does it feel to hear them?
   - Lies (even "white lies") that you tell. How does it feel to tell them? Does it make you happier?
   - Truths you tell (especially, give yourself credit for telling the truth when truth-telling is difficult). How does that make you feel inside?

At the end of the week see how you did. Then set a goal for improvement. For example, you might aim to go an entire day (or some other reachable goal), only telling the complete truth—no white lies, no deceit, no excuses to save face. Ask yourself, "What is the worst that could happen if I told the truth? What is the best thing that could happen?"

The Fearless, Searching, Kind Moral Inventory

Character Strength	Rate Yourself from 1-10. 10 means you are living this strength as well as a person can.	Describe a time in the past when you demonstrated this strength	Describe what you could do to demonstrate this strength better and more often.
Courage means persisting in doing the right thing despite the pressure to do otherwise.			
Honesty means you speak only the truth, always. No "white lies," half-truths (truth can be tactful and kind), cheating, or stealing.			
Integrity means your behaviors match your values and that you show your sincere, authentic self without pretense.			
Respect means you honor people and treat them as worthwhile; are civil and courteous.			
Fairness means you play by the rules, do not take dishonorable advantage of others, and treat others impartially.			
Loyalty, faithfulness, and trustworthiness mean you keep commitments and confidences, don't speak ill of others behind their backs, and are reliable.			
Responsible means able and willing to respond to valid needs and duties; dependable; protects self and others.			
Kind, caring means you are concerned for the welfare of others, and desire to help and support their growth; considerate, generous, tenderhearted.			
Sexual integrity means sexual expression is used in the context of love and concern for the other, and never used in a selfish or exploitive way.			

Tolerant means you are patient with differences and imperfections of others; forgiving			

Reflections on Moral Strength

- Happiness and moral duty are inseparably connected. (George Washington)
- Being good can live with suffering. Feeling good cannot. (William J. O'Malley)
- Nothing can bring you peace but the triumph of principles. (Ralph Waldo Emerson)
- I've never met a man with moral courage who wouldn't, when it was really necessary, face bodily danger. (WWII British general)
- Morality is very important. There are lots of dirty cops. If you know what you are doing is right, then you can deal with the pressure. (TK, veteran of thirteen years as a cop, six in undercover narcotics)
- Happy is he that condemneth not himself. (Rom 14:22)
- There is no friendship more valuable than your own clear conscience. (Elaine S. Dalton)
- No man is free who is not master of himself. (Epictetus)
- Tis substantially true, that virtue or morality is a necessary spring of popular government. Can it be that Providence has not connected the permanent felicity of a Nation with its virtue? (George Washington)
- Honesty is the first chapter in the book of wisdom. (Thomas Jefferson)
- Give me beauty in the inward soul; may the outward man and the inward man be as one. (Socrates)
- You can't play in the dirt and not get dirty. (Coach John Wooden quoting his father)
- If you tell the truth, you don't have to remember anything. (Mark Twain)
- No government at any level and for any price can afford the police necessary to assure our safety and our freedom unless the overwhelming majority of us are guided by an inner personal code of morality. (Ronald Reagan)
- I do nothing but go about persuading you all, old and young alike, not to take thought for your persons or properties, but first and chiefly to care about the greatest improvement of the soul. I tell you that virtue is not given by money, but that from virtue comes money and every other good of man, public as well as private. (Socrates)
- Rather fail with honor than succeed by fraud. (Sophocles)
- Be more concerned with your character than with your reputation, because your character is what you are, while your reputation is merely what others think of you. (Coach John Wooden)
- America is great because America is good, and if America ever ceases to be good, America will cease to be great. (Alexis de Tocqueville)
- An honest man's pillow is his peace of mind. (Anonymous)
- It is better to suffer wickedness than commit it. (Socrates)
- Set your heart on doing good. Do it over and over again, and you will be filled with joy. A fool is happy until his mischief turns against him. And a good man may suffer until his goodness flowers. (Buddha)

- You can only sell your reputation one time. Once it's sold, it's sold. It is difficult for anyone to trust anything you say after that. (Arthur Brooks)
- Live a good, honorable life. Then when you get older, and think back, you'll be able to enjoy it a second time. (Dalai Lama)
- They say the world has become too complex for simple answers. They are wrong. There are no easy answers, but there are simple answers. We must have the courage to do what we know is morally right. (Ronald Reagan)
- The happy life is thought to be virtuous; a virtuous life requires exertion, and does not consist in amusement. (Aristotle)
- The real things haven't changed. It is still best to be honest and truthful. (Laura Ingalls Wilder)

Chapter 19

Suffering

No one escapes this life without suffering. There is a saying that we are strengthened by that which does not kill us. While this is often true, it is certainly not always true. Not everyone who survives great suffering gains. Some are weakened and defeated by it. So it is critically important to be psychologically prepared for suffering in order that we can withstand it and perhaps even turn it to gain.

Happy people know how to retain happiness despite and amidst suffering. This chapter will help prepare you for life's inevitable suffering, and offer ideas that will help to preserve happiness and sanity in difficult times.

This preparation includes recognizing that suffering is a complex, double-edged sword—a mixed bag with the potential for both good and bad. Some bend and even break before recovering, while others get permanently bent out of shape—or break and don't mend.

The Problem with Suffering

The Chinese word for trauma consists of two characters representing hurt and creation. The difficulty of suffering arises when the hurt overwhelms the creation. For example, some traumatized individuals:

- Feel overwhelmed, defeated, crushed, dispirited, vulnerable, and less worthwhile.
- Develop a mental illness, such as PTSD, anxiety, or depression. These may not resolve with time alone. Some who don't develop a full-blown mental illness nevertheless develop troubling symptoms.
- Lose their spiritual beliefs.
- Lose hope and turn cynical.

While anyone can be overwhelmed by excessive suffering, we have learned that certain tendencies diminish one's capacity to triumph over suffering. It is helpful to recognize these pitfalls, which keep people stuck in suffering:

- *Blaming.* This leaves one feeling helpless because the offender or circumstance is given the power over the survivor's happiness.
- *Dwelling on how the suffering could have been avoided.* Thinking "I should have known better" gives but an illusion of control.
- *Condemning the self* (e.g., for imperfect performance, allowing something bad to happen, having symptoms).
- *Resisting or denying the pain.* We do this by trying to avoid, escape, discount, or ignore it. When we deny legitimate pain, we cannot process it or make sense of it. Feelings get suppressed and are likely to erupt later in destructive ways. Without confronting pain, we can't problem solve or learn new ways to deal with pain. If we expect to "get over it quickly" without facing the pain, we might become discouraged when the reality hits that some wounds require more time and effort to heal. Those who resist pain are more likely to misuse alcohol, drugs, or

tobacco, which carry their own risks and can interfere with healing and growth. Unrealistic and simplistic optimism can be a way to intellectually deny pain ("It's all good, there's no problem, all is well"). Unrealistic optimism prevents us from realistically anticipating and preparing for challenges. "To escape a prison, it is necessary to see the prison itself" (Hayes, Strosahl, & Wilson, 1999, p.183). Allowing oneself to remain stuck in depression or anxiety can be a way to avoid problem solving.

- *Dwelling on negative thoughts and emotions* (e.g., worrying about what you can't control, obsessing over feelings of depression or inadequacy, repeating statements such as "I'm damaged goods" or "I'm broken"). Trauma therapists often remind clients, "You are not broken, you are just stuck for now."
- Clinging to unworkable spiritual assumptions (e.g., "God will prevent all suffering"; "Only bad people suffer"; "My suffering means I've been abandoned or am being punished"; "A loving God wouldn't allow suffering to happen"; "God's job is to keep me comfortable"). Such assumptions can keep one stuck in anger, blame, and/or disbelief.

The Potential of Suffering

The hidden gift of suffering is it's potential to create a stronger, wiser, happier individual. Happy, resilient individuals have an attitude and a skill set regarding suffering. They recognize that:

- *Growth and distress coexist.* Studies of various survivor groups (combat, POW, AIDS, cancer, etc.) indicate that the greater the distress, the more beneficial growth, change, and adaptation occur—up to a point. In trying to reduce suffering, adversity challenges us to stretch beyond our pre-suffering condition and develop strengths that better prepare us for future calamities. Survivors of severe suffering often report that they changed for the better, including:
  - Committing to make the most of the present and valued relationships; to appreciate life's beauties more
  - Acquiring self-discipline, the ability to cope with adversity, wisdom, and self-confidence
  - Becoming more altruistic, less materialistic, and more genuine (because genuine inner confidence has been acquired, there is less need to impress)
  - Strengthening spirituality
  - Strengthening self-esteem (e.g., "I'll never again let negative circumstances determine the way I view myself.")
  - Gaining a clearer sense of direction; more meaning and purpose. Great adversity can spur questions, such as, "For what purpose did I survive? What is most important?"
  - Becoming more open to new directions and opportunities

In plants, growing in difficult environmental conditions (such as cold, drought, or poor soil) boosts beneficial phytochemicals and stimulates natural defenses, compared to plants grown in more comfortable environments—even though the more comfortably grown plants look better on the outside. In plants, as with humans, it takes challenges to strengthen one inwardly.[1]

- *Personal strengths are discovered in one's darkest hours.* Survivors often report that adversity revealed previously unknown or only partially-recognized capacities to:
  - Take care of self and others
  - Accept what can't be changed
  - Maintain hope
  - See strength in vulnerability. For example a survivor might view the ability to endure and bounce back from intense adversity as a strength ("If I survived this I can survive anything")
- *Suffering reveals our weaknesses.* If we acknowledge them, we stand to turn them into strengths, or at least wisely recognize them as limits to work with.

Strategies to Turn Suffering to Your Advantage

1. *View suffering as an important process*—"a necessary path to awakening"[2]— with aspects that are good and bad. Sometimes growth comes only with time, patience, and effort. Often we might first have to heal before we can grow. Often we learn things in the process of healing that facilitates growth. Suffering is an impermanent process, like a tree with changing seasons. Leaves fall off, and then the tree sprouts leaves.
2. *Feel a sense of mastery* for surviving and adapting as well as you did. Recognize how difficult some circumstances are and that you did your best under such circumstances. Recognize human limits with acceptance, while still striving for optimal, high-level functioning.
3. *Determine to persist, to make life more meaningful.* Identify values and goals, which help us persevere through the dark times and make the best of any given situation. Do not expect perfection, but do persist, mistakes and all.
4. *Be active, not passive.*
   - Be open to suffering. Turn into it with an open attitude. Embrace it with a comforting stance, much as you would hold a crying child with a skinned knee. Eventually, the child is comforted and returns to play. Understand what happened, as best you can. A cop sent me this note after a resilience training workshop: "Grant that I may be provided the appropriate difficulties and sufferings in my life, that my heart may be truly awakened, and that my practice of liberation and universal compassion be truly fulfilled (author unknown)."
   - If your usual way of handling things is not working well, try different tools. For example, if immersing yourself in work does not help, then use other skills. If you can, solve the problem. You can also confide in writing, worry in writing, and replace cognitive distortions or attitudes that are not working. In chapter 26 you'll learn ways to change your response to problems, without necessarily changing the problems. Forgiving is another way to problem solve (see chapter 23).
5. *Aim to be challenged, not overwhelmed.* If you can, seek an intermediate level of challenge for the greatest growth. Hardship can inoculate us if we are able to make

sense of it and develop strengths. If overwhelmed, however, we might feel defeated and helpless, or turn cynical. So if there is too much on your plate, try to spread out demands or not take on new ones. If you do get overwhelmed, you might later become inoculated if you remain open. Christopher Reeve, for example, initially felt suicidal after an accident left him paralyzed. He eventually turned his tragedy into a meaningful and satisfying cause. Again, you might need time for healing or a period of safety before growth can occur.

6. *Be aware of weakness with acceptance.* Realize that weaknesses are not necessarily permanent. Often, they can later be turned into strengths.

7. *Maintain self-esteem, optimism, and social support,* which are consistently related to post-traumatic growth. For example, optimists are more likely to try to make sense of trauma. Social support lightens burdens. Those who try to go-it-alone deprive themselves of suggestions, comfort, encouragement, and perspective that others who are safe and trusted can provide. Supportive others can help us overcome denial, helping us go to the depths of our feelings, and surrounding wounds with love so that healing is facilitated.

8. *Experience positive emotions.* Remember wholesome distraction, amusement, gratitude, and altruism (this includes caring for and comforting others). Humor is also consistently associated with adaptive coping. Among its many benefits, humor can (see chapter 17 also):
   - Break up the heaviness, giving a needed respite from pain and lightening mood
   - Remind us that we are bigger than the tragedy—able to restore a sense of normalcy and gain a measure of triumph over suffering
   - Give us another way to recognize and discuss pain
   - Strengthen social bonds

9. *Cultivate hardiness.* Hardiness is an attitude that is linked to better performance, health, job satisfaction, leadership, and protection from combat stress. Hardiness:
   - Views adversity as a challenge and opportunity to grow and learn
   - Approaches adversity with the assumption that one is capable
   - Commits in hardship to making one's contribution meaningful

10. *Nourish religious faith and spirituality* (see chapter 20).

Triumph Over Suffering: Three Stories

○ At the University of Maryland, Elizabeth Meejung Lee was a sophomore business major, dreaming of financial success in the corporate world, even though she wasn't passionate about her major. She lost her sight when her ex-boyfriend shot her and then committed suicide. The doctor thought she wouldn't make it, but following multiple surgeries, she did—although she lost her eyesight and sense of smell. After a year of recovery, she returned to school. Deciding that helping people was more important than financial security (which no longer seemed important), she changed her major to sociology. Said Elizabeth, "I can honestly say I'm happier now. I am closer to God, my family and my friends. I've gained a lot more than I've lost." Those close to her describe her as a person of faith, strong, optimistic, positive, cheerful, sweet, patient, and willing to learn.[3]

- Harvard Medical School's Ronald Kessler studied more than 800 residents of three Gulf states following Hurricane Katrina. The prevalence of any mental illness nearly doubled following Katrina, but there was no rise in suicidal thinking. Survivors said they felt closer to loved ones and their community, and more religious; they found greater purpose and meaning as they mobilized inner resources to fight the problems. Some people changed the way they saw themselves (e.g., "I never thought I would do something like jump in the water and save a kid").[4]
- Tony Dungy, when coaching the Indianapolis Colts, called Mark Lemke, a truck driver whose son, who was also his best friend, had died in a motorcycle accident. Dungy was calling with condolences. You see, Dungy's son had recently committed suicide. They formed a friendship and talked often, even amidst the pressures of the Super Bowl season. They commiserated about how hard it is to think about their sons. Dungy gently reminded Lemke that if they keep their faith they'll see their sons again. Dungy has quietly given a hand up to others who were similarly grieving.[5]

Activity: Turning Adversity to Gain[6]

Looking back on a traumatic or otherwise very difficult event, consider the strengths that you demonstrated and complete the sheet below:

Strengths	How and when did you show this strength?	How could you make this strength a greater part of your life?
Courage		
Determination, persistence, perseverance		
Altruism, kindness		
Responsibility		
Hope, optimism, keeping the dream alive		
Judgment, wisdom		
Humor		

Openness to learning		
Confidence		
Self-Discipline		
Integrity		
Flexibility		
Appreciation of life/beauty		
Calmness		
Patience		
Spiritual/religious faith		
Leadership		
Other Strengths		

Activity: Visual Imagery[7]

This imagery exercise provides a breather, a temporary respite from suffering.

1. Sit comfortably in the meditator's posture. Feet are flat on the floor; hands are resting, unfolded comfortably in the lap with palms up or down. Your back is comfortably erect. Imagine the spine aligned like a column of golden coins resting one atop the other. The torso is held with dignity and grace, like a majestic mountain.
2. Allow your eyes to close. "See" in your mind's eye a beautiful mountain meadow on a high plateau. The sun is shining warmly, and snow glistens brightly on the top of a nearby peak. The meadow ends at an edge of a sharp precipice.

3. Imagine yourself climbing the mountain. You feel the bright, warm sun beating down on your body, warming you. Your skin begins to glow as you begin to perspire. You feel hot and tired, and then come upon this lovely, refreshing meadow.
4. Stop and rest for a while in its peace and beauty. Imagine how it looks; how it sounds; how it smells. Enjoy the rewards of all the hard work it took to get there. Breathe in deeply the cool mountain air, and relax down into the soft grass; stay as long as you like. Notice the clouds blowing by.
5. When ready to leave, go to the edge of the precipice and throw over anything that has been bothering you—anything that you wish to be rid of in your life. Picture it as a glaring, jagged-edged word, a chain, a brick, or any other image that helps you symbolize it as undesirable. When the "visit" is completed, thank yourself or whatever you see as your higher power for the release of your burden; then walk peacefully back through the meadow and down the mountain.

Reflections on Suffering

- In the depths of winter, I finally learned that within me there lay an invincible summer. (Albert Camus)
- When it's dark enough you can see the stars. (Ralph Waldo Emerson)
- Affliction comes to us all—not to make us sad, but sober; not to make us sorry, but wise; not to make us despondent, but by its darkness to refresh us, as the night refreshes the day; not to impoverish, but to enrich us. (Henry Ward Beecher)
- If there is no struggle, there is no progress. (Frederick Douglass)
- Prison life taught him how little one can get along with, and what extraordinary spiritual freedom and peace such simplification can bring. (POW, quoted by Anne Morrow Lindbergh)
- Problems call forth our courage and our wisdom; indeed, they create our courage and our wisdom. It is only because of problems that we grow mentally and spiritually. When we desire to encourage the growth of the human spirit, we challenge and encourage the human capacity to solve problems, just as in school we deliberately set problems for our children to solve. (M. Scott Peck)
- So it is more useful to watch a man in times of peril, and in adversity to discern what kind of man he is; for then, at last, words of truth are drawn from the depths of his heart, and the mask is torn off, reality remains. (Roman philosopher and poet Lucretius)
- There's a crack in everything; that's how the light gets in. (Leonard Cohen, poet, songwriter)
- We all leave childhood with wounds. In time, we may transform our liabilities into gifts. The faults that pockmark the psyche may become the source of a man or a woman's beauty. The injuries we have suffered invite us to assume the most human of all vocations—to heal ourselves and others. (Sam Keen, psychologist)
- When heaven is about to confer a great responsibility on any man, it will exercise his mind with suffering, subject his sinews and bones to hard work, expose his body to hunger, put him to poverty, place obstacles in the paths of his deeds, so as to stimulate his mind, harden his nature, and improve wherever he is incompetent. [Meng Tzu, also known as Mencius)

179

- He who learns must suffer.
  Even in our sleep,
  Pain which we cannot forget
  Falls drop by drop upon the heart,
  Until, in our own despair,
  Against our will,
  Comes wisdom,
  Through the awful grace of God
              (Aescshylus, Greek dramatist)

Chapter 20

Religion & Spirituality

Karl Marx called religion "the opiate of the masses." Freud called it "obsessional neurosis" that leads to guilt and repressed sexuality. Were their assumptions correct? Not according to the research. Since the 1980s there have been thousands of studies on religion and health. The vast majority document religion's positive effects, including:

- Greater happiness (an immense amount of data indicates that religious people are happier than secular people)
- Greater optimism
- Greater resilience and better mental health (better cognitive function; less depression, anxiety, stress, and worry; better ability to recover from depression; less disturbance from hardships such as bereavement, illness, unemployment, and divorce; greater recovery and growth after trauma; more calmness)
- More altruism (religious people are more giving of their time and money to both religious and non-religious causes)
- Better health (longer lifespan; lower blood pressure; fewer strokes; better immunity and heart function)
- More satisfaction with marriage and sex
- Less drug/tobacco use, crime, divorce, suicide, guilt, and fear of death

In addition, spiritually-based therapies for PTSD often effectively address "wounds of the soul" that conventional therapies may not.[1]

Religion or Spirituality?

Spirituality is the search for the sacred.[2] For most this means striving to draw closer to God, others, and the highest values of humankind.

Religion comes from the Latin *religio*, meaning "to bind together," and suggests our attempts to connect to the sacred goals mentioned above. A religion refers to the beliefs and practices that unite a community.

In the scientific literature, religion is usually measured by:

- Involvement/practice (e.g., attending worship services, praying or studying sacred writings at home, living ethically and charitably)
- Beliefs

In the research, it is not affiliation or denomination (e.g., whether one calls oneself Methodist, Jew, or Catholic) that predicts benefits of religion, but the degree to which people actually live their religion. Especially predictive of benefits are attendance (e.g., those who attend worship services weekly are far happier than those who attend rarely or not at all) and religious certainty (e.g., faith in God and the truth of one's beliefs, such as life after death).

Wholesome religion supports spirituality. Resilient people often cite religious faith as important to their survival.[3] Depending on the poll, 85-95% of Americans believe in God, consider religion important, and think they are religious, or spiritual, or both.

Why Is Religion Beneficial?

Religious beliefs and practice can:
- *Nurture spiritual support.* The importance of children feeling attached (or bonded) to loving parents has been well documented. Feeling securely attached to God—feeling God's love, presence, and support—is to many the deepest form of attachment. In one study, feeling near to God was the strongest predictor of happiness across all ranges of age.[4] Resilient survivors often mention how their beliefs helped them to endure crises—knowing that a loving and good God is over all and that they can hope and trust in ultimate meaning, goodness, and the resolution of suffering. Others relate how they asked for and received the strength needed to change adverse circumstances or endure what could not be changed. Spiritual intimacy might replace the feelings of being disconnected and groundless, and might explain why religion protects teens from drug, premarital sex, and participation in gangs.

  Nearly all of the world's religions have the following healing themes in common:[5]
  - Love and compassion (e.g., infinite Divine love for individuals despite their imperfections)
  - Eternal worth of individuals
  - Redemption/reconciliation/forgiveness—an answer to guilt
  - Hope—which is broader and deeper than optimism
  - Inner peace through excellence of character[6]
  - Meaning, purpose, and growth
  - Solace in trials; shared burdens (e.g., "God is in control; I don't have to do it all myself.")
  - Perseverance; strength to endure ("God doesn't give trials that we can't handle.")
- *Promote social support.* Religious communities can provide companionship, emotional support in crises, a needed helping hand, and healing rituals, such as funerals and memorial services. Such communities encourage beliefs and practices associated with happiness (such as belief in an afterlife, ethical behavior, altruism, gratitude, non-materialism, and care of the body). Conversely they can support people in the avoidance of beliefs and lifestyle choices associated with unhappiness (such as drugs, premarital sex, and divorce).
- *Put us in touch with moral beauty*—including love, goodness, and kindness. For example, viewing the documentary of Mother Teresa giving selfless service to the poor typically lifts the mood and immune functioning of even cynical viewers (Mother Teresa was both religious and spiritual).

When Is Religion Not Beneficial?

Religion correlates with unhappiness only when one has an unhappy image of God. In several studies those who regard God as kind and caring are happier than those who regard God as punitive, unresponsive, and unloving. [7]

Spiritual ambivalence or confusion can also be unsettling. For example, holding, but not living by beliefs, can undermine spiritual security. Agnostics are less happy than atheists, who are less happy than believers (Brooks, 2008).

Pathways to Beneficial Spirituality

In western cultures, people might invest untold hours in work, golf games, or hobbies, but very little time in cultivating spirituality. Perhaps we expect, as some do with happiness, that spirituality will flourish without effort. You might recall what has fed you spiritually in the past and call again upon these resources. The following suggestions might be helpful:

1. *Seek professional help for mental illness.* Mental illness, especially PTSD, can numb spiritual feelings. So it is good to get help for the healing process. You might consider a therapist who shares, or at least is respectful of, your spiritual views. A *Newsweek* poll found that 72% of Americans would welcome a conversation about faith or spirituality with their doctor.

2. *To strengthen beliefs, actively participate in religious practices for intrinsic reasons.* That is, practice what is dictated by your deepest inner beliefs, not external rewards, such as social standing, success in business, or so forth. An intrinsic orientation has been linked to greater happiness. Those who frequently participate religiously with full commitment benefit more than those who participate less frequently or with weaker commitment.[8]

3. *Consider giving up dysfunctional ideas* that are linked to mental distress (also see chapter 7). Below are a few of these, with their counterarguments:

   - *If God really loved me, God wouldn't let me suffer like this. I'm abandoned and punished. God doesn't care.* Job, Peter, and Jesus, to name a few, suffered greatly. Does that mean they were not loved? Suffering is not necessarily an indication of divine disfavor, just as comfort does not necessarily indicate divine favor. Suffering is part of life; it can ultimately deepen compassion, be a means for growth, and stimulate our most meaningful work in a way that comfort will not. Think, for example, of Candice Lightner, whose daughter was killed by a drunk driver. She went on to found Mothers Against Drunk Driving, an organization that has helped so many people.

   - *God should ensure that only good happens. God shouldn't let this happen.* This can keep us stuck in anger and blame. In an imperfect world where people have free choice, bad sometimes happens—sometimes through the fault of others, sometimes through our own fault, and sometimes randomly. An alternative thought might consider that the ultimate purpose in adversity might not be immediately obvious. Sometimes we create the meaning in adversity by our responses to it.

- *God won't forgive me for* <u>that</u>. Where is that written? Bouncing back from mistakes and starting anew is one important form of spiritual resilience. Everyone has the right to try again.
- *It is selfish to take care of myself.* If you are not spiritually nourished, you won't be of much good to anyone, including yourself. Dedicate time to spiritual growth, much as you would set aside time to eat or exercise.
- *I must forget my troubling past.* This isn't possible. Instead, one can bring it to God, the master healer. It is then possible to remember the past, but without feeling the same emotional distress.
- *Religion and being good will protect me from adversity.* These won't always, but they *can* provide the inner peace and strength needed to meet adversity without hatred or bitterness.[9]
- *My lifestyle choices or mistakes make me bad to the core.* Mistakes make us human, not worthless or irretrievable. There is a difference between guilt (I *made* a mistake) and shame (I *am* a mistake—bad to the core and unlovable). Guilt can lead to a useful resetting of our course in life. Shame is not useful. Let it go.

4. *Pray regularly.* You might try meditative prayer—focusing on maintaining a relationship with God, feeling God's presence, or inviting God into your life. Those who do are happier than those whose main focus in prayer is petitioning.[10] Try sitting quietly, letting go of thoughts, and simply be aware of divine presence. You might use imagery, such as resting beside still waters, or feeling a divine embrace. When petitioning, don't expect prayer to fix everything. In addition to asking for desired outcomes, we might simply ask more frequently for the strength to endure life's challenges.

5. *Seek comfort in sacred writings.* One WWII survivor of the abhorrent Japanese prison camps told me that what got him through was remembering a scripture he'd learned as a youth: "Casting all your care upon him, for he careth for you" (1 Peter 5:7). Another recalled that Jesus, who himself felt abandoned for a time, gave this solace, "Remember, I am with you always, to the end" (Matt 28:20). You might record such writings in a place where you can retrieve them when under distress.

6. *Connect with a faith community* that helps fill needs for security, attachment, understanding, and affirmation of one's basic worth. A place of worship can often prompt the relaxation response. Members of faith communities are sometimes called "holders of hope" (Day et al., 2005, p.126). You might seek the support of clergy or members or the congregation in meeting life's challenges.

Trauma involves loss, such as the loss of innocence, dreams, safety, opportunities, or relationships. Faith communities can help with the grieving and reconciliation process. Be aware, however, that some congregants might not relate to trauma survivors, who might feel rejected by the community or abandoned by God. This is to be expected until those congregants either themselves experience trauma or are taught to understand it. Don't take this personally. Also, be wary of those who judge unkindly, such as assuming that pain is necessarily a result of sin or weak faith. Don't let imperfect individuals interfere with meeting your spiritual needs.

7. *Find comfort in rituals.* For example, the Jewish chaplain at American University, Rabbi Ken Cohen, commemorated the anniversary of 9/11 with the Blast of the Shofar: One sustained blast signified "I am whole"; three short blasts, "I am broken"; staccato blasts, "I am utterly disconsolate"; and finally, very long, sustained blasts signified, "I am whole again" (Day et al., 2005). A minister, a Vietnam veteran, likened the ritual of visiting the Vietnam Memorial to the Valley of Death (Day et al., p.126):

> Hope can creep up on you slowly when you've stopped expecting it. For me the most powerful example of this is the Vietnam Veterans Memorial in Washington, D.C., which most Vietnam veterans call "the Wall." As you walk on the pathway by the memorial, at first the Wall is hardly noticeable. Then as you continue to walk, the top is up to your ankles, then your knees, then your neck—and then like the war itself, you're in over your head. When I visit the Wall, I feel swallowed at this point. When you've walked far enough, the Wall towers over you. It's inescapable, it's overwhelming, you are totally immersed in it. If you let yourself, you can feel the despair of feeling swallowed up by something much bigger than you, and it feels as if there's no way out. There is nothing to do but to keep on walking, and as you do, eventually the path rises, and it's not so overwhelming, you can see out above it once again, and then it is only knee height, then ankle height—no longer overpowering but still present. At some point along the way, you can feel hope again.
>
> Visiting the Wall and letting yourself be overcome by it is an experience of despair, and hope, of death, and resurrection, of being lost and then being found again, of dying and being reborn.

For many, the simple act of regular worship is a ritual that deepens spirituality.

8. *Don't be surprised if faith initially weakens after trauma.* Spiritual growth is not simple, nor is it necessarily linear. Although adversity can deepen one's faith, about 30% of people experience a weakening of faith after trauma. Initially one might feel numb, angry, or spiritually adrift. With time—especially if one turns to God for support, worships, seeks forgiveness for errors, and engages in other positive religious practices—guilt and distress tend to abate, while spirituality can grow (Day et al., 2005). Ironically, the greatest spiritual growth often follows the greatest spiritual difficulty after trauma, as old, simplistic assumptions are shattered and give way to better ones, and as the relationship with deity deepens.[11] For example, of his five-and-a-half years as a POW in North Vietnam, John McCain ((1999, p.253-254) wrote:

> Faith in myself was important, and remains important to my self-esteem. But I discovered in prison that faith in myself alone, separate from other, more important allegiances, was ultimately no match for the cruelty that human beings could devise when they were entirely unencumbered by respect for the God-given dignity of man.
>
> To guard against such despair [that God has forsaken you], in our most dire moments, POWs would make supreme efforts to grasp our faith tightly, to profess it alone, in the dark, and hasten its revival. Once I was thrown into another cell after a long and difficult interrogation. I discovered scratched

into one of the cell's walls the creed "I believe in God, the Father Almighty." There, standing witness to God's presence in a remote, concealed place, recalled to my faith by a stronger, better man, I felt God's love and care more vividly than I would have felt it had I been safe among a pious congregation in the most magnificent cathedral.

Elvia, a former nun, came to America from Columbia, knowing no English. Her son was her special gift and inspiration. Two years after her husband died, her boy was murdered in a random shooting at a convenience store. Because of political connections, the murderer went unpunished. For years Elvia suffered, asking, "Why did this happen? Where was God? Why did the murderer go free?" Eventually, after four years, her faith re-awakened. She related, "Murder taught me to surrender to Him. Otherwise I go insane or seek revenge. God saved my life." Elvia now works in an intensive care unit in a large city, helping people with grief. She continues, "I have a sure belief in God's grace. I hug people and tell my story. They say, 'If you can make it, so can I.'"

9. *Try spiritual imagery.* For example, you might try this at the end of the day: Relax, breathe in, and acknowledge your concerns. Breathe out and give your concerns over to God to keep for the night, feeling as a child being tucked in bed by a loving parent might feel (Day et al., 2005). Alternatively, locate your pain in your body. (Remember, we feel emotions in our body.) Give it a shape and color. Now push the pain away, and see the pain forming a barrier, such as large boulder—with a size, shape, and different color. Now see yourself walking around that barrier and being greeting by an infinitely loving being, who gives you a loving embrace and utters consoling words. Experience that embrace.

A Story of Spirituality In Suffering

Air Force captain Larry Chesley spent nearly seven years in the Hanoi Hilton, a facetious name given to the squalid building in which American prisoners of war were held during the Vietnam War. Much of the time was spent in solitary confinement. He described their special Sunday practice (Chelsley, 1973, p.21, 58):[12]

[W]e made love of God and our country the paramount theme and an anchor to our souls throughout those years. Each Sunday we would pass the [knocking] signal around, then each man would kneel in his separate room, offer a prayer, and recite the Twenty-third Psalm or the Lord's Prayer. Then we would pledge allegiance to the flag.

We were all aware of the words of Jesus, "Where two or three are gathered together in my name, there am I in the midst of them": ...separating walls were insignificant...we were together in spirit... I learned that God never deserts us if we put our trust in him and try to do his will.

Reflections on Spirituality

- Our creator is the same and never changes despite the names given Him by people here and in all parts of the world. Even if we gave Him no name at all, He would still be there within us, waiting to give us good on this earth. (George Washington Carver)
- Science and technology cannot replace the ago-old spiritual values that have been largely responsible for the true progress of world civilization as we know it today. (Dalai Lama)
- We [too often] regard God as an airman regards his parachute; it's there for emergencies but he hopes he'll never have to use it. (C.S. Lewis)
- But God will look to every soul like its first love because He is its first love. Your place in heaven will seem to be made for you and you alone, because you were made for it—made for it stitch by stitch as a glove is made for a hand. (C.S. Lewis)
- Life in Ravensbruck [concentration camp] took place on two separate levels, mutually impossible. One, the observable, external life, grew every day more horrible. The other, the life we lived with God, grew daily better, truth upon truth, glory upon glory. (Corrie Ten Boom)
- All I have seen teaches me to trust the creator for all I have not seen. (Ralph Waldo Emerson)
- The deepest consolation comes from one's relationship to the divine...I don't pray to invoke blessings, but to know God's will, and have the strength to carry it out. (Arthur Ashe)
- Of all the dispositions and habits which lead to political prosperity, religion and morality are indispensable supports...let us with caution indulge the supposition that morality can be maintained without religion. Whatever may be conceded to the influence of refined education on minds of peculiar structure, reason and experience both forbid us to expect that national morality can prevail in exclusion of religious principle. (George Washington)
- When asked by a pastor if the Lord was on the Union's side, Abraham Lincoln said, "I am not concerned about that, for I know that the Lord is *always* on the side of the *right*. But it is my constant anxiety and prayer that I and the nation should be on the *Lord's* side.
- Science without religion is lame, religion without science is blind. (Albert Einstein)
- With all your science, can you tell me how it is that light comes into the soul? (Henry David Thoreau)
- Let nothing disturb thee,
  Nothing affright thee;
  All things are passing;
  God never changeth.
  —Saint Teresa of Avila, Spanish nun

188

Chapter 21

Money: Attitudes and Management

Wealth, materialism, more academic degrees, and prestigious jobs don't lead to lasting happiness. For example, the wealthiest Wall Street stockbrokers suffered a disproportionately high rate of depression in one study, while even thinking about money tends to make people less interested in helping others.[1] So is there anything related to money that does affect happiness levels? It appears that happy people, irrespective of wealth level, manage their money differently than unhappier people. They also have different attitudes toward money than the unhappy do. This chapter will summarize what we've learned about the way people think about and manage money.

Materialism and Happiness

We'll begin with a brief understanding of materialism. Materialism—the preoccupation with accumulating wealth and material possessions as a primary life goal—is negatively related to overall life satisfaction and satisfaction with one's standard of living.[2] Materialists set unrealistically high standards based on social comparisons with others, who appear to be making more without working harder. They equate their worth as a person to income, and base their happiness on their standard of living, rather than other domains of life. They also tend to overspend, believing happiness comes from consuming. Finally, materialists watch more television, which itself is related to drops in mood.

Money and Happiness

A growing amount of research suggests that the following steps might increase happiness levels:
1. *Spend money on memories.* Lasting happy memories are more likely to come from a vacation, concert, trip, or meal, rather than from material objects such as jewelry or clothes.
2. *Spend some money in making others happy.* As mentioned in chapter 16, altruism increases happiness. So spending some of our wealth on gifts, making memories for others, or charity tends to increase happiness in the giver.
3. *Budget wisely.* Happy people tend to make a written budget and live within their means. They also tend to pay bills as they come in, have wills, and purchase insurance (life, disability, etc.). Peace of mind comes from a sense of control over our resources, not necessarily the amount of wealth we possess. So it appears wise to have a budget and to review it several times a year.
4. *Save 5-10% of your income.* Aim for an amount in savings equal to at least three to six months of your present earnings.
5. *Avoid debt as much as possible.* Interest on loans accrues constantly, even when we sleep and vacation. Avoid using credit cards for luxuries or extravagant purchases,[3] and only use them when you have sufficient cash to cover the purchase. Beyond a modest home or car, or needed education, try to avoid debt.

6. *When you think about money, try not to compare yourself to other people.* Wealth does not change one's intrinsic worth. View your salary not as a status symbol, but as an affirmation of your contributions and meaningful efforts.

7. *Live simply and be content with what you have.* Know when enough is enough. It is not material affluence, but having time to enjoy life and do what is meaningful, that is associated with happiness. The story is told of a Harvard MBA who tries to convince a contented Mexican villager to push himself in order to expand his fishing enterprise over a twenty-year period, so that he could retire and enjoy the good life. The fisherman asked the MBA what the good life was. Upon hearing the explanation, the modest fisherman explained that he already had it—time with family, time for a nap, time for a stroll along the shore, and time to enjoy life. "Rat race" is the name given to overworked people suffering from time poverty as they pursue more material wealth. You might be thinking, "I hear you, but just a little more would make me happier." Those who earn "just a little more" tend to escalate their expectations for wealth. And happiness decreases as the gap between what one has and expects to have increases. So it is wise to find contentment in things that do not cost much. As much as you can, release attachment to material objects, which is a major source of unhappiness. If you tell yourself, "I must have that car (house, property, etc.) in order to be happy," you probably won't be happier for long when you do get it. If you don't get it, of course, you'll make yourself unhappy. Instead, we might think, "It would be nice to have that, but I can still enjoy life with less possessions."

    Henry David Thoreau, in March of 1845, moved for two years to Walden Pond, living on property owned by his friend Ralph Waldo Emerson. Thoreau made a cabin, planted a garden, and existed with no clock. He spent his time writing, studying nature, visiting the local community, and enjoying conversation with invited guests. Of his friend, Emerson said: "[Thoreau] knew how to be poor without the least bit of squalor or inelegance. He chose to be rich by making his wants few, and supplying them himself." Happiness prefers adequate, but does not require perfect, conditions.

8. *Recognize money's limitations.* Wealth confers certain advantages,[4] but tends to isolate the wealthy—building walls, literally and figuratively. Possessions also require time to acquire and manage, depriving us of time to reflect and enjoy the simpler pleasures of life. In addition, additional wealth can increase tension and anger, perhaps because of the sacrifices we make to acquire and maintain it. Acquiring wealth does not reduce worries overall, just the type of things we worry about. So ask yourself what you really need to be happy. A happy home, relationships, inner harmony, a meaningful cause, and time to reflect are more related to happiness than material wealth.

9. *Recognize when shopping is meeting emotional needs, such as the need for power or the need to take care of yourself.* Material pleasures might temporarily cover up pain, but don't heal it. Don't count on finding peace at the shopping mall.

10. *Be happy at work.* Happiness does not equate to pay.[5] However, happy people enjoy their work more, finding satisfaction in investing their strengths, helping others, accomplishing, and making friends with co-workers.

A Story of Simplicity

Although he is now educated and materially comfortable, Enrique Fiabella speaks nostalgically of his earlier years in Guatemala:[6]

> Riches were not a part of my childhood. We were a family of five: my father and four siblings. My mother had passed away when I was five years old. My father's meager income was used to buy our food; the purchase of clothing was put off as long as possible.
>
> One day, somewhat bothered, I came up to my father and said, "Daddy, why don't you buy me some shoes? Look at these; they're worn out, and you can see my big toe through the hole in the shoe."
>
> "We'll fix that up," he replied and, with some black polish, gave a shine to my shoes. Later on he told me, "Son, it's fixed up."
>
> "No," I answered, "you can still see my big toe."
>
> "That can also be fixed," he told me. He again took the polish and put some on my toe, and before long it shined like my shoes. So it was early on in life I learned that happiness does not depend on money.

Reflections on Money

- How much money does it take to be happy? A little bit more than he's got. (John D. Rockefeller)
- A thatched roof once covered free men; under marble and gold dwells slavery. (Seneca)
- Many wealthy people are little more than janitors of their possessions. (Frank Lloyd Wright)
- Don't pursue circumstances and take your eye off happiness. (Jennifer Michael Hecht)
- One ought to be able to be equally happy sleeping in palace one night and hut the next. (Marcus Aurelius)
- Do not spoil what you have by desiring what you have not; but remember that what you now have was once among the things only hoped for. (Epicurus)
- The essence of philosophy is that a man should so live that his happiness shall depend as little as possible on external things. (Epictetus)
- If it makes you happy, why are you so miserable? (paraphrasing Sheryl Crow's 1996 hit "If It Makes You Happy")
- Don't envy the rich, whose benefits are counterbalanced by their troubles. (Ecclesiastes)
- There are two ways to get enough. One is to continue to accumulate more and more. The other is to desire less. (G. K. Chesterton)
- We live in a society today where the middle class has more luxury than kings or queens did during most of human history. There is always something in our lives that we can appreciate. (Jacob Teitelbaum)

- A man will never grow rich until he is willing to be poor without feeling deprived. (Puritan adage)
- I think that a person who is attached to riches, who lives with the worry of riches, is actually very poor. (Mother Teresa)
- Too many people spend money they haven't earned, to buy things they don't want, to impress people they don't like. (Quoted by Will Smith)
- I lost a lot when I got money. I lost a lot more when I got fame. As time went on, I needed [my friends] more and more. Other than my family and God, they are all I got that matters. The rest can go away in a minute. (Mariano Rivera, New York Yankee)
- Happiness comes from relationships, not money, and relationships are based on trust, not money. (Anonymous)

Reflections On Simplicity

- Simplicity is the ultimate sophistication. (Leonardo da Vinci)
- Simplicity, simplicity, simplicity! I say let your affairs be as two or three, and not a hundred or a thousand; instead of a million count half a dozen. (Henry David Thoreau)
- I would not give a fig for the simplicity on this side of complexity, but I would give my life for the simplicity on the other side of complexity. (Supreme Court Justice Oliver Wendell Holmes)
- To be a poor, content, and happy person is better than being one who is rich, worried, and afflicted with greed. (Chin Kung)
- The simpler the life, the happier the life. (Chin Kung)
- Our lives are wasted in our attempts to attain things. (Chin Kung)
- [T]he beggar, who suns himself by the side of the highway, possesses that security which kings are fighting for. (Adam Smith)
- To be content with what we possess is the greatest and most secure of riches. (Marcus Tullius Cicero)
- He is richest who is content with the least; for content is the wealth of nature. (Socrates)
- The secret of contentment is knowing how to enjoy what you have, and to be able to lose all desire for things beyond your reach. (Lin Yutang, Chinese writer)

Activities

1. Consider what you really need to be happy—shelter, some food, relationships, good books, time, sleep, and so forth. How much money does it take to meet these needs?
2. Make a list of simple pleasures that you have enjoyed in the past, or could enjoy now. Try to list especially those pleasures that cost little or nothing.
3. Consider what might bring greater financial peace:
   - Make a written budget, listing your income and your expenses. Determine what is left to spend. Try to minimize unnecessary expenses, such as frequently eating out or purchasing what you could make yourself, such as

lunch. If possible, budget some money for savings, making others happy, and creating a happy memory.

- Make a will.
- Buy needed insurance (life, disability, home, etc.).

4. Make a plan to get out of debt. If you have multiple debts, pay off the smallest first. Pay back more than the minimum payment due each month in order to reduce interest payments. When that debt is paid off, apply that payment to the next biggest debt.

Chapter 22

Meaning and Purpose

He who has a why to live can bear with almost any how.
Nietzsche

People who sense that their lives have meaning and purpose are happier and more resilient. Meaning and purpose make life and work more satisfying, give us a reason to persevere through tough times, and help to protect against post-traumatic stress symptoms and mental disorders generally.

Purpose refers to what one determines to do—goals one intends to reach. Meaning implies that one's purposes and actions are worthwhile or significant to the person.

The much-admired survivor of the WWII concentration camps, Viktor Frankl, expressed perhaps the most profound thoughts on the subject of meaning and purpose.[1] He noticed that those who had a reason for living withstood their suffering better. He marveled that some people in the most dire straits found joy in serving their comrades. He himself transcended the meaningless, miserable world of prison camp by envisioning his beloved wife's love, and by seeing himself at some future time lecturing to others on the lessons of the concentration camp. He also realized that one could take consummate pleasure in something as simple as watching the sunrise through the barbed wire. From his own experience, he boldly asserted that one might imprison your body, but no one can take away your inner freedom—the freedom to choose your attitude toward suffering and your ability to impose meaning upon even the worst of circumstances. The school of psychotherapy that he developed, logotherapy, helps people find meaning in their lives. In his own life, Frankl found great satisfaction in helping others find meaning and purpose. He said, "What the human being needs is not a tensionless state but rather a striving and struggling for some goal worthy of him."[2]

Life usually presents circumstances that help us discover meaning and purpose. For example, prisoners sick with typhus needed Frankl's medical skills. He responded by volunteering to care for them, at great risk to his own health. However, meaning and purpose are mostly created as we respond to circumstances from our values, abilities, experiences, understanding, desires, and loves. This creative process is intensely personal, heartfelt, and unique—no one else will combine the ingredients you have in the same way. Meaning and purpose derive from absorption in challenging, satisfying activities.[3] Unlike fleeting material pleasures, the satisfaction from meaningful, purposeful endeavors tends to persist and even increase with time as we invest and grow our talents.

How to Build Meaning and Purpose

How are meaning and purpose discovered or increased in our lives? It can be useful to consider three domains: life in general, jobs, and crisis.

Life in General

Viktor Frankl said that there is no universal pathway to meaning and purpose; the pathway is discovered by each individual in a unique way and on his own timetable. As an exercise to stimulate ideas, place a check beside an item that might be of interest for you to pursue, either now or at a future time. As you complete this checklist, consider what you really want from life and what you want to contribute to it. The items are grouped in three broad areas. The most satisfied people will generally strike a balance among the three areas:[4]

Giving something meaningful to the world. Contributing in ways that make the world a better place:

_____ establishing or joining a social or political cause that excites you (family, politics, science, church or synagogue, Mothers Against Drunk Driving, Parents of Murdered Children, urban sanctuaries for children, youth mentoring, etc.)

_____ creating art, poetry, writing; other creative expression that makes something new, beautiful, or useful

_____ giving money or material support to a worthy cause

_____ altruistic service, self-transcendence, building up or helping others

_____ giving, even in small ways that are useful to others, like picking up trash by the road, beautifying your yard for your neighbor's benefit—not yours, giving a co-worker, spouse or neighbor a hand unexpectedly, lifting anyone in any small way (a smile, a thank you, listening ear, etc.)

_____ committing to do your best at your job today

_____ simply observing what you do to meet others' needs

_____ sharing with others what you have discovered to reduce your own suffering

Experiencing and enjoying life's wholesome pleasures/beauties. Enjoy:

_____ nature (e.g., get up early and watch the sunrise; gaze at the constellations at night)

_____ intimate love

_____ friends

_____ connecting with neighbors

_____ recreation

_____ exercising your body

_____ notice what you appreciate in others; tell them

_____ cathedrals

_____ faces

_____ teamwork

Developing personal strengths and attitudes:

_____ peace of mind

_____ personal growth, holiness, goodness of character, self-actualization

_____ courage, taking responsibility for your own life. (The "I can't" often means "I won't take responsibility for my own life," a form of avoidance.5)

_____ refraining from criticizing, complaining, whining, backbiting, and other negatives

_____ improving the mind

_____ understanding, empathy, patience, compassion

_____ loyalty and honesty

Meaning and purpose spring from our deepest values. A wonderful question that can clarify our values is: What would you do if you didn't have to make a living?

Jobs

Many people find meaning and purpose in their jobs. Ideally, find a job that you love to do. As one said, "figure out what instrument your heart plays."6 If can't do the job you most love, figure out how to love your job.

How might you turn your job or career into a vocation where your strengths are utilized in a meaningful and satisfying way? How might you redefine your job from drudgery to a calling? As an exercise, rewrite your job description so that people would want to apply. Highlight the benefits. Especially consider those aspects of the job that call forth your strengths, skills, and values—and give you the greatest pleasure, including interactions with others. What about the job might attract another person to apply? Then hire yourself. Keep that new job description handy. Reread it when you get frustrated with your boss or when you wonder why you are doing the work you are doing.

Amy Wrzesniewski and colleagues found that a third of a hospital cleaning staff considered their work a calling to make the hospital experience positive for patients and staff alike. While others complained about the degrading work and low pay, this minority considered the ways their work beautified the environment—helping patients to heal and the medical staff to be more effective. They went beyond their job requirements, bringing flowers and smiles to patients.7 Likewise, a police officer might turn cynical as she considers the crude people she constantly must confront. Or, she might find meaning in knowing that she is cleaning up the streets for the benefit of others. She might find a sense of purpose in treating offenders as worthwhile people on a downward slope, with no negative judgments—even considering that incarceration might prevent the offender from further harming himself through bad choices. I again think of the cop who shared with me a prayer he carried around with him by an unknown author: "Grant that I may be provided the appropriate difficulties and sufferings in my life, that my heart may be truly awakened, and that my practice of liberation and universal compassion be truly fulfilled."

Each job can be meaningful. In WWII, General George Patton told his truck drivers that without them the war would be lost. If the whole job is not satisfying, what parts can you find satisfaction in completing? If completing a task is not possible in the near future, can you find satisfaction in the process of making progress?

You might reconsider your goals and expectations for working. For example, a physician might focus on prestige, income, and pleasing his parents with the status associated with his job. Alternatively, he might focus on the more intrinsically satisfying goal of service. (Recall that clergy, firefighters, and educators are among the happiest with both their work and life in general, despite relatively low wages.)

The father of the positive psychology movement, Martin Seligman, notes that lawyers are the most highly paid but most dissatisfied career. Their risk for depression exceeds that of the general population and all other professions, while rates of alcoholism, illegal drugs, and divorce rates are above average. These findings are perhaps not surprising when we consider that lawyers are trained to be aggressive, judgmental, pessimistic, adversarial, and analytical and emotionally detached. Their bottom line is frequently not the highest good, but winning. In their early years, many lawyers also spend much time alone researching. Seligman suggests mediation and pro bono work as ways to add meaning and purpose to their job.[8] The need for having balance in their lives, apart from work, is strongly suggested (see chapter 25).

Crisis

Barbara Frederickson and colleagues[9] have found that resilient people feel more positive after crises because they are more likely to find positive meaning. They suggest that meaning and purpose might be the most powerful way to cultivate positive emotions during crisis. (Recall that positive emotions help to improve performance under pressure.) It is understandable that we will likely feel negative emotions as we deal with life's difficult situations. However, finding positive meaning can help us to cope better during and after such situations. They suggest the following questions relating to current adversities. First identify a current problem or problems, such as conflict, an ended relationship, too much to do, troubled family members, a move, major life changes, illness or death of loved one, or your own illness. Take time to ponder and then respond to these questions in writing.

- Have you thought about how this problem could change your life in a positive way?
- Which of your strengths does this situation require?
- Did anything good come out of dealing with this problem?
- How might you find benefit in this situation in the long-term?
- How might this situation prepare you for adversity in the future?
- How might others find benefit in the long-term as a result of this situation and/or the things you've suffered?
- What might you learn from this experience?
- What can you still feel good about?
- What is left that is important to you?

Meaning Making: A remarkable story

During WWII, Corrie ten Boom and her sister Betsie were imprisoned in a German concentration camp for helping Jews in Holland escape from the Nazis. During that terrible ordeal, they, like Viktor Frankl, found ways to give meaning to their adversities:[10]

Corrie asked her sister what they could do for the feebleminded people who had been degraded by the concentration camp. "Can't we make a home for them and care for them and love them?" Corrie said. Betsie replied, "Corrie, I pray every day that we will be allowed to do this. To show them that love is greater." Later Corrie learned that Betsie was planning to establish a "concentration camp" for the guards after the war, a home where "people who had been warped by the philosophy of hate and force could come to learn another way." This camp would have no walls or barbed wire, and the barracks would have window boxes filled with flowers that grow and help to teach about love.

Although Betsie died in the prison camp, Corrie found that those times beside her sister were joyous ones. Betsie was so kind that even the meanest prison guard softened toward her. Before her death, Betsie said, "We must tell people what we have learned here. We must tell them that there is no pit so deep that He is not deeper still. They will listen to us, Corrie, because we have been here." After the war, Corrie made her sister's dream her own. The German government turned over a former concentration camp, which she used from 1946-1969 to rehabilitate those in need of rest and care. In Holland she opened another home for ex-prisoners and other war victims in need. She died on her ninety-first birthday on April 15, 1983, after a lifetime of service.

Common Themes

Although there is no single road to meaning and purpose, many of the pathways contain common themes. Much of meaning and purpose is about developing our strengths and investing them in something larger than self. Much of what is meaningful relates to using our strengths to elevate, serve, or love others—in short, helping to make others happier, which is the ultimate source of happiness (see resources for identifying strengths in Appendix 9). These efforts are uniquely personal, consistent with our individual capacities. *Flow* is the name given to our absorption in meaningful and satisfying activities that are challenging but not overwhelming. Flow calls us to invest our best selves. Flow is associated with happiness. Being overwhelmed is not. So seek meaningful pursuits. Do what you can, but don't overdo it.

Each life can matter, as this poem suggests:

Thank You For Being My Dash
Author Unknown

I read of a man who stood to speak
At the funeral of a friend
He referred to the dates on her tombstone
From the beginning...to the end.

He noted that first came the date of her birth
And he spoke the following dates with tears,
But he said what mattered most of all
was the dash between those years (1934-1998).
For that dash represents
all the time that she spent alive on Earth...

And now only those who loved her
Know what that little line is worth.
For it matters not how much we own;
The cars...the house...the cash,
What matters is how we live and love
And how we spend our dash.

So think about this long and hard...
Are there things you'd like to change?
For you never know how much time is left,
That can still be rearranged.

If we could just slow down enough
To consider what's true and real
And always try to understand
The way other people feel,
And be less quick to anger
And show appreciation more

And love the people in our lives
Like we've never loved before.
If we treat each other with respect
And more often wear a smile
Remembering that this special dash
May only last a little while.

So when your eulogy is being read
With your life's actions to rehash,
Would you be proud of the things they say
About how you spent your dash?

Activity

Ponder how you would wish to remember your life, and how you would wish to be remembered. This activity can help to clarify what is most important to you. What specific goals does this activity suggest?

Reflections on Meaning

- The primary motivational force in man is his striving for meaning. (Viktor Frankl)
- It did not really matter what we expected from life, but rather what life expected from us. (Viktor Frankl)
- Identify your regrets. This tells you something about what you still value, what matters to you, what is meaningful. (John Burt)
- Without a firm idea of himself and the purpose of his life, man cannot live, and would sooner destroy himself than remain on earth, even if he was surrounded with bread. (Russian novelist Fyodor Dostoyevsky)
- One cannot live without meaning. (Camus)
- Hate won the day. But it cannot win the war [against those who have hope, bond together, value helping others, and are courageous in defending freedom]. (Remembrance: September 11, 2001)
- At one time I used to say that all those guys died [in Vietnam] for nothing. Now I know better. Any man that lays down his life so others can be free is not only rich, I believe he sits at God's right hand. (Sergeant David A. Somerville[11])
- [Instead of wasting my survival of a war I considered meaningless], I could give meaning to what had happened by learning from it and helping others with that knowledge. I knew I finally had a true mission, one I could accomplish and be proud of. (Paul Cohen, MSW, former Vietnam vet with PTSD, now a therapist)
- Taste the joy that springs from labor. (Henry Wadsworth Longfellow)

Chapter 23

Social Intelligence

You can always tell a real friend: When you make a fool of yourself, he doesn't feel you've done a permanent job.
Laurence Peter

Social intelligence can be lifesaving. Daniel Goleman (2006) relates that in Iraq a group of American soldiers approached a mosque to ask a cleric for help in distributing supplies. A mob surrounded the small unit. The unit's commander shouted to the soldiers to take a knee, point their rifles toward the ground, and smile. The commander had correctly read the mob's hostility and sensed what would calm them. Social skills also enable small children to disarm bullies with good-humored remarks, and workers and spouses to defuse potential conflicts.

Social intelligence is not simply having knowledge about relationships, but also being able to quickly and effectively apply people skills in diverse situations. Those with social intelligence:

- Get along harmoniously with a wide range of people in many different situations
- Are likeable
- Form strong and warm relationships
- Work well with others; build teamwork; handle conflict well
- Read emotions, facial expressions, and other body cues, and know how to respond (e.g., disarming aggression)
- Are caring, kind, respectful; seek the good of others
- Lift others' spirits—encourage, build them up, put them in a good mood (making them feel more joy, calmer, energized, valued)
- Appropriately state their preferences and say no to undesired pressure (i.e., refusal skills)
- Effectively summon needed help
- Effectively motivate and persuade others
- Solve problems in relationships

Socially intelligent people have been found to enjoy a wide range of benefits. They tend to:

- Be happier (strong social bonds are strongly linked to happiness; relationships provide pleasures that endure and increase, unlike many physical pleasures)
- Experience less cognitive decline with aging
- Be healthier—fewer medical and psychological problems, live longer (e.g., those with strong social bonds are less vulnerable to PTSD, depression, anxiety, and stress; they rebound better from heart attacks and have fewer colds)
- Be professionally successful—lasting longer in their jobs, functioning better on the job, and getting ahead—getting more raises and promotions (As a resilient WWII survivor once told me, "It's hard to keep focus when you are lonely.")
- Behave more morally (morality presupposes caring about others)

- Make better leaders (bosses with social intelligence get more productive work from their employees)

In terms of relationships, quality and (to a lesser degree) quantity matter. Bonds with family and friends are both important. Particularly in high-stress jobs, bonding with coworkers has great survival value. Many are the people with high IQ whose social and professional lives have derailed because of a lack of social intelligence.

This chapter will explore a wide range of social principles and skills that can be mastered through practice. Let's start with a thorough self-assessment.

THE SOCIABILITY[1] CHECKUP

This is a useful checkup to help you gauge your people skills. The large number of items perhaps suggests why cultivating and maintaining successful interpersonal relationships can be so challenging. It also suggests the great potential for growth. Without judgment, see how you are doing. Remember that no one scores high on all of these items, and most won't do any of these all the time. Rate how well each item describes you, according to the scale below, and circle an item you'd like to work on improving:

1=strongly disagree   2=disagree   3= mixed opinion   4= agree   5= strongly agree

I....

_____ 1. form satisfying relationships fairly easily
_____ 2. make reaching out and connecting with others a priority
_____ 3. get along well with a wide range of people in a wide range of different situations
_____ 4. pay attention to what others are feeling by reading facial expressions and bodily cues
_____ 5. know what to do when others get upset
_____ 6. am regarded as friendly, caring, kind, considerate, respectful, and truthful
_____ 7. am good at building teamwork
_____ 8. influence others to work together
_____ 9. can usually get others to see my viewpoint
_____ 10. actively strive to see others' point of view
_____ 11. build people up (encourage; support; make them feel valued and accepted)
_____ 12. help others feel better (e.g., calmer, more joyful, energized)
_____ 13. disagree or say "no" agreeably
_____ 14. usually resolve conflicts in a way that strengthens relationships
_____ 15. am comfortable with a wide range of emotions around people
_____ 16. have developed a wide support network—family, friends, neighbors, coworkers, leaders, professionals, mentors, and/or members of a faith or social community
_____ 17. have at least one "best friend"—one with whom I can share my honest feelings and who provides encouragement, advice, salve for wounds, companionship, uplift, an example of good coping, etc.
_____ 18. know at least one person well—deeply, not superficially

_____ 19. isolate myself from others infrequently

_____ 20. engage people I'd like to know better and work myself into their heart by positioning myself near them, showing warmth and interest (e.g., by smiling, asking questions or spending time with them), showing appreciation for their attention, responding to their interest, and lifting their spirits

_____ 21. form and keep mature relationships

_____ 22. choose people for relationships wisely (e.g., avoid those who are manipulative, controlling, or abusive)

_____ 23. make people around me smile/laugh

_____ 24. am generally upbeat in my moods

_____ 25. don't smother people or make unreasonable demands

_____ 26. am loyal, steady, and committed in my relationships

_____ 27. understand my needs and find people who meet them

_____ 28. apologize when I am wrong

_____ 29. communicate my wants and disappointments without blowing up

_____ 30. nourish my relationships by actively planning together time—phone calls, talks, visit, dates, meals, recreation, birthdays, celebrations

_____ 31. respect others' will: I sense when to give and when to receive, when to push and when to ease up

_____ 32. compliment often and criticize rarely

_____ 33. can be a sounding board, without offering unsolicited advice

_____ 34. am in tune to what other people are feeling and needing

_____ 35. help others in a variety of ways without expecting rewards (e.g., giving a ride to the library, listening, providing information or advice, giving a helping hand, providing material support)

_____ 36. ask for and obtain the help I need

_____ 37. accept the faults of people I am close to, and don't expect too much from them

_____ 38. listen closely to what intimates are expressing—verbally and non-verbally

_____ 39. express affection verbally and non-verbally (e.g., smiles, touch, hug)

_____ 40. am reliable (honest, dependable, punctual, faithful, keep confidences, control my temper, avoid unnecessary risks)

_____ 41. like people of all ages and persuasions

_____ 42. think of people as equals

_____ 43. actively try to create good will in every possible encounter

_____ 44. politely request, rather than boss others

_____ 45. let people know me—my thoughts, feelings, likes, dislikes, desires

_____ 46. join groups (family, teams, neighborhood, social, service, and/or religious)

_____ 47. am polite

_____ 48. treat people, including family and other drivers, with respect

_____ 49. strive to eliminate habits that weaken my relationships

_____ 50. don't make unreasonable demands of others

_____ 51. make people feel that I like them overall, despite their flaws

_____ 52. allow my mate privacy/independence without feeling jealous or insecure

_____ 53. do not focus conversations too much on myself, but keep an appropriate balance (some people disclose too little about themselves, and others too much)

_____ 54. make my requests of others clear

_____ 55. treat others as I wish to be treated.
_____ 56. fit well into varied groups and work well with others
_____ 57. engage in pleasant conversation with many
_____ 58. deal effectively with group tensions and different personalities
_____ 59. inspire people in groups to work together and keep them moving in the desired direction
_____ 60. frequently express affection and appreciation, and ask about others' thoughts and feelings

The General Principles of Social Intelligence

1. *Be likeable.* Convey the feeling that you regard others as intelligent and worthwhile. This is an attitude of the heart and is often conveyed without words. Be genuine, hard working, reliable, trustworthy, helpful, interested, playful, and conscientious. Dishonesty, arrogance, and manipulative behavior do not wear well.

2. *Create good moods in others by being calm, cheerful, positive, and enthused.* Putting yourself in a good mood helps you to respond better to others' needs and makes it more likely that others will listen to you.

3. *When confronting negative feelings in self or others be fully present and sincere.* Sometimes we get the best relief from unpleasant feelings by experiencing them fully and without fear.[2]

4. *Have something to offer.* Everyone uniquely contributes to relationships just by being fully present. Be aware of your strengths and use them in relationships (e.g., humor, organization, ability to listen and affirm). Cultivate your passions and hobbies so that you have something to share. We might also become expert in certain relevant areas. Offer your expertise with good-natured humility.

5. *Have good hygiene and appearance.* Within reason, look and smell as pleasant as possible.

6. *Be approachable.* In the mirror, practice removing grimaces or angry expressions. Look into the eyes of others with a cheerful countenance and smiling eyes. Each morning, you might start out the day reciting, "May I be welcoming and friendly. May I be helpful." Speak in a friendly, pleasant tone of voice, avoiding unpleasant hand gestures or harsh tones.

7. *Be appreciative.* Genuinely thank people for their contributions.

8. *Show interest.* When people approach you, appear welcoming. Signal your willingness to talk by initiating conversation. Any question will do. It needn't be witty or clever, just sincere.

9. *Be real.* It can be endearing to hear someone we respect be honest about their faults and struggles, or that they don't know an answer but are open to discuss and learn. In the *Likeability Factor*, Sanders (2005) encourages people to write a personal history. Describe your challenges, milestones, best and worst times, good luck, what you've learned, what you are looking for and hoping for, and how you are evolving. This exercise reminds us who we really are, and that we each have much valuable and interesting experience to share.

The Basic Principles of Effective Communication

1. *Listen more than you speak.* Or, as Stephen R. Covey (1990, p.235) has stated, "Seek first to understand, then to be understood." Most people rate themselves as good listeners, when in fact the practice of listening with full intent to understand, without interruption, is a rare skill that changes the fundamental dynamics of relationships.
2. *Create an open, safe environment that is free of censure and criticism.* In thriving relationships, compliments and positive emotional experiences outnumber criticisms by at least five to one. When it is necessary, criticism focuses on how one can improve (e.g., "I'd like to see you do this..."), rather than name calling or character attacks. The skillful listener puts his or her ego on the shelf, regards criticism as potentially useful feedback, and explores criticism for ways to improve the relationship.
3. *Clearly communicate expectations.* For example, "I'd like you to complete this by tomorrow night and let me know when you have. Will you do that?"
4. *Follow-up group meetings with personal interviews.* Frequent one-on-one interviews let an individual know he matters. It is an opportunity to listen, check for understanding, and head off many problems before they occur.
5. *Praising strengths and accomplishments usually motivates more than harsh criticism.*

Empathy

Empathy is a critically important aspect of social intelligence that merits special attention. Empathy is the ability to sense or attune to another's emotions and thoughts in a caring way.[3] It is more than simply being able to label another's feelings. It is understanding what is going on inside—experiencing those feelings with the other person, seeing that person's viewpoint—and being able to respond from the heart. When other people have empathy, we feel understood, that they are feeling what we feel—compassionately and without judgment.

Empathy is vital to building consensus, resolving conflict, and creating harmony in relationships. Those with empathy read peoples' wants and needs, and are therefore in touch with what might build the relationships. They are attuned to threats and can thus anticipate how to respond. People with empathy are more popular, better adjusted, more resistant to stress, and more successful in relationships of all kinds—from friendship to marriage and leadership. Conversely, aggressive and antisocial people lack empathy, behaving without regard for others' feelings, while leaders without empathy create resentment.

The brain is wired for empathy. Mirror neurons fire when we are in the presence of someone who is feeling. That is, the same areas of our brain become activated as the person who is experiencing the feeling—if we are attuned. Thus smiling and laughter are contagious. So are negative emotions. Mirror neurons prepare us for movement and physiological changes. Thus, when we see a smile, we tend to feel more cheerful, and smile as well.[4] Attuning to another's pain moves us to help.

How to Build Empathy

Neuroplasticity allows empathy to grow. Following are a number of useful exercises to develop empathy:

1. *Five-minute emotional attunement exercise*
   - Read another person's emotions. With warmth, acceptance, and curiosity, primarily watch the person's mouth and eyes for the basic seven emotions: sadness, anger, fear, disgust, interest, surprise, and happiness. Also pay attention to bodily cues (e.g., posture, gestures, tension) and to voice tone. Take your time to tune in. Notice changes in emotions. Be fully present, with no intention of changing the person's emotions or viewpoint. Notice how that person's feelings make you feel emotionally and physically. Then try to feel what the other person is feeling.[5]
   - Try to understand what that person wants, needs, and might be thinking. For example, for an angry person, you might ask yourself, "Why is he behaving that way? Has he had a bad day? What are his needs right now (e.g., understanding, a nap, appreciation, relaxation, a sense of accomplishment, happiness)? Is he thinking that he is being treated unfairly, or that he is a failure?"
   - Do this exercise frequently.
2. *Happiness drill.* Ask someone to identify two or three of his/her three happiest memories, and then describe them to you. Feel and envision those memories along with the person.
3. *Understanding exercise.* Notice when another person is upset. Study the face, posture, gestures, and tone of voice and try to understand what is going on inside. Say something like, "Are you upset?" If the answer is yes, say "I'm trying to understand your feelings better. Would you please tell me what you are feeling?"[6] Then, "Would you help me understand what is making you feel that way?" Your goal is simply to accurately understand the other person's feelings and thoughts. A similar drill could be tried for positive emotions ("You seem happy. What's made you feel that way?"). Empathetic accuracy is characteristic of successful people in a wide range of fields.
4. *Have a partner identify an event that elicited fairly strong emotions, and then re-experience the emotions without explaining the event.* Try to resonate with the person's non-verbal cues: match the person's facial expressions, posture, gestures, and so forth. Notice how that feels. When you are ready, say, "I think you are feeling _____ because _____." Then, for your understanding, the partner describes the event and explains what she was feeling and why.
5. *Put the ego on the shelf.* Rather than trying to persuade someone to your point of view during a disagreement, try to see the others point of view, and say, "I see what you mean. You're feeling...because....Is that right?" Then, "That makes sense. I can see why you would feel that way."
6. *Watch.* Notice a person who is in a very difficult situation (e.g., poverty, grieving the death of a loved one, going through a divorce, living with an abusive spouse, chronic illness). Imagine how you would feel in that situation.

7. *Compassion meditation.* Empathy requires compassion, a feeling for people's sufferings. Try this meditation to cultivate this feeling:
   - Think of people you've loved the best. Feel that love in your heart.
   - Reflect on someone treating you with compassion and affection. Breathe in and receive that compassion and affection. Create the intent to feel happy, as you say to yourself, "May I be happy. May I be free of suffering." (Everyone wishes to be happy and free of suffering. Compassion and happiness help us endure suffering.)
   - Visualize someone who is suffering acutely—either physically or emotionally in pain from an unfortunate situation. See him as having the same capacity as you to experience joy and pain—desiring to be happy and not suffer.
   - Generate compassionate and affectionate feelings for the person.
   - Breathing in, see yourself taking upon yourself that person's feelings of suffering. Breathing out, see your compassion and affection flow toward the suffering person. Think, "May you be happy and free of suffering."

Socially Intelligent Leadership

Leaders come in all shapes and sizes: military commanders, bosses, parents, teachers, coaches—even the lowest ranking members of units lead by example. Although there are rare exceptions to the rule, the most effective leaders are typically high in social intelligence. Research has shown that:
   - Workers are more productive when they like, rather than fear, their bosses. Workers tend to like managers who make them feel positively. They are also more productive and satisfied with their job when managers pay attention and show concern.
   - The most effective managers are caring and warm, and verbalize their thoughts and feelings.
   - Emphasizing workers' strengths and what they are doing right improves performance substantially, while emphasizing weaknesses substantially degrades performance.

What Socially Intelligent Leaders Can Do

In *Leadership is an Art*, Max DePree (1989, p.xx) defines leadership as "liberating people to do what is required of them in the most effective and humane way possible." Leaders, he continues, enable people to realize their full potential, bringing out and polishing their gifts and respecting the varying gifts of individuals. Although there is no perfect leader, we can approach the ideal by striving to:
   - *Become credible.* Learn your craft so well that others will respect what you say and follow you.[7]
   - *Live with integrity.* Most people expect excellent character of leaders. Without this there is no respect, and only reluctant obedience. DePree notes that good leaders develop, defend, and exemplify civility, values, and good manners.
   - *Promote cohesion within the unit.* Especially in high-risk groups, social support—call it camaraderie, friendship, unit cohesion, or espirit—protects and uplifts

people. Workers who say they have a best friend at work are happier and more productive. Yet many adults don't actively seek friends among their co-workers. So wise leaders help to foster bonding by training as teams, keeping units serving together over time,[8] and organizing socials and other recreational events. Before hiring new employees, try to ensure that they will mesh socially with others.

- *Communicate expectations clearly and calmly.* Teach and encourage the importance of friendship and the values that cultivate it, such as loyalty, dependability, teamwork, and courtesy. Understand the complexities of your mission so well that you can explain what workers are to do plainly and simply. Try to let them know in advance what is required of them and why (this helps people anticipate and makes them feel more secure). As much as possible, communicate why their work matters. If workers see that leaders find great satisfaction and meaning from their work, they will be more motivated to follow.

- *Consider your role as a servant-leader.* The most effective leadership is in the service of others—helping others to succeed and develop as individuals, team players, and future leaders. Servant-leaders ensure that people have needed resources. They remove barriers to success when the followers can't do this themselves, and they provide opportunities for those they lead to stretch. This altruistic approach to leadership is one reason why effective leadership is so satisfying.[9]

- *Lead with respect, not fear.* Respected workers feel more secure and function better under extreme pressure.[10] Respect is a heartfelt attitude that is communicated without words. Respect honors the unique value, strengths, and potential of all people. Respectful leaders consider themselves as equally worthwhile—no better than their followers in terms of worth as people. They consider the input of others, even if the leader's ultimate decision differs with a follower's opinion.[11] They know that losing one's temper and intimidation tend to degrade performance.

Respectful Leadership

At West Point, plebes had to memorize the following passage. I considered it the best leadership lesson we learned, one that really applies to all types of leadership:

The discipline which makes the soldiers of a free country reliable in battle is not to be gained by harsh or tyrannical treatment. On the contrary, such treatment is far more likely to destroy than to make an army. It is possible to impart instruction and to give commands in such a manner and such a tone of voice as to inspire in the soldier no feeling but an intense desire to obey, while the opposite manner and tone of voice cannot fail to excite strong resentment and a desire to disobey. The one mode or the other of dealing with subordinates springs from a corresponding spirit in the breast of the commander. He who feels the respect which is due to others cannot fail to inspire in them regard for himself, while he who feels, and hence manifests, disrespect toward others, especially his inferiors, cannot fail to inspire hatred against himself.

Maj. Gen. John M. Schofield[12]

- *Focus on people's strengths and accomplishments.* Most leaders tend to focus on improving weakness, even though emphasizing strengths and accomplishments garners far better results. From time to time, ask people what they consider to be their strengths. You might have to prompt them by mentioning those you have noticed. Publicly acknowledge what has gone right (praise reinforces strengths and motivates people to build on them). Most workers want to hear "good job" or "thanks." As much as possible, adjust tasks to the individual's strengths. When weaknesses need to be addressed, train methodically and patiently. You might encourage your people to take web tests that identify individual strengths (see Appendix 9). Encourage people to use these strengths and attribute successes to them. Doing so tends to improve productivity and self-confidence.[13]
- *Make people feel secure.* We perform better when we have a secure base. Bosses can help people feel more secure by:
    - Paying attention to them as individuals on a daily basis. Ask about how their work is going and if they have the resources needed to succeed. Ask about their families and interests. Especially pay attention to those who seem isolated.
    - Challenging, but not overwhelming them. Give them freedom to experiment and sometimes fail.
    - Being with them "in the trenches." Sharing your people's discomfort lets them know that you are concerned and are available as a resource. During the Vietnam War, platoon leader Rick Rescorla was respected by his men for his tactical competence, but also for his social competence. When his men were surrounded and greatly outnumbered, he would calm them with encouragement, banter, or songs. He brought those same strengths to his job as vice president for security for Morgan Stanley-Dean Witter. Through his thoughtful planning and training, he instilled the idea that employees at the World Trade Center could function well in a terrorist attack. During 9/11 they did. Calmly following his leadership, nearly 2700 employees made it safely out of the building before it collapsed. He was one of seven who did not make it out. He was still "in the trenches," trying to ensure that all his people were safe. When people feel secure—knowing that they are led by concerned, involved, reasonable leaders—then unit socials will matter.
    - Discussing after a mission what went well and how this was accomplished. Then discuss what *we'll* work together to improve through training and practice.
    - Normalizing psychological symptoms resulting from great distress and encouraging treatment so that workers can be more happy and productive. Reassure them that suffering will abate, that things will get better—others have gone through this, too; you are not alone.
- *Empower individuals.* Instill the idea that skill and effort bring success. Your people are not powerless; their fate is not determined by outside forces.
- *Stay generally upbeat.* Leaders set the emotional tone of a group. So nourish your own happiness daily. Keep the emotional climate friendly and fun, remembering that happy workers are more productive.[14] Happiness is contagious. A ripple effect has been observed such that a happy boss leads to

happier workers, leading to happier families, friends, and neighbors. Remember the attributes that have been universally associated with good leaders: empathy, humor, humility, calm, being encouraging, being fully present, and being appreciative. Bad bosses are associated with being angry (loss of temper), self-centered, distrusting, arrogant, detached, over-demanding, and over-critical (Goleman, 2006).

- *Maintain self-control.* Keep an even keel. Don't get too high or too low. Getting too high can set one up for disappointment; getting to low can be depressing and sap motivation. Most achievements require steady, sustained efforts. Don't get discouraged if you did your best to prepare and execute, but fell short. Instill this attitude in your followers, as well.
- *Keep groups on task.* When groups lose focus, you might try saying the following (Chaffee, 1998):
  - "That's an interesting idea. Perhaps you can explain how it relates to the issue at hand."
  - "In the interest of time, let's refocus on our task, which is...."
  - "Since we have to bring this to a close, are there any final comments that introduce points we haven't already considered?"

  To deal with problem members, you might say:
  - "Your criticism might be right—can you suggest a better idea?"
  - "That's a good idea. I'm putting you in charge of implementing that idea."

Leadership Drills

- Catch workers doing something well and let them know you appreciate their contributions.
- Listen fully to someone you are leading, without judgment or attachment to a preconceived outcome. Let them know that even negative feedback, given respectfully, is OK.

Basic Interpersonal Skills

A new line of research on shyness, led by Bernardo Carducci, Ph.D.,[15] has shed much light on interpersonal skills that are useful for people generally. Carducci directs the Shyness Research Institute at Indiana University Southeast. It turns out that nearly half of all people are shy, meaning they are uncomfortable and lacking in confidence around others.[16] Shy people have learned certain thoughts and behaviors that maintain their discomfort. Typical thought distortions include:

- *Unfavorable comparisons* ("Javier is the life of the party. He's so interesting and funny. I'm just a wallflower.")
- *Mind reading* ("People are always watching and judging me negatively.")
- *Overgeneralizing* ("No one wants to talk to me.")
- *Shoulds/musts/oughts* ("Everything I say must be fascinating or witty and come out perfectly. I must not be awkward. I must be socially graceful, quickly and without effort.")

- *Catastrophizing*
  - "It's awful to stumble socially. I'm not capable of having a genuine relationship."
  - "I can't handle rejection. It's awful." (The renowned psychologist Albert Ellis overcame his shyness in approaching young women by approaching hundreds of them. Eventually he realized he could stand rejection, and in the process got quite adept at meeting new people. Ellis called forcing yourself to face the "unbearable" *shame-attacking behavior*.)
- *Fortune telling* ("I know this person won't like me.")
- *All or none*
  - "If everyone (or a certain person) doesn't like me I'm a loser."
  - "Either I'll be the center of attention or a flop; fascinating or a loser."

This kind of thinking typically leads to shyness behaviors, such as:
- *Avoidance* (e.g., relying on alcohol in social settings instead of social skills; staying away from people and social situations)
- *Self focus.* Shy people concentrate on controlling their own self-talk. For example, they'll think, "I'm good enough, they'll like me," rather than focusing on the conversation.

Shy people generally do fine once they are in a secure relationship. They just use ineffective strategies to initiate new ones, such as:
- Forced extroversion that comes across as unnatural.
- Expecting others to draw them out, which cedes control to others.

The good news is that shyness can largely be overcome, and doing so tends to improve the mood of introverts. Social confidence comes from learning and practicing social skills—much like practice develops athletic skills. Social competence improves with face-to-face contact. Drawn mainly from Carducci, the following strategies can be useful generally:

1. *Prepare in advance.*
   - Check your self-talk now, not during conversations. Tell yourself, "If I'm friendly and willing to talk, some people will probably like me. If they don't, will that really kill me?"
   - Keep expectations realistic. "I don't have to be a superstar, just genuine. I don't need fireworks with every encounter, but I can reasonably anticipate some pleasant experiences."
   - Stay up-to-date on current events so as to have something to talk about.
   - In the mirror, practice looking friendly—smiling, having a cheerful expression, and having relaxed and friendly body language. Don't look neutral, disinterested, or hostile. Don't hunch over or lower your head, but stand tall. Think about a time your felt secure inside and outside, and then bring that feeling forward.
   - Mentally rehearse beforehand what you will do and say. Plan ahead for uncomfortable silences, thinking of questions to ask and things to say.

2. *Arrive early* at events, allowing yourself time to feel comfortable in the new setting and to meet people gradually.

3. *Don't worry about saying just the right thing.* It's better to be warm and sincere. Just ask a question, any question, to signal your willingness to be friendly and talk. If asked a question, try to give a little extra information to facilitate the conversation. For example, if asked where you live, you might say, "On Maple Street, just near that great Italian restaurant."

4. *Shift the focus from yourself to others.* Accept your shortcomings and self-consciousness. You're not great on small talk? That's OK. Normalize your body's arousal as a signal that you "want to do well and your body is ready to help" (Casriel, 2007, p.73). Then actively pay attention to the others' feelings and the conversation. Concentrate on listening, putting them at ease, and making them feel interesting.

5. *Practice being sociable in small day-to-day exchanges.* When you buy something from the store, focus on the seller. Thank them for their help. Help others out.

6. *Invest in your social life.* Become a student of sociability, observing interactions so you can improve. Mix and mingle more. Accept invitations. Actively plan gatherings in your home and outings with those you'd like to know better. Surround yourself with others. Invite others along to lunch or other things you normally do.

7. *Expect others to respond positively when approached.* If they don't, that's OK.

8. *Make a social recon.* Before jumping into a conversation, observe others and actively listen. Watch expressions to gauge people's interest. See if they want to be left alone or are receptive.

9. *Enter the conversation gracefully in a lull in the conversation.* Make comments related to the conversation without calling attention to yourself (be interested, not necessarily interesting). Fit into the conversation by asking a deft question or offering a summary ("So you're thinking..."). Elaborate on what someone else said ("That's an interesting point. I also heard...").

10. *Handle failure matter-of-factly.* Rebuffs happen to everyone, even the popular. Don't pessimistically assume the causes are personal ("I'm not likeable; I can't make friends"), permanent, and pervasive. Rather, think, "Maybe he's in a bad mood, shy, or needing privacy"; "We're not compatible"; "My skills need polishing"; "I'll keep persevering—maybe I'll get a different response next time or from others").

11. *Rebound from rebuffs.* If someone declines an invitation, you might ask, "Well, can we reschedule for next week instead?" Or you might invite the other person to a smaller date, to which getting a "yes" is more likely. If success is unlikely, move on to another group.

12. *It's OK to end conversations politely* with "It's been nice visiting," or ""Good meeting you." This is useful for someone who is latching on or when you wish to meet others.

13. *Be comfortable with differences of opinion in conversations.* You have a right to have an opinion, and it's OK if people disagree. Make sure they've heard you. Practice expressing yourself clearly (this takes practice and time). Think of lively interchanges as a way to sharpen the thinking of yourself and others.

14. *Regulate emotions.* As a general rule, concentrate on upbeat topics. Likeable people restrain expressions of depression, anxiety, and anger in social settings, and don't dwell on downers. Turn off constant bitterness, rancor, complaining, and criticism. Instead, focus on topics that are beautiful, interesting, and amusing, such as good movies and books, what people are doing well, funny stories, being playful. Be humble, kind, and forgiving when it would be easy to harshly criticize. And this leads us into the next important social skill.

Forgiving[17]

Once thought of simply as a theological concept, forgiveness has been linked in hundreds of studies to sound mental health. Let's briefly explore it as a vital social skill.

Forgiving means releasing bitterness, hatred, and desires for revenge for past offenses—canceling the debt owed by the offender.[18] We choose to forgive not necessarily because the offender has asked for or deserves it,[19] but because we no longer wish to be chained to the suffering caused by yesterday's wounds. Forgiveness does not mean forgetting the offense. It does not necessarily mean we again trust the offender. However, in forgiving we strive to replace negative feelings toward the offender (such as resentment or indifference) with compassion (someone who does that must himself be wounded) and wishes for their happiness. Thus, we can be wiser from our experience, but without the strong distressing feelings that cripple us. We see, then, that forgiving is a gift we give ourselves

The literature is full of accounts of resilient survivors who have forgiven unspeakable crimes. For example, the story appropriately entitled "From Darkness to Light" recounts the story of Christopher (Hugh) Carrier (2005). As a trusting ten-year-old, he climbed off the school bus thinking of Christmas. David McAllister said to him, in effect, "I'm a friend of your father; could you help me find him a gift?" Hugh got into McAllister's motor home and was driven to open fields. There, McAllister repeatedly stabbed him with an ice pick in revenge. (Hugh's father had fired McAllister for being drunk on the job.) McAllister then shot the boy in the left temple, leaving him blind in Florida's alligator-infested Everglades. After being unconscious for nearly a week, Hugh staggered to a road, where a motorist spotted him and took him to the hospital.

Hugh's life followed a downward spiral. He was afraid to sleep alone or go outside, deeply resentful, and self-conscious about his drooping, half-shut eye. Three years after the accident, he was struck by a message of forgiveness. He graduated from college, earned a master's degree, and married. He felt gratitude for miraculously surviving the Everglades. He realized why God had kept him alive when he held his baby and saw the many youngsters who realized all he'd been through and opened up to him readily.

Twenty-two years after the crime, McAllister admitted his guilt in a nursing home. The police called Hugh, who had wondered what he'd do if he were ever to confront his offender. Outside the room, Hugh took a deep breath, summoning all his courage to go in. Walking into the room, Hugh introduced himself to a withered seventy-seven-year-old man weighing seventy pounds. At first, McAllister said, "I don't know what you're talking about." Then he trembled and cried. Reaching out, he said, "I'm sorry. I'm so sorry."

Hugh told McAllister that what he did was not the end of meaning in his life. It was a beginning. McAllister squeezed Hugh's hand and whispered, "I'm very glad." Hugh visited nearly every day for the next three weeks. McAllister shared his life story: no father, juvenile halls, drinking heavily by his teen years, no friends, a life of anger and shame, believing God is only something suckers believe in. With Hugh's help, McAllister began to pray. Eventually McAllister said to Hugh, "I'm planning on going to heaven and I want you there too. I want our friendship to continue." That night McAllister died in his sleep. Hugh reflected, "Strange as it seems, that old man did more for me than he ever could have known. In his darkness I found a light that guides me still. Forgiving David McAllister gave me a strength I will have forever."

Notice that forgiving was difficult. At first the offended was not sure he could do it, but he persisted. Forgiving was a process that began as a teen, but was completed many years later. In this case offender and offended met face-to-face and reconciled. This won't always be possible. As bitterness was released, the positive aspects of Hugh's life became clearer

Bitterness costs. If forgiving gives away distressing anger and helps people to bounce back from past wounds, then we would expect research to demonstrate beneficial effects of forgiving. It does. The practice of forgiveness helps people to:

- Be happier
- Have higher self-esteem and greater hope
- Experience less stress, depression, anxiety, hostility, chronic pain, and relapse from substance use disorders
- Be more flexible
- Sleep better
- Have lower blood pressure
- Have greater empathy and spirituality

How to Forgive Others

Even serious offenses can be forgiven. Although the process is not usually easy, it is usually liberating. These steps can help:

1. *Process the hurt.* Acknowledge the offense and the pain it caused. You might confide your pain in writing, describing what happened and what you thought and felt. Consider the positives that have resulted from the pain (e.g., "I channeled my anger to a constructive cause").

2. *Try to understand the offender.* Why might she have behaved that way? Without condoning the offense, acknowledge that the offense does not fully define the offender, just as your mistakes don't fully define you.

3. *Don't take it personally.* The offense reflects a wounded person and is not a statement of your worth. Many have been hurt in the same way and many have overcome the resulting bitterness.

4. *Let go of thoughts that keep you bound to the past* (e.g., "I can't believe one I loved could do that; I can't go on"). In fact, imperfect people behave imperfectly, and you *can* go on when you detach from the offender through forgiveness and

liberate yourself from past offenses. No one, no matter how respected or beloved, was ever treated well by everyone.

5. *Begin the process and give it time.* You might start the process by writing a forgiveness letter:

> Dear _____,
>
> You hurt me when you_____. I felt_____
> because_____.
> I wish you instead had_____.
> To the best of my ability, I now release my negative feelings toward you and free you and me to live fully again.
> Signed,

Depending on the offender, you might choose to burn, rather than send, this letter. Don't be surprised or discouraged should negative feelings return. This does not negate your progress. The process might be two steps forward and one back. Forgiveness might come unexpectedly once the intention is formed.

6. *Take the offender to zero.* Forgiving is easier when the offender acknowledges his hurtful action and his determination to improve. Often, the offender will not apologize or reform. In this case, try this approach, described by Baker and Greenberg (2007). Accept that the offender is not the person you wish he were. That person does not exist. If you can't feel positively toward the offender yet, let go and take him to zero. Think, "He hasn't earned my love or trust. So I take him to neutral, nada, zip, zero. I don't even waste time thinking about him or remembering him." Diagrammed, this looks like this:

Hate	Neutral	Love & trust

How to Forgive Self

Which is harder: forgiving self or others? Many find it very difficult to forgive themselves, thinking, "But I knew better!" Perhaps they grew up in a critical home, and tell themselves that they can never change. Nevertheless, forgiving self is a critical aspect of bouncing back, and is as important as forgiving others.

Hayes, Strosahl, and Wilson (1999) describe forgiving as giving that which we had before. When we forgive ourselves, we give ourselves permission to go back and start again from where we were before the error. We refuse to stay mired in negative judgments and self-condemnation, but determine to go forward.

1. *Allow the idea that forgiveness is a gift available to everyone.* Ed Tick (2008) takes veterans back to Vietnam to heal. Many carry harrowing guilt for committing "unforgivable" wrongs against the people there. Many are surprised that their former Vietnam "enemies" now forgive and befriend them,

understanding that people make mistakes in war. Now that the war is ended, their only desire is that their former enemies, who share a common warriors' history, heal. This experience reminds the veterans that forgiveness is a choice. Anyone may release the past and resolve to flourish again. There is no benefit to self-condemnation, only to improving behavior.

2. *Go back to the stuck point.* Acknowledge the wrong and apologize with a heart open to compassion.[20] It can be very healing for both parties when the offender says the words, "I know I hurt you. I was wrong. I am sorry and will try to never hurt you or others that way again. Please forgive me." Make amends as much as possible. If we can't undo the damage, perhaps we can do something constructive. Vietnam veterans, for example, often get involved in building schools or hospitals in Vietnam.

3. *Remind yourself that your error is not the sum total of who you are.* Remember that getting turned around does not negate what you still value, nor does it disqualify you from having a good life. Said Confucius, "Our greatest glory is not in never falling, but in rising every time we fall." After forgiving yourself, try gratitude recall, remembering what you did well and what you have learned from your experience.

4. *Accept what you can't control.* No one controls the universe. We can't always control the fact that a buddy gets killed in the course of duty. A buddy wouldn't expect a friend to grieve forever.

5. *Try writing yourself a letter of forgiveness,* reminding yourself of these points and your right to go on.

Forgiveness Reflection

- I do not hunch my back with yesterday. (Danny Thomas, when asked how he could be so kind to one who wasn't kind back)

Chapter 24

Socially Intelligent Families

Families have great potential for good and bad. While harmony at home positively affects the happiness, health, and job effectiveness of family members, family discord has the opposite effect. A balanced home life gives people a sense of security, while tension at home creates insecurity. Among the longest-living peoples, Okinawans, Sardinians, and Seventh Day Adventists all put family first. In this chapter we'll extend the principles and skills of social intelligence to strengthening couples and family.

Strengthening Couples

We start with couples, who lead the family. It is not marriage, per se, that benefits people. It is happy, enduring marriage to one's best friend that confers significant mental, physical, and economical benefits to the partners. Faithfully married couples are more sexually satisfied than all other sexually active groups (e.g., Michael et al., 1994). Yet the general trend in America is for divorce rates to be rising, while marriage satisfaction rates are declining.

Fortunately, considerable research has demonstrated the keys to strengthen marriage. We have learned, for example, that satisfied couples balance shared enjoyment with handling conflict in ways that strengthen the relationship. That is, they spend time together building respect, trust, and fond memories. They also solve problems constructively (calmly and as *equal* members of a team, with no hostility, withdrawing, or discouragement), and tolerate differences that can't be resolved (most couples have these).

Helpful Ideas

It is quite liberating to realize that:
- Among those who describe their marriages as very unhappy, 80% of those who stick it out for five years will say their marriage is happy (Waite et al., 2002).
- It typically takes ten to fifteen years for couples to reach high quality intimacy and mutuality, states marriage and family therapist Liberty Kovacs, Ph.D.[1] During this time they move through six stages: (1) At first couples depend on each other—romantically thinking that their partner is perfect, able to fulfill all their needs. (2) Partners recognize differences. They fear the partner is changing and putting other priorities first, and they don't know how to be close. (3) Power struggles occur, wherein childhood issues surface and each partner fears giving in. (4) Couples draw apart, becoming more *independent* and finding ways to make themselves happy. (5) Couples cooperate, viewing independence as normal. (6) Couples choose to stay together, cooperating and *interdepending* because they enjoy being a team.

In other words, it typically takes time for good relationships to unfold—and good relationships are likely to develop if couples persist.

Complementary Gender Differences

Ask yourself: Who is more likely to talk about problems in the relationship—men or women? Which gender is more likely to avoid such discussions?

Generally speaking, men and women process things differently. Much of this can be explained by brain differences. While there are certainly exceptions to the general rules, understanding gender differences can help to strengthen relationships. It is helpful to view these differences as complementary, not bad or good. We have learned, for example, that:[2]

1. *Women, having larger right brains and more interconnections between hemispheres, can process more aspects of a situation and do so more quickly.* Thus, in an emotional situation women will tend to pick up more emotional and intuitive cues and be able to verbalize more easily. Men might need to say, "I'm taking time to process this." While most men want to discuss deeper issues (like affection of spiritual topics) they might find it more difficult to put feelings into words.

2. *Men are more likely to say they want discussions to be calm and follow predictable rules, in order to think through issues logically* (think of engineers). Thus, if they see women becoming emotionally aroused, men are more likely to withdraw to avoid conflict. Conversely, women, having so much to process and say, and being more adversely affected by relationship difficulties, will typically want to talk about the issues. Problems can result if the male is withdrawing while the woman wants to talk.

3. *Women tend to feel closer through harmonious talking.* Men are more likely to enjoy playful debating and bonding through activities. (Thus, women tend to prefer talking agreeably across a table, while men might prefer talking while driving or engaging in recreation.)

4. *Men prefer to problem solve when they talk*—wanting to fix the problem efficiently and quickly. If they ask for advice, they are more likely to want a solution. Because they are processing more complexities, women tend to prefer to talk about all aspects of the situation first. Thus, men might tend to offer a quick fix when they see their partner struggling, which can unintentionally communicate, "I don't think you are smart enough to figure this out." Often women really just want a sounding board to help them consider all the angles of the situation so that they can better decide what to do. Women might need to say, "I'm not asking you to solve the problem; I'm asking you to help me consider all the angles." Men might need to say, "Do you want advice or shall I be a sounding board?"

Despite these differences, both genders want the same thing: to be treated with respect and equality. The important skills that follow incorporate these principles. They have been shown to predict marital satisfaction. These skills are: building an emotionally safe climate, resolving conflict, and enhancing fun and intimacy.

Building an Emotionally Safe Climate

Validating[3] is a simple, powerful skill upon which the other skills are built. Rather than criticizing, arguing, or giving advice, validating builds relationships by simply showing that you care.

Suppose a wife says, "I'm so upset about this!" The spouse might wish to "fix" the problem by saying, "Just do this" (which might make her feel inadequate or resentful of unsolicited advice) or "You shouldn't feel that way" (which invalidates her feelings). A validating response would be, "Oh, tell me about it."

Validating is the process of acknowledging and legitimizing the other person's feelings. As marriage and family therapist Gary Lundberg and wife Joy, authors of *I Don't Have to Make Everything All Better* (1999), explain, it is walking alongside another emotionally without changing his or her direction. It says, "You are not weird. I can see how you feel. You *and* your feelings are worthwhile."

The Lundbergs explain the four principles of validating:

1. *Everyone needs to feel respected and worthwhile, that their feelings matter, and that someone cares.*

2. *Trying to solve your spouse's problems is not why you exist.* In fact, there are many problems that we can't solve (e.g., the death of a loved one). It is often best to create a safe, supportive climate that helps them work through it themselves. We can help people experience the depths of their feelings, and compassionately support them in rising above them. Once they have risen from the depths of their negative feelings, we might then validate positively ("I know you can do it"; "I trust you").

3. *Validating really means tenderhearted listening with full attention to another's emotions and needs, and not just their words.* This is the essence of empathy. Once you understand, only then respond.

4. *Give people their agency, not advice.* They know more about the problem than you do. When someone is hurting, you might say, "That would hurt. What are you going to do?" Leave the choice with the person, who will feel more empowered by figuring out the best course of action.

How to Validate

Validating is done by kind, gentle, and respectful phrases. Listen for the word that carries the person's emotion, and respond in kind. If someone feels frustrated, you might say, "That *would* be frustrating. I'd feel frustrated too." Other phrases are:

- "Tell me more."
- "I'm sorry to hear that."
- "That had to be hard."
- "That's too bad. I know how much that meant to you."
- "Wow, that's great! I'm happy for you." (It's important to respond enthusiastically to someone's good news, too.)
- "What a good idea!"

Validating is also done through respectful questions to understand, not accuse, such as:

- "What happened?"
- "What was that like?"
- "Did that hurt your feelings?"
- "What's making you feel sad?" (after someone says he or she feels sad)
- "How did you feel about that?"
- "What did you do?"
- "What would you like to do?"
- "What do you think would work next time?"
- "What do you think would happen if you...?"
- "I think I understand, but I'm not sure. Can you help me understand that better?"
- "What helped you get through that?"

Avoid accusatory questions such as "Why did you do that?" (If you really want to understand, try, "I'm just trying to understand. Could you tell me why you felt that way?"), or "Why are you so defensive?" (You might instead ask, "Are you feeling defensive?")

Some applications

1. Validate your partner's dreams. Instead of "You know we can't afford that!" try, "That would be nice to go on that cruise, and someday we will."
2. Your spouse is discouraged from the weight she's gained. Instead of saying, "Why don't you go to the gym?" or even "I'll go to the gym with you," try, "Tell me about it. Is there anything I can do to help?"
3. For grief, "Oh, I'm so sorry it hurts. What can I do to help?"

Resolving Conflict

All couples have conflict; it is inevitable. Marital satisfaction is predicted not by the absence of conflict but by how the couples handle conflict. In fact divorce can be predicted with a high degree of accuracy by simply watching the way couples handle the first minutes of conflict. Socially intelligent couples:

- Stay calm and respectful—no rolling the eyes, name calling, contemptuous looks, character attacks (e.g., "You're irresponsible!"), sweeping generalizations (e.g., "You never help me out!"), or yelling
- Solve problems as a team, thinking in terms of "us" not "me"

Howard Markman and colleagues (1994) at the University of Denver have developed an approach to handling emotionally charged issues that has halved divorce rates and improved marital happiness. The approach, called the speaker-listener technique, takes into account the male-female differences. Recall that males prefer to have structure and rules, and that discussions be free of strong emotions. They tend to withdraw from conflict. Women tend to talk in order to feel close. They are less interested in solving the problem, but are more interested in the feeling content of the issue and want her mate to help her explore the whole situation. They need to know that

222

the partner will not walk away from the discussion before it is completed. The hotter the issue, the greater is the potential to escalate, and the more important it is to use the speaker-listener technique. The key elements of this technique are:

- *Exploration of the problem.* Before jumping to *solve* the problem, there will be a full *exploration* of the problem to ensure that both partners fully understand the problem and empathize with their partner. A single issue will be explored. Both partners put their ego on the shelf and consider conflict as an opportunity to strengthen the relationship.[4] The couple agrees to a time (not in the heat of the moment). A partner might say, "I have a concern I'd like to talk with you about. Would tonight be a good time for us to use the speaker-listener technique?"

- *The speaker's role.* The speaker holds an object, which symbolizes that he or she has the floor. This could be, say, a pen or a book. The speaker's job is simply to speak for herself, describing her thoughts, feelings, and concerns. There is no mind reading, or speaking for the partner. The speaker keeps her comments short and relatively simple, and then pauses to allow the listener to respond. You might start with the XYZ technique: "When you do X, in situation Y, I feel Z."

- *The listener's role.* The other partner is the listener. The listener's role is only to understand what the speaker is saying. There is no rebutting or interrupting. The listener demonstrates understanding by paraphrasing what the speaker has said ("So you are feeling....because....." Or, "I hear you saying that you were disappointed when you were running around and I didn't offer to help you.") Then the listener checks to see if he got it right. The speaker will acknowledge that the paraphrase is correct. If it isn't she will politely clarify and ask the listener to paraphrase again. (The only time an interruption is OK is when the listener respectfully asks to paraphrase the speaker's comments when those comments are becoming too long or complex. If the listener doesn't understand, it is alright to ask the speaker to restate or clarify. Otherwise, no questions are permitted.)

- *Changing roles.* The dialogue continues until the speaker feels heard and understood. At this point, the symbol is exchanged and the roles are reversed. The new speaker continues until he/she feels heard and understood. The back-and-forth process continues until both partners feel understood and agree that the issue has been adequately discussed.

- *Problem solving agenda.* Once the issue has been fully discussed, and only then, will the couple arrange a time to solve it. During the problem solving session the couple brainstorms lots of possible solutions, without discussing if they are workable or not. After brainstorming, the couple will discuss the pros and cons of each idea, before agreeing upon the best idea or combination of ideas to try. Set a time, say within a week, to evaluate how the plan is working.

- *Timeouts.* If at any time feelings are about to boil over, ask for a timeout to regroup. You might say, "I want to talk about this but I'm getting too upset. I'll be back in _____minutes." During the timeout, take a walk, write out your thoughts and feelings, or do whatever else will help you regain your composure.

- *A positive ending.* Try to end on a positive note ("Thanks for talking." Note what's been going well, shared values, and what you appreciate about your partner. Express your love and commitment.[5])

Enhancing Fun, Positive Feelings, and Intimacy

As important as it is to know how to disagree constructively, preserving and enhancing positive feelings in the relationship appears to be even more important. A sense of security grows when partners know that they enjoy each other's company. Having fun together allows partners to be themselves. Consider the habits of highly effective couples below. Circle those that you would wish to practice. Effective couples:

1. *Focus on the partner's strengths, not weaknesses.* Appreciate, don't criticize, at every opportunity. ("Thanks for listening." "You were so thoughtful to do the dishes." "I like the way you do that.") Accept that there will be differences and imperfections. Forgive. Appreciate the intent when the execution is less than perfect. Consider what first attracted you to your partner. Avoid teasing and sarcasm as a way to change your partner. Remember your partner's potential.

2. *Structure time for fun and friendship.* Friends are glad to see each other, and don't have immediate plans to change each other (Lundberg & Lundberg, 1999). They have fun being together. Brainstorm enjoyable events. Take turns picking the events to try. Have a weekly date night. Sometimes "plan spontaneity"—just set aside a block of time with only general plans and see what happens. Keep these times off limits for arguments or discussions of issues. Other times to reserve for enjoyment are bedtime chats, meals, lunch dates, and working together. Recording your feelings of such times helps to preserve the good feelings. Passive events like television are not usually as fulfilling as active ones, such as hobbies, gardening, learning, or hiking.

3. *Have a weekly couple's meeting* to anticipate possible problems, plan, and value the partner. Emphasize what is going well. This can be as short as a half hour. Try to keep it fun.

4. *Say you're sorry for mistakes.* A sincere apology is endearing.

5. *Put your spouse first.* Greet your spouse warmly before you greet others. Be courteous—use please and thank you often. Secretly help each other, without being asked or seeking credit (which can make the other feel obligated). Make phone calls or leave love notes just for fun. Show affection—gentle touching and caressing triggers the release of oxytocin, which reduces stress.

6. *Seek to value, not control, your spouse.* Both partners are happiest in relationships where there is equality and mutual respect. Don't push too hard. If a gentle invitation doesn't work, calm yourself, ease up, and try another approach.

7. *Work at intimacy.* Ask your partner what would make sexual intimacy more enjoyable. Often, what come up are things like spending time to talk, being alone together, kindness, or giving a helping hand.

8. *Be 100% honest and faithful.* These strengths characterize happy couples.

9. *Always consult your partner before making a decision that concerns them.* This makes the partner feel valued and increases trust.

Relationship Enhancement Activities

- *List the things you most appreciate in your partner.* Share one a week. Make it playful sometimes ("You know what I like about you...?"), but always sincere.

- *Each day, notice something that your partner does* (takes out the garbage, makes the bed, spends time with the children, and so on). Give your partner a hug and express appreciation for it.
- *Ask your partner about his/her hopes, dreams, or fears.*
- *Check your positivity ratio.* Respected marriage researcher John Gottman found that happy couples have a ratio of at least five positive interactions (such as humor, showing interest or affection, sharing good news or something fun that happened, validating, complimenting, gratitude and appreciation, reassurance, kind deeds, and praise) to every negative (e.g., anger, withdrawing, criticism, nagging, contempt, insults, defensiveness, trying to control, pointing out flaws in what the partner does, showing indifference to good news, and discounting accomplishments). Track your ratio for a week and make needed adjustments.
- *Go online to read research-based articles and complete two related exercises each week.* This has been found to work as well as attending seminars or workshops on marriage. The website www.foreverfamilies.net has compiled many such articles and exercises.
- *Describe in writing what it would be like living with you if you were your spouse.* Explain why you do what you do. Ask your spouse to do the same. Exchange what you've written. Discuss and listen in a way that seeks understanding. This often reveals fears and concerns that are not being understood, and changes anger to empathy.[6]

Strengthening Families

Highly effective parents raise children who feel valued and respected. These parents communicate expectations ("I expect you to...."), set limits ("That's not acceptable"), and emphasize accomplishments and rewards rather than punishments and weaknesses. Consider the habits of such parents and circle those you'd wish to try. Effective parents:

1. *Cultivate the family-as-team ethic.* They repeat, "We have to work as a team; we need to pull together." They explain the purpose of chores (it's more about building relationships than getting the work done) and work alongside their children.
2. *Hold weekly family nights.* These are weekly events where the purpose is having fun together. This can involve games, discussions, gardening, or learning.
3. *Hold regular family councils.* This is like a couple's meeting that includes the whole family to coordinate calendars, share goals, go over chores, plan, and encourage. The environment is open, safe, and positive. In one family, for example, all members shared their goals from the previous month and their progress. One child said, "My goal was to run every day and I was 50% successful." The whole family cheered. I thought to myself how much more motivating that was than focusing on the lapses. Try posting an agenda, where each person can add an issue they'd like to address, with a tentative solution. This trains children to be problem solvers. During the council, the whole family brainstorms, listing ideas without critiquing them yet. (All ideas are accepted as having merit; you never know what will emerge.) Then the problem solving strategy is used wherein each alternative is weighed and the best one is selected to try.

225

4. *Follow up family meetings with regular mom or dad interviews with each child.* Plan a regular, anticipated time to encourage and listen to the child, and hopefully ward off problems. Tell the child, "This is a time for you to talk about your interests and concerns, accomplishments, goals, and so forth. What do you need to talk about?" Make sure you keep the atmosphere positive—avoiding criticism, and communicating your love and concern. Be sure you listen much more than you speak. As children learn they can speak freely without censure, they will open up.

5. *Correct in private.* All children need parents who love them enough to set limits. Correcting in private avoids resentment.

6. *Tap the power of the family dinner.* In families that eat dinner together the children perform better at school, are better nourished, and experience fewer mental health problems. When the parents are home for dinner, the parents feel greater personal and family success, and are more satisfied and productive at their jobs. Wise managers, then, will help their employees get home for dinner— perhaps offering flextime, encouraging workers to make it home for dinner, or encouraging them to go home and come back if necessary. Wise parents will plan regular dinnertime, and let children know that they are expected to be there. Turn off the phone and television, ask the children to contribute in the preparation and/or cleanup. If you buy a meal out, pick it up and eat it at home.[7]

7. *Make each child feel loved and appreciated.* Remember validation and expressing appreciation and affection. Have special parent/child date nights. (One family held VIP nights where a child could stay up a little later with a parent. Years later, the child reminisced fondly of times spent folding laundry and talking with Dad.) Make scrap books with photographs, recorded memories and impressions, report cards, notes and art created by the children, etc.

8. *Parent the child you have, not the child you wish you had.* Children are all different and have different needs, capabilities, and strengths. Don't be surprised. If gentle requests are not working, be willing to set boundaries that hold children accountable and enforce consequences

Chapter 25

Balance

In interviewing resilient WWII combat survivors who were on average eighty years of age, I was struck by the degree of balance they had maintained throughout their lives. This chapter will look at various important aspects of balance in life.

Balancing Work with Pleasure

Nearly all of the resilient WWII survivors had been actively engaged in a wide range of interesting and pleasant activities over the course of their lives (Schiraldi, 2007).[1] Pleasant activity helps to keep the brain sharp and the mood upbeat. It is also among those factors outside of the workplace—including sleep, exercise, diet, and social bonds—that appear to improve work performance.

   Peter Lewinsohn and colleagues (1986) observed an interesting downward spiral in depressed people. First, they became stressed, as typically happens among those who are "crazy busy." To save time, they stopped doing the pleasant things that had kept their moods up. As the mood became depressed, they pessimistically assumed that nothing could lift their moods again, so they stopped trying to engage in those mood-enhancing activities. Lewinsohn's team developed the Pleasant Events Schedule to help depressed people again engage in pleasant pastimes. Doing so, he found, measurably improved the mood. The modified version of Dr. Lewinsohn's schedule, found below, helps functioning people check their lives for balance and make needed adjustments in order to optimize mood. Completing this is very effective, and is highly recommended.

Directions for Pleasant Events Scheduling

STEP 1: The Pleasant Events Schedule* beginning on the next page lists a wide range of activities. In Column 1, check those activities that you enjoyed in the past. Then rate from 1-10 how pleasant each checked item was. A score of 1 reflects little pleasure, and 10 reflects great pleasure. This rating goes in Column 1 also, beside each check mark. For example, if you moderately enjoyed being with happy people, but didn't enjoy being with friends/relatives, your first 2 items would look like this:

   √ (5)   _____   1. Being with happy people

   _____   _____   2. Being with friends/relatives

---

*The "Pleasant Events Schedule" and the instructions for using it are adapted with permission from Lewinsohn, P., Munoz, R., Youngren, M., & Zeiss, A., (1986), *Control Your Depression*, New York: Prentice Hall, © 1986 by Peter M. Lewinsohn. Not to be reproduced without written permission from Dr. Lewinsohn. This modified version originally appeared in Schiraldi, G. R. (2001). *The Self-Esteem Workbook*, Oakland, CA: New Harbinger.

PLEASANT EVENTS SCHEDULE

I. Social Interactions. These events occur with others. They tend to make us feel accepted, appreciated, liked, and/or understood.*

COLUMN 1   COLUMN 2

_____	_____	1.	Being with happy people
_____	_____	2.	Being with friends/relatives
_____	_____	3.	Thinking about people I like
_____	_____	4.	Planning an activity with people I care for
_____	_____	5.	Meeting someone new
_____	_____	6.	Going to a club, restaurant, tavern, etc.
_____	_____	7.	Being at celebrations (birthdays, weddings, baptisms, parties, family get-togethers, etc.)
_____	_____	8.	Meeting a friend for lunch or a drink
_____	_____	9.	Talking openly and honestly (e.g., about your hopes, your fears, what interests you, what makes you laugh, what saddens you)
_____	_____	10.	Expressing true affection (verbal or physical)
_____	_____	11.	Showing interest in others
_____	_____	12.	Noticing successes and strengths in family and friends
_____	_____	13.	Dating, courting (this one is for married people, too)
_____	_____	14.	Having a lively conversation
_____	_____	15.	Inviting friends over
_____	_____	16.	Stopping in to visit friends
_____	_____	17.	Calling up someone I enjoy
_____	_____	18.	Apologizing
_____	_____	19.	Smiling at people
_____	_____	20.	Calmly talking over problems with people I live with
_____	_____	21.	Giving compliments, back pats, praise
_____	_____	22.	Teasing/bantering
_____	_____	23.	Amusing people or making them laugh
_____	_____	24.	Playing with children
_____	_____	25.	Others: _____

II. Activities that make us feel capable, loving, useful, strong or adequate.

_____	_____	1.	Starting a challenging job or doing it well
_____	_____	2.	Learning something new (e.g., fixing leaks, new hobby, new language)
_____	_____	3.	Helping someone (counseling, advising, listening)
_____	_____	4.	Contributing to religious, charitable, or other groups
_____	_____	5.	Driving skillfully

*You might feel that an activity belongs in another group. The grouping is not important.

_____ _____   6. Expressing myself clearly (out loud or in writing)
_____ _____   7. Repairing something (sewing, fixing car or bike, etc.)
_____ _____   8. Solving a problem or puzzle
_____ _____   9. Exercising
_____ _____ 10. Thinking
_____ _____ 11. Going to a meeting (convention, business, civic)
_____ _____ 12. Visiting the ill, homebound, troubled
_____ _____ 13. Telling a child a story
_____ _____ 14. Writing a card, note, or letter
_____ _____ 15. Improving my appearance (seeking medical or dental help, improving my diet, going to a barber or beautician)
_____ _____ 16. Planning/budgeting time
_____ _____ 17. Discussing political issues
_____ _____ 18. Doing volunteer work, community service, etc.
_____ _____ 19. Planning a budget
_____ _____ 20. Protesting injustice, protecting someone, stopping fraud or abuse
_____ _____ 21. Being honest, moral, etc.
_____ _____ 22. Correcting mistakes
_____ _____ 23. Organizing a party
_____ _____ 24. Others: _____

III. Intrinsically Pleasant Activities

_____ _____   1. Laughing
_____ _____   2. Relaxing, having peace and quiet
_____ _____   3. Having a good meal
_____ _____   4. Doing a hobby (cooking, fishing, woodworking, photography, acting, gardening, collecting things)
_____ _____   5. Listening to good music
_____ _____   6. Seeing beautiful scenery
_____ _____   7. Going to bed early, sleeping soundly, and awakening early
_____ _____   8. Wearing attractive clothes
_____ _____   9. Wearing comfortable clothes
_____ _____ 10. Going to a concert, opera, ballet, or play
_____ _____ 11. Playing sports (tennis, softball, racquetball, golf, horseshoes, frisbee)
_____ _____ 12. Trips or vacations
_____ _____ 13. Shopping/buying something I like for myself
_____ _____ 14. Being outdoors (beach, country, mountains, kicking leaves, walking in the sand, floating in lakes)
_____ _____ 15. Doing artwork (painting, sculpture, drawing)
_____ _____ 16. Reading the Scriptures or other sacred works
_____ _____ 17. Beautifying my home (redecorating, cleaning, yard work, etc.)
_____ _____ 18. Going to a sports event
_____ _____ 19. Reading (novels, poems, plays, newspapers, etc.)
_____ _____ 20. Going to a lecture

_____	_____	21.	Going for a drive
_____	_____	22.	Sitting in the sun
_____	_____	23.	Visiting a museum
_____	_____	24.	Playing or singing music
_____	_____	25.	Boating
_____	_____	26.	Pleasing my family, friends, employer
_____	_____	27.	Thinking about something good in the future
_____	_____	28.	Watching TV
_____	_____	29.	Camping, hunting
_____	_____	30.	Grooming myself (bathing, combing hair, shaving)
_____	_____	31.	Writing in my diary/journal
_____	_____	32.	Taking a bike ride, hiking, or walking
_____	_____	33.	Being with animals
_____	_____	34.	Watching people
_____	_____	35.	Taking a nap
_____	_____	36.	Listening to nature sounds
_____	_____	37.	Getting or giving a backrub
_____	_____	38.	Watching a storm, clouds, the sky
_____	_____	39.	Having spare time
_____	_____	40.	Daydreaming
_____	_____	41.	Feeling the presence of the Lord in my life; praying, worshipping
_____	_____	42.	Smelling a flower
_____	_____	43.	Talking about old times or special interests
_____	_____	44.	Going to auctions, garage sales, etc.
_____	_____	45.	Traveling
_____	_____	46.	Others

STEP 2: In Column 2, check if you've done the event in the last 30 days.

STEP 3: Circle the number of the events that you'd probably enjoy (on a good day).

STEP 4: Notice if there are many items you've enjoyed in the past that you are not doing very often (compare the first and second columns).

STEP 5: Using the completed Pleasant Events Schedule for ideas, make a list of the 25 activities that you feel you'd most enjoy doing.

STEP 6: Make a plan to do more pleasant activities. Start with the simplest and the ones you are most likely to enjoy. Do as many pleasant events as you reasonably can. It is suggested that you do at least one each day, perhaps more on weekends. *Write* your plan on a calendar, and carry out this written plan for at least two weeks. Each time you do an activity, rate it on a 1-5 scale for pleasure (5 being highly enjoyable). This tests the stress-induced distortion that *nothing* is enjoyable. This rating may also help you later replace less enjoyable activities with others.

Some Tips

- Tune into the physical world. Pay less attention to your thoughts. Feel the wind, or the soap suds as you wash the car. See and hear.
- Before doing an event, set yourself up to enjoy it. Identify three things you will enjoy about it. Say, "I will enjoy _____ (the sunshine, the breeze, talking with brother Joe, etc.)." Relax, and imagine yourself enjoying each aspect of the event as you repeat each statement.
- Ask yourself, "What will I do to make the activity enjoyable?"
- If you are concerned that you might not enjoy some activity that you'd like to try, break it up into steps. Think small, so you can be satisfied in reaching your goal. For example, start by only cleaning the house for ten minutes, then stop. Reward yourself with a "Good job!" pat on the back.
- Check your schedule for balance. Can you spread out the "need to's" to make room for some "want to's"?
- Time is limited, so use it wisely. You needn't do activities you don't like just because they're convenient.

Balancing Past, Present, and Future

Those who create time affluence—sufficient time to reflect and pursue what is pleasurable and meaningful—are consistently happier than the "rat racers," who are rushed, materialistic, and overworked (Kasser & Ahuvia, 2002). However, recent research by Philip Zimbardo and John Boyd (2008) has also found that the happiest, healthiest, and most successful people have balanced attitudes about the past, present, and future.

- About the past, this group has warm, nostalgic memories, without clinging to the past. Activities that cultivate this perspective include keeping scrapbooks of mementos, feeling gratitude for positive memories, tracing your genealogy, and participating in events that celebrate the culture you came from. At the same time, this group does not dwell on bad things from the past. Writing about the past, for example, might help to process and settle negative memories. Forgiving and accepting that all people experience bad things can also help.
- This group feels moderately invested in the future without obsessing about it, which can make us crazy busy and angry at interruptions, such as slow traffic or computer glitches. Activities that foster this perspective are making value driven plans and being flexible with those plans—not being so goal oriented that they can't relax and focus in the present. Lennis Echterling and colleagues (2005) suggest this anticipation exercise: Generate positive emotions (e.g., by smiling and recalling pleasant memories). Then think ahead. "When _____ (some problem or obstacle) is resolved, I'll feel even more at ease, comfortable, happy, etc." A reasonable investment in the future allows one to exercise discipline to do difficult tasks in order to enjoy the long-term satisfaction and feeling of accomplishment.
- About the present, this group is enthused and committed to finding pleasure in the opportunities life presents without being unreasonable, unrealistic, or

demanding. They feel capable of finding something to enjoy in each situation. This orientation can be cultivated by "planning spontaneity,"[2] and by being more open to life's simple pleasures (actively look for something to enjoy in any circumstance).

Balancing Technology with Tranquility

In his book on happiness, Nick Baylis, Ph.D., (2009) considers how we can gain freedom from the crippling bonds of technology. He quotes the brilliant scientist Albert Einstein regarding "time-saving technology." Decades ago, Einstein said (p.254), "Why does this magnificent applied science, which saves work and makes life easier, bring us little happiness? The simple answer runs: because we have not yet learned to make sensible use of it." Ponder the electronic devices in your life, such as computers, cell phones, email, and Facebook, and ask yourself: Do they connect me or isolate me from the following? Check the appropriate box:

My electric devices....

Connect me to	Isolate me from	
		Other people
		Nature
		Myself (what I feel and need; who I am)
		Reflection and relaxation time
		Being fully present "in the moment"
		Simple pleasures
		Hobbies or other pleasurable recreational pursuits
		My creative side
		Sleep, exercise, and good eating

In your journal please write your reactions to this reflection:

Virtual reality isn't real. Spending hours on Facebook isn't the same as sitting face-to-face with a friend for hours. Will the world end if we were to turn off the Blackberry during dinner or at a restaurant? Do we really need to spend hours on email, Facebook, MySpace, Skype, texting, *and* video conferencing, or might we select and use one or none of these? Is your technology a boon or an addiction? Is it energizing or creating a frenzied exhaustion? Could we better limit our technology time and expand our tranquility time? What would happen if you turned off the news and went to bed earlier tonight?

Balanced Goals

Robert Emmons, Ph.D., (1986) found that setting goals and progressing toward them predicts happiness. Goals set our course so we can relax and enjoy the trip more. The goals that happy people make are:
- *Specific and concrete, not vague.* A specific, concrete goal is to lose two pounds by the end of a month's time; a vague goal would be to become leaner. Being

kinder by saying hello to one new person each day links a worthwhile, but abstract, goal (being kinder) to a concrete, specific goal.

- *Intrinsically motivating.* Money, status, prestige, praise, recognition, or aiming to impress others are generally less motivating than investing your strengths in a cause that *you* truly value and enjoy working toward. Ask yourself what you would do for no pay at all. Loving what you do and doing what you value enables you to persist when you don't feel like it. Don't pay excessive attention to bad, or even good, judgments from others. These can sidetrack you from freely choosing what is most important to you.
- *Realistic and reachable.* It's better to attain smaller goals than to be frustrated with bigger ones, so make goals challenging, but obtainable. Feel satisfaction for progressing toward the goal, even if that goal is imperfectly realized.
- *Approach, not avoidance, oriented.* It is more motivating to set a goal, say, to improve my appearance by reducing my waistline by an inch than to say I will avoid having a premature heart attack like Dad did by dropping five pounds.
- *Flexible.* Don't freak if you fall sort, but try again, try a new approach, or modify your goal.
- *Balanced.* Address all valued domains of life: relationships, physical health/fitness, intellectual/educational pursuits, emotional health, leisure/recreational/enjoyment, profession, citizenship, spiritual/personal growth, and legacy.

The Valued Life Activity

Consider very strong negative feelings you've experienced, such as anger, depression, shame, or fear that perhaps keep you stuck. What do these feelings tell you about what you value? For example, if you get very angry when your spouse is disrespectful, perhaps this suggests that you value harmony and respect in your intimate relationships. Imagine something happens to change those negative feelings and enable you to pursue these values constructively. How would your life be improved? Write about this in your journal. This activity can clarify and reinforce what you most value in life, and perhaps suggest how to progress toward these values.

Value-driven Time Management

Value-driven goals help us to persist. A sound time management plan helps us to pursue those goals efficiently. Imagine that you have overcome all "stuck points" that you possibly can—all obstacles to reaching your most valued goals in life.

STEP 1: Values. Rank order the following nine domains of life. That is, place a 1 by the domain you consider most important, a 2 by the next most important, and so on:
_____ 1. Relationships (family, friends, intimate, colleagues)
_____ 2. Physical health/fitness (sleep, exercise, nutrition, medical care)
_____ 3. Intellectual/educational pursuits
_____ 4. Emotional health
_____ 5. Leisure/recreational/enjoyment (e.g., travel, hobbies, culture)

233

_____ 6. Profession

_____ 7. Citizenship/community

_____ 8. Spiritual/personal growth (e.g., integrity, humor, optimism, responsiveness to beauty)

_____ 9. Legacy (something I'll leave behind; a meaningful impact I'll have on the world)

STEP 2: Life Goals. Finish the following sentence stems. Write as quickly as you can. Do not worry about whether what you write is doable or makes sense. Just write quickly.[3]

- My personal definition of success is.... (Try to think beyond the material. People whose central goals are solely financial tend to have poorer mental health.)

- If I were to live more fully functioning and happily I would be more _____ and less _____. (For this stem, indicate personal traits.)

- My life overall would be just about ideal/complete if I were to.... (Imagine you were taking a video of yourself. What would you see yourself doing?)

- My retirement goals are...

- My goals for 10 years from now are...

- My goals for 5 years from now are...

- My goals for 1 year from now are...

- If someone looking into a crystal ball were to tell me that I had only six months to live, I would do the following:

STEP 3: Balance Check. At step 2, you have just made a substantial list of goals that are important to you. Now you'll check your goals for balance. Each goal will likely fall under one or more of the nine domains listed in step 1. Beside each response to the sentence stems in step 2, place a 1, 2, 3, 4, 5, 6, 7, 8 and/or a 9 corresponding to the appropriate domain. When you finish this step, pause. What do you notice? Are your goals balanced? Do they especially reflect the domains you most value? Make any desired adjustments.

STEP 4: Backward Planning. In this step, translate your general life goals to more specific goals. Create a Five-Year Goal sheet with the following headings:

Five-Year Goals for Period Beginning_____ and Ending _____

Goals	What I'll Do to Reach Goals	Starting Date	How I'll Know I Reached Goal	Evaluation at End of Period
Relationships **Physical Health (etc....)**				

In the first column, list several goals under each of the domains you consider relevant. Try to make each goal as specific and measurable as possible. For example, instead of the vague physical health goal of "improve appearance," you might write "lose one inch off waistline." Instead of "improve personal relationships," you might write, "spend 15 minutes of uninterrupted time with my son each day." In the second column, list specific steps that will enable you to reach each goal. For example, a way to lose one inch from the waistline might be to walk 30 minutes six days a week. In column three, specify when you will begin to work on each goal. In column four, describe how you will measure/observe the successful achievement of each goal (e.g., achieve waist measurement of 33"). The last column is completed after the five-year time period. Continuing the backward planning process, complete a One-Year Goals sheet in the same way.

STEP 5: Monthly Planning. Next, complete a monthly calendar for the upcoming month. Indicate what you will do each day to bring you closer to your five- and one-year goals. Also anticipate and record here all important events coming up during the month, such as medical or professional appointments, work tasks, and recreational dates. (You might wish to make or buy a monthly planner.)

STEP 6: Weekly Planning. Plan a typical week—hour by hour for each day, as on this sample:

Weekly Work and Recreation Schedule

Hours	Sunday	Monday	Tuesday	Wednesday	Thursday	Friday	Saturday
6-7 a.m.							
7-8 a.m. etc.							

It is wise to start by blocking out the essentials, such as sleep, eating, exercise, and recreation, before you block out other demands (commuting, work, or meetings). Think of life as a marathon. You'll run farther and accomplish more if you are conditioned, rested, and nourished. You'll probably want to include perhaps an hour of time at week's beginning to plan the upcoming week.

Pause here for a moment. Have you allowed time each day for emotional, spiritual, and physical nourishment? If not, you will probably not give your best to self, others, or your tasks. Is there ample time allocated to accomplish your monthly goals? If overloading is evident, what would happen if you softened expectations or spread out the less essential goals? Remember, you can do almost anything you choose to do, but you can't do everything, and you can't do it all at once. Do what you can, and then release worry as much as you can.

STEP 7: Daily "To Do" List. Keep a *single* list of things you choose to do for the upcoming day, by priority. Do the highest-priority items first. Try to make a list with reasonable expectations, allowing sufficient time to accomplish each item. If you don't get to all the items, place the unfinished items on tomorrow's "to do" list, again listed by priorities. You might wish to make a "to do" list at least an hour or two before retiring, and review it at the start of the next day. It is also suggested that you keep all your planning sheets together, perhaps in a single notebook or electronic planner, with your daily "to do" list first, where you can refer to it often.

Chapter 26

Meditation

It's a perfect combination of aggressive action taking place in an atmosphere of total tranquility...just totally peaceful.
Billie Jean King

Meditation may be thought of as experiencing our true, happy nature. It is not surprising, then, that adding meditation to happiness training gives an added boost in happiness, while giving additional reductions in anxiety and depression (Smith, Compton, & West, 1995). In fact, meditating has been found to confer many other beneficial effects, ranging from improved cognitive abilities to improved medical health and heart rate variability (related to heart coherence.) In this chapter we'll explore two particularly effective methods of meditating: mindfulness mediation and integral yoga meditation.

Mindfulness Meditation

If the time available for resilience training were severely limited, mindfulness would likely be the one skill I would teach. It is that effective. Since being introduced into Western medical circles in 1979, researchers have concluded that mindfulness:
- Increases positive and decreases negative emotions[1]
- Enlarges various regions of the brain, including the hippocampus and prefrontal cortex, and strengthens connections between brain regions
- Improves the ability to pay attention; synchronizes various brain regions involved in mood and cognitive functions
- Improves reaction time, productivity, empathy, relationship satisfaction, inner security, hardiness, [2] vitality, and sleep quality
- Boosts immune function; reduces chronic pain, blood pressure, psoriasis, and a wide range of other medical symptoms
- Reduces impulsivity and reactivity to criticism, conflict, and other stressors (even torture); increases comfort with adversity; increases resilience and the ability to cope with stress

Mindfulness changes the way we *respond* to our environment without attempting to change the outer world—or even our thoughts. Instead of *fighting* with what is, or *reacting* with strong emotions, mindfulness practice teaches us to be fully aware of each moment with calm, compassion, and equanimity. Eventually, mindfulness helps us to experience even the strongest, most distressing emotions, thoughts, and bodily discomforts calmly and without undue distress. This is why mindfulness training is often included in PTSD treatments.

Mindfulness derives from Eastern teachings. However, the practice of mindfulness readily harmonizes with nearly any tradition imaginable.

In the Eastern view, each person is of two minds, the wisdom mind and the ordinary mind. Visualize two concentric circles, as in Figure 26.1. At the center is our wisdom mind, or true happy nature—who we truly are. The wisdom mind is happy, wise, compassionate, good humored, dignified, humble, hopeful, whole, and peaceful. When we are grounded in our wisdom mind, we respond to the world in the most effective way. Problems arise, however, when we are pulled away from our wisdom mind into the ordinary mind. The ordinary mind is characterized by swirling, effortful, and scattered thoughts. The ordinary mind endlessly thinks, plans, worries, regrets, obsesses, judges, avoids, hurries, dramatizes, and fights against the way life is—with resulting emotional and physical distress. You've undoubtedly heard the expression of people being beside themselves with worry, anger, or other strong negative emotions. This means they are separated from the wisdom mind and stuck in the ordinary mind. Racing thoughts actually block our ability to focus. The ordinary mind covers the wisdom mind and causes most of our suffering. It attaches to things that are not necessary for our happiness, such as pride, jealousy, or material goods. So the idea of meditation is to get underneath the ordinary mind, grounded in the peaceful wisdom mind. Mindfulness is not a way of thinking; it is a way of being.

Figure 26.1
THE NATURE OF MIND

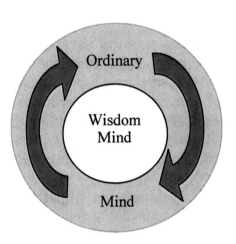

In Eastern teaching, the word for mind also means heart. Mindfulness is about connecting with the innate attitudes of the heart. We shall highlight seven of these attitudes.[3]

- *Compassion* is the most important attitude. Compassion is often translated as gentle friendliness or loving kindness. Compassion means feeling sorrow and empathy for suffering and the desire to help. Eastern masters, however, teach that it is as important to feel compassion for oneself as it is to feel compassion for others. When we respond to stressors with compassion we are calmer and happier. When we are calmer and happier, we respond more effectively to daily challenges.
- *Vastness*. The wisdom mind is broad and deep, large enough to embrace any stressor compassionately. The wisdom mind is often likened to a vast ocean. At its depths the ocean is calm. Looking from the calm depths, we view stressors as waves at the surface. The waves swell, and then are absorbed into the vast deep ocean, leaving the inner depths unchanged. This perspective reminds us that the

surface can constantly change, but our center has all the resources needed to fully embrace whatever storms arise confidently and calmly.[4]

- *Acceptance.* To accept is to see with full awareness what is, without judging, criticizing, or over-thinking the situation. When we accept, we simply notice, without trying to fix, change, or escape the situation. That is, we bring compassionate awareness to the situation, trusting that the appropriate response will eventually arise. Notice that acceptance does not mean passive resignation. It simply means that we fully take in the situation before we do anything. This stance has important implications. Often people experience anger (an ordinary-mind reaction) as a sign that they are afraid to face fear or pain. They might drink to escape the fear and pain. Mindfulness teaches us to simply acknowledge the fear and pain without judgment—to gently turn *toward* our experience. Compassion eventually soothes those distressing emotions.[5] We greet them cordially, watch them rise like the waves, and eventually be absorbed into the ocean. In day-to-day living, acceptance teaches us to first see clearly the way the situation is, not the way the ordinary mind says it is, before attempting to solve, fix, or change the problem. Acceptance is the primary response. Sometimes it is the only response needed.[6] Paradoxically, acceptance is associated with effective planning and action,[7] whereas avoidance keeps us stuck.[8]

- *Non-attachment.* Attachment is the root of unhappiness. We lock on to the thought that "I must have something to be happy." That something might be a material possession, such as a car. Then we push ourselves feverishly to obtain that car, and feel sad if we don't get it. If we get it, we worry that something might happen to it, or get angry if someone scratches it. Or, we could be attached to status, appearances, prestige, a relationship, or even happiness. Attachments keep us tense and battling in the ordinary mind. When we release the attachment and allow ourselves to come home to the wisdom mind, we realize that we already have within what is needed to be happy. Notice that we can still actively pursue what we value. However, in mindfulness practice we release the vice-like grip and don't strive for anything in the moment. Later, if we choose to, we can act with greater relaxation, clarity, and efficiency.

- *Beginner's mind.* The expert learns little. The child who is fully open usually learns more. In mindfulness we do not prematurely foreclose our experience with preconceived judgments or expectations, such as "I can't meditate," "I'll never improve," or "I must do this just right." We simply practice with an open, flexible mind, being neither overly optimistic nor cynically pessimistic. We just allow the experience to unfold and notice what happens, without trying to make anything happen.

- *Equanimity.* We greet whatever we experience, whether positive or negative, with the same calm response. In mindfulness, both positive and negative emotions are considered important, and each is greeted in the same calm, non-judgmental, unattached way.

- *Commitment.* Those who practice mindfulness meditation usually find that starting with twenty minutes per day, and progressing to 45 minutes per day or longer, six days a week, is most effective. Practice even if you don't feel like it; the beneficial effects of practice accumulate over time.

239

Jon Kabat-Zinn, Ph.D., introduced mindfulness meditation to Western medical circles at the University of Massachusetts Medical School. His eight-week training program is called Mindfulness-based Stress Reduction, which we will overview here in abbreviated and somewhat modified form.[9] It all starts with the humble raisin. Practice each exercise in sequence, since each builds on the one before it.

Exercise: The Raisins

The purpose of this exercise is to eat two raisins mindfully with full awareness over a ten- to fifteen-minute period.

1. Hold two raisins gently in the palm of your hand with a curious, good-humored attitude.
2. Pick one up and notice all the details of the raisin—the ridges, stem, translucence, color, and aroma. Notice the sensations in your fingers as you feel the surface of the raisin. Roll it between your fingers next to your ear and notice what that sounds like.
3. Notice your body as you hold it, noticing tension as you move it slowly toward your mouth. Sense the air against your skin as your hand moves slowly, much as you'd feel the water against your hand in the bath. Notice whether your body is signaling hunger. Pay attention to all the sensations in your hand and moving arm.
4. As you get ready to put the raisin in your mouth, you might notice yourself thinking things like: "I like (dislike) raisins. Mom used to give them to us for snacks. I'd like to eat lunch. I really don't have time to do this raisin exercise. There are probably a lot of calories in this raisin. What's this got to do with resilience?" This is good! Each time such thoughts arise, greet them cordially (thinking is what the ordinary mind does), and simply bring back your attention to eating the raisin.
5. Notice how your mouth accepts the raisin. As you let the raisin sit on your tongue, just sense it there and notice what it feels like before eating it. After a while place it on different areas of the tongue. Notice whether you salivate and taste the raisin.
6. Take a single bite and notice the flavor. You might notice a burst of flavor that is more intense than it seems when you mindlessly eat raisins.
7. Chew slowly, paying attention to what that is like, and then notice the intent to swallow. As you swallow, follow the raisin down into your stomach. Notice the aftertaste and sensations in your body.
8. When you finish, do it again with the second raisin, being fully and calmly present for the experience.

Most of the elements of mindfulness are introduced in this exercise: being calmly present for an experience moment by moment without judging or emotionally reacting; being aware of the wandering mind, and gently escorting it back to the present moment without judging; the beginner's mind (even though you might think all raisins are the same, eating the second raisin is not the same experience as eating the first); and realizing how much of life we miss when we are not mindful. Many people notice that the experience of eating a raisin is more intense when the mind is focused on the present moment, and that they really notice flavors that they miss when they are in a hurry. Some say that they'd probably eat less if they were mindful because they'd enjoy each bite more and would notice when hunger signals stop. Can you see how situational awareness would increase as we practice being fully aware of everything in our environment?

Exercise: Mindful Breathing

This is a very effective meditation practice that helps us learn to be more peaceful in our own bodies, and to get under the racing thoughts in our heads. It takes about ten to fifteen minutes. Practice it once a day for a week or more.

1. Sit comfortably in the meditator's posture: Feet are flat on the floor; hands are resting, unfolded, comfortably in the lap, with palms up or down. The back is comfortably erect. Imagine that the spine is aligned like a column of golden coins resting one atop the other. The head is neither forward nor back; the chin is neither up nor down. The torso is held with dignity and grace, like a majestic mountain. The mountain is constant and secure, despite the clouds that cover it or the storms that batter it.

2. Allow your eyes to close. Release tension in the shoulders, neck, and jaw. Let the abdomen be soft and relaxed. Permit your body to relax and settle. Let yourself begin to settle in the wisdom mind.

3. Gently and with good humor be aware for a moment of the attitudes of mindfulness that already exist within, such as compassion, vastness, acceptance, and nonattachment. In this meditation, you are not striving to make anything in particular happen. Just notice what occurs.

4. Let awareness go to your breathing, as you breathe abdominally (allow your upper body to be relaxed and still; the only movement is your abdomen rising as you breathe in and falling as you breathe out). Notice your breathing as you would watch waves flow in and out from the shore of the beach. As your breath is flowing, sense the parts of your body that are moving. You might sense the rising and stretching in your abdomen as you breathe in. You might notice the breath moving through your nostrils and throat and in and out of your lungs. Perhaps you notice your heart beating, slightly faster on the in-breath and slightly slower on the out-breath. Each breath is different, so pay attention to the entire breath with the beginner's mind.

5. As you breathe, thoughts will come and go. To fight them is to increase tension, so simply notice your mind wandering, and each time you notice that it has wandered, gently bring it back to focusing on the breath. The object is not to stop yourself from thinking. Rather, it is to feel satisfaction each time you notice your mind wandering. This is what the ordinary mind does. Congratulate yourself each time you mindfully notice thoughts arise, and gently, kindly, patiently return your awareness to the breath without judging. Think of this as practice in responding to life with loving kindness.

6. Release, relax, and rest in the breath. Notice fully each part of the in-breath, the out-breath, and each subtle changing moment. Rest your mind in your belly, sensing what this is like.

241

7. And now feel the breath as if it were a wave filling the entire body. Underneath the breath notice a deeper calm, the peace within.
8. When you are finished notice how you feel. Let that feeling go, just as you let awareness of the breath come and go.

Exercise: Body Scan

We feel emotions and physical sensations in the body. Yet we often try to manage these in the head. We might think, "Oh, no. I don't want to feel that emotion. Not again. I've got to stop feeling that." Or, "This pain is terrible; I've got to find a way to kill it." The more we fight the feelings and sensations, the more we suffer. We are often quite out of touch with the body as we live in our heads, being more connected to television, computers, or cell phones than to our bodies. We might be obsessed with the image of our body in the mirror without being in tune with our body, just as we may eat without really tasting. The body scan meditation will prepare us to eventually experience emotional and physical discomfort with kindness and calmness, without trying to push it away, run from it, or think ourselves out of it. This meditation teaches us to simply welcome in each sensation. We watch it kindly and dispassionately, and then let our awareness of the sensation dissolve. As we simply watch sensations, we notice that they often change; they come and go. When we do not tense up, but instead relax into the sensation, our response to the sensation changes. Many people observe that they feel grounded when they are centered in their bodies instead of their heads—peacefully observing the comings and goings of bodily sensations, and holding whatever comes up in calm awareness. The idea in this meditation is not to *think about* each region of the body, but to place your awareness deep inside it, feeling from inside. Practice this meditation for about forty minutes daily, for at least a week.

1. Lie down on your back in a place where you are unlikely to be disturbed. Close your eyes. Remember especially the attitudes of loving kindness, acceptance, non-judgment, letting go, and good humor.
2. Breathe and let your mind settle; let your mind rest calmly in your body.
3. Notice how your body as a whole feels at this moment without judging. Feel your skin against the bed or floor. Notice the temperature of the air around you and how it feels. Be aware of how your body feels—is it comfortable, or is there any tension, pain, or itching? Notice the intensity of these sensations and whether they change or stay the same.
4. In a moment you will breathe in and out of one region of your body several times, paying full attention to all the sensations that you experience. It is as though your mind is resting in that area of the body. Then when you are ready, you will release your awareness, letting awareness of that region dissolve as you also release tension in that area. Then you'll bring your awareness in a similar way to the next region. Each time your mind wanders, gently bring it back to the region on which you are focusing without judging. Let's begin. We'll give directions starting with the toes of your left foot. Then we'll progress in a similar fashion to the other regions of the body.
5. Bring kind, openhearted attention to the toes of your left foot, letting your mind rest there. Imagine that you are breathing in and out of your toes. Perhaps you imagine air from your in-breath flowing down through your nose, lungs,

abdomen, and legs into your toes, and then, with your out-breath, out from your toes, up through your body, and though your nose. Allow yourself to feel any and all sensations in the toes—pressure from a sock, temperature, blood flow, pulsing, relaxation, tension, and so on. Notice any changes in these sensations as you breathe. If you feel nothing, that is okay. Just notice whatever there is to experience without commenting or judging. When you are ready to leave this region, take a deeper and more intentional breath, following the in-breath down to the toes once again. As you exhale, let awareness of the toes dissolve, releasing any tension or discomfort your body is willing to release at this time, as you bring awareness to the next region of your body (your left sole). Let your awareness stay in the next region in the same way for several breaths before moving on. As thoughts arise, silently and without judgment say, "Thinking, just thinking." Gently return your awareness to the region of the body and your breathing. Approach each region with the beginner's mind, as though you've never before paid attention to that region. Watch whatever you experience without tensing or judging, but with kind, gentle, softhearted awareness. Repeat the process for each body part, following the list below.

- Left sole
- Left heel
- Top of left foot
- Left ankle
- Left shin and calf
- Left knee
- Left thigh
- Left side of groin
- Left hip
- Toes of right foot
- Right sole
- Right heel
- Top of right foot
- Right ankle
- Right shin and calf
- Right knee
- Right thigh
- Right side of groin
- Right hip
- Pelvic region, genitals, and buttocks
- Lower back
- Upper back
- Spinal column
- Stomach
- Chest
- Ribs
- Heart
- Lungs

- Shoulder blades
- Collar bones
- Shoulders
- Fingers of left hand
- Left palm
- Back of left hand
- Left wrist
- Left forearm
- Left elbow
- Left upper arm
- Left armpit
- Fingers of right hand
- Right palm
- Back of right hand
- Right wrist
- Right forearm
- Right elbow
- Right upper arm
- Right armpit
- Neck and throat (notice air flow)
- Nose (notice air flow and smells without judgment)
- Left ear
- Right ear
- Eyes
- Cheeks
- Forehead
- Temples
- Jaw and mouth
- Face
- Crown of head

6. Now be aware of your whole body, breathing in peaceful stillness. Go beneath your thoughts and feel the wholeness of the body. Notice what is moving or changing. Breathe through imaginary air holes in your head and feet: Breathe in through the head, following the breath down to the stomach, and, on the out-breath, follow the breath down the legs and out the toes. Then breathe in through the feet, following the in-breath to the stomach, and breathe out through the head. Ultimately feel the entire body breathing, like waves on the surface of the ocean, as you watch from the calm and peaceful depths.

Exercise: Smile Meditation

This beautiful meditation reminds us that happiness already exists within us as part of our true, happy nature. It is good to practice this at the beginning of the day, and throughout the day. Allow about ten to fifteen minutes for this meditation.

1. Assume the meditator's posture, sitting comfortably erect, with feet flat on the floor, and hands resting comfortably in the lap. The spine is straight like a stack of golden coins. The upper body is relaxed but erect, sitting in graceful dignity like a majestic mountain. Allow your eyes to close. Let your breathing help you to settle into your restful wisdom mind.

2. Be aware of the playful, good-humored aspects of your true happy nature, or wisdom mind. Imagine for a moment what it would be like to smile. Perhaps you notice that just the idea of a smile tends to evoke feelings of being content, happy, relaxed, and softhearted. Just the thought of smiling relaxes and softens your face.

3. Now allow a half smile to form on your face—perhaps a little twinkle that causes your eyes to sparkle, relaxing your face and jaw. The smile spreads across your face, bathing, soothing, and comforting your face.

4. Imagine that the smile spreads to the neck and throat, bringing happiness with it. Just sense happiness in that region, letting your mind rest there.

5. Now let happiness spread to the lungs, sensing the comfort it brings to that area. Perhaps happiness feels like a warm light there. Whatever it is, just accept that and allow it to be.

6. Now, let that feeling of happiness fill the heart, warming, and soothing it. Breathe and let the mind rest there. Just allow happiness to settle in your heart.

7. Let the happy feeling of that smile spread to the stomach and any other areas of the body in turn that you wish to focus on. Just sense happiness in each region of the body.

8. Hold any thoughts that arise in kind friendliness, and return to experiencing the smile and happiness in the body. Conclude by sensing your whole body breathing and being comforted by the soothing, happy feeling of a smile.

Exercise: Sitting with Emotions

The meditation skills explained earlier in this chapter have prepared you for the following very powerful method of calming distressing emotions, and thereby taking care of yourself. This meditation teaches us to be calm and non-reactive in the presence of whatever emotions arise, good or bad.

In our Western culture, we are taught to flee or cover pain with pain killers, work, shopping, risky behaviors, or other forms of sedation that do not address the pain. When tired, we might take stimulants, instead of listening to our bodies and "taking sleep." This meditation teaches us to turn gently toward pain with kind awareness. Softening our response changes the way we experience pain.

The wisdom mind is indeed vast, loving, and accepting—wide and deep enough to hold any distressing emotion. Thus, we can be open to whatever exists, penetrating distressing emotions with healing loving kindness. Instead of fighting thoughts, memories, and feelings, we can learn to just embrace them, remembering compassion. It is like sitting with your beloved who is in pain, listening, and saying: "Tell me about it. Whatever it is, it's okay." We listen without judging until the pain subsides and/or the person changes his response to the pain—relaxing, rather than fighting the pain.

In this meditation, we learn to watch distressing emotions from the vast, detached perspective of the wisdom mind. The pain is impersonal; we don't identify with the pain. We think, "There is pain," rather than "I have pain" or "I am the pain." Remembering that the ordinary mind creates much suffering as we resist pain ("Why do I have to suffer?"; "It's not fair!"; "I can't stand this pain!"), we change our response to pain by allowing the pain in. However, instead of bracing and tensing as we fight it, we relax into the pain with full acceptance. We don't judge emotions as bad or good; instead, we accept both with equanimity, allowing love to penetrate and dissolve the pain. It is recommended that this meditation be practiced for thirty minutes or more each day for at least a week.

1. Assume the meditator's posture, sitting comfortably erect, with feet flat on the floor, and hands resting comfortably in the lap. The spine is straight like a stack of golden coins. The upper body is relaxed but erect, sitting in graceful dignity like a majestic mountain. Allow your eyes to close. Let your breathing help you to settle into your peaceful wisdom mind.

2. Remember the key attitudes of acceptance, compassion, and vastness. Remember that you are already whole. Use the beginner's mind as you explore a new way to experience feelings.

3. Be aware of your breathing for several minutes. Let your belly be soft and relaxed, watching it rise and fall as you breathe in and out, becoming still, peaceful, settled, grounded, and really present.

4. Be aware of any feeling in your body, any sensation as it comes and goes, without judging or trying to change it.

5. Whenever you find your mind wandering, congratulate yourself for noticing this. Remember that thoughts are not you, and bring your awareness gently back to breathing and sensing your body.

6. Recall a difficult situation, perhaps involving work or a relationship—and the feelings of unworthiness, inadequacy, sadness, worry about the future, or any other feelings that arise. Make a space for this situation. Give deep attention to these feelings. *Whatever* you are feeling is alright. Greet those feelings cordially, as you would greet an old friend.

7. Notice where in the body you feel the feelings (your stomach, chest, or throat, for instance). Let yourself feel the feelings completely, with full acceptance. Don't think, "I'll tighten up and let these feelings in for a minute in order to get rid of them." This is not full acceptance. Rather, create a space that allows the feelings to be completely accepted.

8. Breathe into that region of the body with great love, as if fresh air and sunlight were entering a long-ignored and darkened room. Follow your breath all the way down through the nose, throat, lungs, and then to the part of the body where you sense the distressing emotion(s). Then follow the breath out of your body, until you find yourself settling. You might think of a kind, loving, accepting smile as you do this. Don't try to change or push the discomfort away. Don't brace or struggle with it. Just embrace it without judging it—with real acceptance, deep attention, loving kindness, and peace. Let the body soften and open around that area. The wisdom mind is vast enough to hold these feelings with great compassion; love is big enough to embrace, welcome, and penetrate the discomfort. Let your breath caress and soothe the feelings as you would your adored sleeping baby.

9. View the discomfort from the dispassionate perspective of the wisdom mind. It is as if you are watching waves of discomfort rise on the surface of the ocean, and then be reabsorbed into the vast ocean. The waves come and go without changing the basic nature of the ocean. If you find it helpful, you might think of loved ones who remind you of loving kindness—and let that loving kindness penetrate your awareness as you remember that difficult situation. Simply notice what happens to the feelings without trying to make them change.

10. When you are ready, take a deeper breath into that area of the body and, as you exhale, widen your focus to your body as a whole. Pay attention to your whole body breathing, being aware of the wholeness and the vast, unlimited compassion of the wisdom mind that will hold any pain that comes and goes. Your attention now expands to the sounds you are hearing, just bringing them into awareness without commenting or judging. Simply listen with a half smile. Feel the air against your body; sense your whole body breathing. Notice all that you are aware of with a soft and open heart.

11. To conclude, say the following intentions silently to yourself: "May I remember loving kindness. May I be happy. May I be whole."

Exercise: Mindfulness-Based Cognitive Therapy

From cognitive therapy (see chapter 7) we learn a useful way for dealing with the drama that plays out in the ordinary mind: we first become aware of our distorted automatic thoughts and then replace these with more constructive thoughts. This tends to reduce the severity of the disturbing emotions that we experience. Further relief can be gained by becoming aware of, and replacing, our inaccurate core beliefs.

In Eastern psychology, automatic thoughts and core beliefs are just thoughts in the ordinary mind that do not reflect the deeper wisdom mind. In fact, trying to fight thinking with thinking can keep one locked in a tense struggle in the ordinary mind.[10] Logic alone may not sufficiently soothe hurt feelings. Mindfulness offers an alternative to fighting thoughts with thinking. In mindfulness, we simply bring compassionate awareness to our thoughts, breathe into them, allow awareness of them to dissolve, and return to resting in the wisdom mind. The neural pathways associated with these negative thoughts degrade through disuse, as we fail to react emotionally to them and instead strengthen the pathways associated with the wisdom mind.

Return to chapter 7. Identify an emotionally charged automatic thought or core belief. Instead of trying to change it, try sitting with it as follows.

1. Sit comfortably in the meditator's posture, breathing softly, resting in the wisdom mind.

2. Bring the thought into kind awareness without judging the thought. Notice where you sense the thought and associated feeling in your body and breathe into that area with loving kindness and complete acceptance.

3. Occasionally, if it is helpful, mindfully remind yourself:
   - "It's just a thought."
   - "Holding that thought in kind awareness."
   - "Feeling compassion."

4. Keep breathing into the area of the body where you sense the thought until you are ready to release awareness of that thought.

5. With a deeper, more intentional breath, let awareness of that area dissolve as you become aware of your environment. Or, you might shift to a smile meditation.

Everyday Mindfulness

We can practice mindfulness in our everyday moments. Practice a smile meditation. Then choose an everyday activity and be mindful. That is, fully experience the activity without getting caught up in judging, criticizing, or over-thinking. Simply bring kind awareness and acceptance to each moment. If you notice yourself being distracted by a thought, just escort your awareness back to the activity. For example, you might mindfully:
- Wake up
- Savor a meal (when eating, just eat—notice aromas, textures, tastes, the experience of chewing and swallowing)
- Wash, shower, or bathe
- Speak with someone (without thinking of what you'll say next or how you'll change the other person)
- Answer the phone
- Hug someone
- Cook
- Wash dishes
- Give a baby a bath
- Watch kids sleep
- Notice weather or seasons
- Notice inner weather (what's going on inside emotionally) without judgment

Integral Yoga: Happy Nature Meditation

Nestled in the beautiful Blue Ridge Mountains of central Virginia, grounds considered sacred by Native Americans, is Yogaville, founded by Sri Swami Satchidananda. Satchidananda (*ananda* means happiness) dedicated his life to teaching people to be happy. A number of years ago, after finishing a book early, I traveled there to learn for a week. Visitors meditated at five o'clock in the morning for seventy-five minutes—an experience so peaceful and refreshing that I always wished it were longer.

Since then, I've taught a meditation based on Swami Satchidananda's Integral Yoga, called the Happy Nature Meditation. Like mindfulness, this form of mediation derives from Eastern teachings, yet is harmonious with nearly all persuasions.

Sincere and good-humored, Swami Satchidananda taught that happiness is what everyone wants—the criminal, the police officer who chases the criminal, you and I. Happiness comes not from chasing things, but from experiencing our true happy nature and from being useful to others. This meditation focuses on experiencing our true happy nature.

A few points of preparatory instruction: Recall that the purpose of meditation is to experience our true happy nature. This meditation will use three kinds of breathing and mantras, whose only purpose is to settle the mind so you can meditate. The three kinds of breathing are:

- *Abdominal breathing.* As taught in chapter 5, this breathing is, as it were, filling the abdomen on the in-breath and deflating the abdomen on the out-breath. It is gentle, rhythmic, and smooth. As you breathe normally, keep awareness on the breath inside. Let your breathing be a signal to release external attachments and go within—settling in your true happy nature. As agitated water is allowed to settle, it becomes very clear. Allow your breathing to settle your mind.

- *Bellows breathing* presumably expels toxins. Early in my visit, I was taught that the trainers at Yogaville had observed that many who are traumatized, anxious, or depressed carry negative emotions in their solar plexus, a mass of nerve cells in the upper abdomen. This immediately piqued my curiosity, given my research interests. It is thought that bellows breathing releases these emotions, and perhaps physical toxins, as well.[11] This type of breathing is done by inwardly snapping, or contracting, the abdominal muscles. This causes air to be expelled from the lungs. When those muscles are then allowed to fully relax, the lungs naturally fill with air. After the lungs fully inflate, again snap the abdominal muscles. Then relax to inhale. This process is repeated, preparing us to relax and rest in the wisdom mind.

- *Alternate nostril breathing.* The brain follows an ultradian rhythm, whereby dominance shifts every ninety minutes between the right and left hemispheres. Whichever nostril is open tells you which hemisphere is dominant (e.g., if the right nostril is open, the left hemisphere is dominant). Alternative nostril breathing is thought to balance the left (logical, linear, externally focused) and right (intuitive, creative, internally focused) hemispheres. This type of breathing is done as follows:
    1. Extend the thumb and ring and little fingers of the right hand. The index and middle fingers are curled and rest in the palm of the hand. Place the thumb against the right side of your nose and the ring and little fingers against the left side of your nose.
    2. Close the right nostril by pressing your thumb against the right side of your nose. Breathe in through the left nostril.
    3. Close the left nostril with your ring and little fingers, and open the right nostril. Exhale and then inhale through the right nostril.
    4. Close the right nostril then exhale and inhale through the left nostril.
    5. Repeat this cycle of exhaling then inhaling through alternate nostrils.

Practice these three types of breaths until you can do them without looking at the instructions.

A *mantra* is a word or word that is chanted. Mantras have a curiously calming affect. Their effect is not based so much on what the words mean, as on the change in the body and mind that they cause.[12] Focusing on a mantra keeps the focus off of negative thoughts and emotions and helps us to settle into the wisdom mind. In my experience, most people in the West quickly adapt to their use. The three mantras that are chanted in this meditation are:
- *Om* (rhymes with *home*). This mantra denotes peace, oneness within, and oneness with all that is without. Some describe the word as the basic, divine vibration—the sound of God humming or awaking; the primary vibration in the

universe heard in the wind, waves, or the hum of an electrical transformer or anything else with power. Chanting the *...mmmmm* portion of this mantra creates a pleasant vibration in the forehead region, or the area of the prefrontal cortex.

- *Hari Om* (Hah-dee Om). This combination of sounds brings awareness from the stomach, to the thyroid, to the top of the head with each successive syllable. This chant helps to ground us in the body and wisdom mind.
- *Shanti Om* (Shahn-tee Om). *Shanti* signifies inner peace. The phrase tends to release tension and suggests lightness.

Practice these mantras until they can be chanted comfortably and naturally. See what happens when you vary the pitch of different syllables, different words within a phrase, or the entire phrase.

Some points about meditation are useful to emphasize. There are thousands of methods to meditate—or experience our true happy nature. The breathing and mantras are simply invitations to release attachments and rest in the wisdom mind. The true happy nature is drama-less. Don't expect fireworks when you meditate. It is more likely that your experience will be quiet, pleasant, and subtle. The instructions for Happy Nature Meditation follow. This adaptation takes about thirty minutes. It is practiced once or twice daily. Try it for about a week to see if you'd like to continue it. The times for each step are merely suggestions.

1. Sit quietly in the meditator's posture, like a dignified and steadfast mountain. Relax the muscles of your body. Adopt a light and friendly, almost playful attitude. Imagine that you have just returned from working in the yard. Pleasantly tired, you have nothing left to do or worry about, so you imagine that you sink into a soft chair. When you are ready, gently close your eyes. Use your abdominal breathing as a signal to settle your mind. Just as agitated water becomes clear as it settles, let your mind settle and clear. Breathe abdominally for about five minutes. Release strivings and graspings, content to simply be—resting in your wisdom mind.
2. Chant for a few minutes. Repeat *Om* aloud for about a minute, pausing to allow your mind to settle between repetitions of the word. Repeat this with *Hari Om* and *Shanti Om*.
3. Do bellows breathing for about a minute. Follow this with a minute of abdominal breathing. Repeat this sequence.
4. Do about three minutes of alternate nostril breathing.
5. Chant for about a minute, using any combination of Om, Hari Om, and/or Shanti Om. Let the chants settle your mind more.
6. Silently meditate. For about fifteen minutes, release, rest, and relax into your true happy nature. Should thoughts intrude, just greet them cordially and let them pass through awareness as you return your focus to resting in your true happy nature.
7. End with:
   - A minute of chanting, using any combination of Om, Hari Om, and Shanti Om.
   - A minute of intentional chants:

- "May I be happy and free of suffering."
- "May I be whole."
- "May all people be happy and free of suffering."
- "May all people be whole."
- "May we all be content."

Before step 7, I like to do a smile meditation, letting happiness spread from the face, to the forehead, and to all other parts of the body in sequence. This adds but a few additional minutes.

PART VII

SUCCEEDING:

PEAK PERFORMANCE
&
ADAPTIVE COPING

Chapter 27

Active Coping

If you are cold, get into the sun.
Betty Brown

You cannot escape the responsibility of tomorrow by evading it today.
Abraham Lincoln

So far we have explored resilience skills related to maximizing brain readiness, calming body and mind, managing negative emotions, and cultivating positive emotions and attitudes. In this part of the book we will build on these skills, adding skills that optimize performance and adaptive coping.

Peak performance means we give our best possible efforts in the service of meeting our goals. Adaptive coping means we adjust to changing circumstances and use whatever is available to our best advantage to solve problems, meet challenges, and move toward our goals.

The general principle of this part is this: Success is most likely when we:

- Set a goal and want to achieve it.
- Believe that we can achieve it—expecting success and having a sense of personal efficacy.
- Commit to achieving the goal—working hard, persisting, and exercising the needed discipline. In the long run, commitment is more important than innate ability. Commitment includes dedication to mental preparation. Many people prepare sufficiently in a physical sense but buckle or choke under real-life pressure because they are not mentally prepared. So we must commit to mental practice at least as much as we do to physical practice.

All of the skills that you have learned so far promote peak performance and adaptive coping. For example, calming skills and managing negative emotions help us to stay composed and focused under pressure. Optimizing brain health enables the brain to function more quickly and effectively. Happiness skills help people to stay open to coping possibilities and implement them more effectively.

In this part of the book we will explore three pillars of success: active coping, creativity/flexibility, and confidence. We'll start with active coping. Considerable research points to the idea that an active stance toward life is advantageous compared to a passive, avoidant stance. Let's consider the differences.

The Active Coper

As mindfulness training teaches, the active coper turns *toward* problems, rather than away from them. This increases the likelihood of finding an appropriate response. People with an active stance toward life do the following. Place a check next to those that apply to you. Active copers:

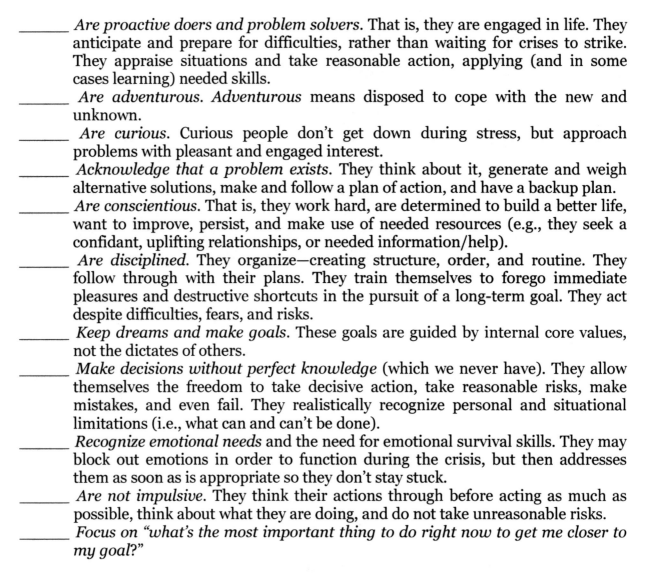

_____ *Are proactive doers and problem solvers.* That is, they are engaged in life. They anticipate and prepare for difficulties, rather than waiting for crises to strike. They appraise situations and take reasonable action, applying (and in some cases learning) needed skills.

_____ *Are adventurous. Adventurous* means disposed to cope with the new and unknown.

_____ *Are curious.* Curious people don't get down during stress, but approach problems with pleasant and engaged interest.

_____ *Acknowledge that a problem exists.* They think about it, generate and weigh alternative solutions, make and follow a plan of action, and have a backup plan.

_____ *Are conscientious.* That is, they work hard, are determined to build a better life, want to improve, persist, and make use of needed resources (e.g., they seek a confidant, uplifting relationships, or needed information/help).

_____ *Are disciplined.* They organize—creating structure, order, and routine. They follow through with their plans. They train themselves to forego immediate pleasures and destructive shortcuts in the pursuit of a long-term goal. They act despite difficulties, fears, and risks.

_____ *Keep dreams and make goals.* These goals are guided by internal core values, not the dictates of others.

_____ *Make decisions without perfect knowledge* (which we never have). They allow themselves the freedom to take decisive action, take reasonable risks, make mistakes, and even fail. They realistically recognize personal and situational limitations (i.e., what can and can't be done).

_____ *Recognize emotional needs* and the need for emotional survival skills. They may block out emotions in order to function during the crisis, but then addresses them as soon as is appropriate so they don't stay stuck.

_____ *Are not impulsive.* They think their actions through before acting as much as possible, think about what they are doing, and do not take unreasonable risks.

_____ *Focus on "what's the most important thing to do right now to get me closer to my goal?"*

In *I Love a Fire Fighter*, Ellen Kirschman, Ph.D., (2004, p.180) described an active stance toward troubling emotions and a model for dealing with them: Act during the crisis, then acknowledge and process distressing feelings. During water rescue training in a storm, a boat capsized. Afterwards, one emotionally courageous firefighter said to his assembled comrades, "I don't know about you guys but I thought I was going to die out there today and I doubt I'm the only one who felt that way." One by one crewmembers opened up—expressing their fears of never seeing family again and of going out on the water again, anger at dying so young, and sadness for an incomplete life. Acknowledging these feelings brought his team together. The next day everyone went out again on the water to train. Until they talked, each felt isolated. Realizing that all were in the same boat emotionally actually helped them move past their feelings and prepare for their training. Conversely, many highly trained and capable emergency service providers are engaged at work in their physical tasks, but then disengage from their feelings when they come home—shutting down or burying their emotions.

In prisoner of war camps, many outward freedoms are taken away. When prisoners could not actively escape, they exercised their freedom to be as active as possible. For example, Larry Chesley (1973) noted that many of his comrades in the Hanoi Hilton exercised to keep in good physical condition, despite the hunger it caused. They walked back and forth in their cell, three paces one way and then back, doing much thinking and planning as they exercised. Others made a competition for sit-ups, pushups (several reached several hundred), and deep knee bends. The prisoners also conspired to use covert communications to keep morale high. On the cell walls, they tapped a code learned in Boy Scouts. Humming or whistling an individual's favorite song let other prisoners know (without speaking, which was forbidden) that the individual was still alive.

The Passive Coper

Passive copers take an avoidant stance toward life. They find ways to leave the problem, leaving it unsolved (see Figure 27.1). Check any of the following that seem to describe your coping style. Passive copers:

_____ *Don't think about troubling thoughts, emotions, or situations*, and thus do little to modify them

_____ *Try to escape or block out negative emotions.* Tactics include excessive humor, drugs, workaholism, whining, worrying, suicide, and overconfidence. Notice that some of these might appear to be active attempts at coping, but each is a maladaptive way to avoid emotions. For example, one can worry obsessively, intellectually trying to understand the problem, without acknowledging the emotions or acting to resolve them.

_____ *Deny something is wrong or minimize problems* (e.g., "Nothing is wrong; it doesn't bother me; it used to bother me but now it doesn't")

_____ *Get stuck or freeze by:*
- Assuming they are helpless and then giving up (There is always *something* to try)
- Blaming self or others
- Dwelling on "Why is this happening?" rather than "What does this situation require of me?"
- Thinking, "I don't believe this is happening"
- Wishing things were better
- Trying to forget something that happened
- Being bewildered, deliberating excessively, and/or waiting for instructions when action is called for
- Giving in to discouragement

_____ *Use cynicism or an uncaring, indifferent attitude* to protect themselves from pain

_____ *Might tackle problems at work, but come home and try to ignore or drown negative feelings* with television, computer games, and so forth

_____ *Withdraw.* They: avoid people, places, or situations that are distressing; isolate themselves and don't tell others what is going on inside; keep feelings inside

Figure 27.1
AVOIDANCE

"Emotional avoidance detour" was illustrated and conceptualized by Joseph Ciarrochi and David Mercer, University of Wollongong, NSW, Australia. Reprinted with permission.

It has been observed[1] that only 10% of people facing a crisis take decisive, constructive action. Eighty percent freeze and wait for instructions. Ten percent do the wrong thing, acting in self-destructive ways. For example, during the attack on the World Trade Center on 9/11 (Ripley, 2008), most of the people were lethargic, not panicked. They waited an average of six minutes before descending the stairs. Some waited as long as forty-five minutes, calling relatives and friends or checking emails. Many milled around, as if in a trance, perhaps fearing embarrassment, perhaps denying the reality of the situation. (A similar response was observed in the 1977 Beverly Hills Supper Club fire, where many who passively awaited instructions died in the fire.) Others died on 9/11 because they wasted time ascending the stairs, trying to exit through doors on the roof that were locked. Ripley asserts that we must acknowledge a threat and thoroughly, repeatedly, and realistically rehearse for it so that everyone knows what to do quickly and decisively during the crisis.

The Consequences of Avoidance

Those with avoidant coping styles don't solve problems. They don't become stronger or more confident through wrestling with and overcoming problems. In addition, research has shown that avoidance is generally associated with:

- Weakened immunity
- Impaired relationships
- Poorer cognitive, job, and athletic functioning
- Mental disorders (those who are unwilling to stay in contact with distressing thoughts, memories, emotions, and bodily sensations long enough to process them are more likely to suffer from PTSD,[2] anxiety, depression, and general distress

Active coping is generally associated with the opposite findings. (We'll explore some exceptions in chapter 28.)

How to Cultivate Active Coping

We can choose our response to adversity, whether to relax into any given situation and act to the best of our ability (which is all anyone can ever do), or to try to escape it. We can:

- *Acknowledge a problem (whether it is family disharmony or the threat of terrorism), develop an action plan, and rehearse it, despite resistance from other people.* Recall that Rick Rescorla anticipated the terrorist attack on the World Trade Center, developed an action plan of escape, and drilled his people repeatedly until they were able to successfully execute the plan under pressure—despite the complaints of those who lacked his vision.
- *Drop the battle with distressing thoughts, memories, emotions, images, and sensations.* Instead of fighting them, avoiding them, or giving into them in passive resignation, we can actively accept them—turning toward them with compassionate acceptance, as mindfulness training directs (see chapter 26). At first we do this in quiet and calm moments. Eventually, we can kindly accept the full range of emotions even in crises, and respond to them calmly so that we can perform optimally. For example, once we acknowledge fear calmly and without judgments, we can then act effectively. Otherwise, fear can immobilize us or lead to frenzied reactions. Also remember to use the skills in part IV to manage distressing emotions.
- *Reframe problems as challenges.*
- *Use calming skills to help see your options clearly, and then act.* (Rehearse calming skills repeatedly under both calm and real-life training conditions.)
- *Approach challenges with optimism, which is the attitude that leads to active coping* (see chapter 13). Likewise, think about your purposes in life—your reasons to survive—as these will motivate you to act productively.[3]

Activity: Increasing Motivation to Successfully Act[4]

Motivation and drive predict performance. Being clear on your motivations can help you to persevere during periods of fatigue, excessive stress, nutritional or sleep deprivation, noise, and over-seriousness. This activity will clarify your motivations and help you develop a motivating success dialogue.

1. Determine what motivates you to act. Place a check beside those that apply to your life:

_____ Mastery	_____ Friendship	_____ Service	_____ Excellence
_____ Enjoyment	_____ Security	_____ Teamwork	_____ Saving lives
_____ Love	_____ Competitive	_____ Personal	_____ Helping the
_____ Courage	greatness	growth	underserved
_____ Healthy pride	_____ Meaning &	_____ A worthy	_____ Novelty/stimulation
in knowing	purpose	cause	
you've done			
your best			

_____ Other values (specify): _____

2. Write down three reasonable training goals that are consistent with the motivations that you checked above, such as:
   • Satisfaction from knowing I'm doing my best in _____ (name a given situation)
   • Improve the bonds of friendship by creating trust and having enjoyable experiences
   • Improve concentration—focusing on my tasks despite noise, confusion, etc.
   • Stay composed and poised under pressure
   <u>Note</u>: Don't focus on the outcome. We can't always control that.[5] Rather focus on the training process. Remember that mental rehearsal is as important as physical preparation.

3. Create a mental rehearsal dialogue, which includes several affirmations for each goal. For example, an athlete in training might create this dialogue, which could easily be adapted for preparing to meet a challenge at home or work:

> I am composed, even more so in the most important games. I feel alert, poised, relaxed, capable, prepared, and focused. I see what is needed and respond calmly and effectively. I concentrate well despite fatigue and distractions. I enjoy working alongside and supporting my friends. I love using my skills with those I care about, doing something I love. I'm looking forward to doing my best. My movements are fluid and nearly effortless. I'm confident in my abilities. I'm committed to doing my personal best, not worrying about the outcome or what others think. I do my best and let the outcome take care of itself. I am in the flow, fully engaged and concentrating, and enjoying the feeling of my best performance. I make decisions quickly and act decisively, without hurrying. I am comfortable with all the emotions that arise, and respond to all in the same calm, non-

judgmental way. Afterwards, I look back on my performance with quiet satisfaction, knowing that I did my best.

4. Relax, visualize the training, and repeat this dialogue repeatedly prior to training or rehearsal experiences, until this active stance becomes ingrained. In chapter 29 we will build upon this dialogue.

Chapter 28

Confidence

One important key to success is self-confidence. An important key to self-confidence is preparation.
Arthur Ashe

Confidence and an active coping stance go hand in hand. An active stance says, "I *will* do my best to succeed—I will do what is needed and persist." Confidence says, "I *can* do that—I have the skills and resources that I need, and know how to apply them effectively."

In the scientific research, confidence is called self-efficacy. Self-efficacy correlates with less avoidance and better performance in various domains. Self-efficacy also correlates with greater self-esteem and pain tolerance, and less anxiety and depression.

Confidence Principles

1. *Confidence must be based on experience.* Confidence improves with success experiences—real or imagined. Both physical practice and mental rehearsal work about equally well. The combination of both kinds of practice is ideal.
2. *Confidence must be realistic.* Overconfidence is a form of avoidance and self-deceit. It can kill, or at the least make failure more likely. One must know what he or she can and cannot do. Without this awareness, we won't make the effort to gain mastery and might make foolish decisions under pressure.
3. *Training must be so rigorous that the real-life challenge is easier.* Legendary coach John Wooden so rigorously trained his basketball players that the games seemed much easier than practice.
4. *To perform confidently, one must know how to regulate arousal and distractions.* Excessive stress degrades performance, and can be regulated with mindfulness practice, abdominal breathing, and relaxation training. Through training we can learn to maintain concentration and composure despite noise, visual distractions, some fatigue, and the like.
5. *Regular participation in exercise (especially aerobic exercise) and sports is firmly linked to greater self-confidence.* At the gym at West Point is displayed the famous quote by General Douglas MacArthur: "On the fields of friendly strife are sown the seeds that on other days and other fields will bear the fruits of victory."
6. *Nearly everyone with average learning ability can achieve professional competence in nearly any field with lots of practice.* Nick Baylis, Ph.D., (2009) explains that it takes about 3000 hours of determined practice to go from novice to a remarkable amateur in music (or nearly any other field)—about two hours per day, six days a week, for five years. It takes about 10,000 hours of concentrated effort to reach a professional standard in virtually any field, and at least ten years of fulltime, dedicated practice to reach world class level. About half of America's leading concert pianists were not precocious and had parents who played no instruments. What they did have, typically, were warm, encouraging parents (or teachers). Those who excel also have tend to have highly

relaxed minds (which absorb more), and the determination to concentrate (multi-tasking degrades concentration and the ability to learn).

7. *Perfectionism degrades confidence.* Focus on doing a good job, even an excellent job, not a perfect job. Baylis (p.212) notes that only about a quarter of Shakespeare's works are celebrated today. Not everything we produce will be a masterpiece, so we can relax, do our best, and enjoy the "occasional gem."

8. *The confident person is poised.* John Wooden (2003) defined poise as just being yourself, not acting or pretending, but performing at your personal best level without undue pressure or concern with others' judgments or expectations. Confident persons watch, learn from, and are inspired by successful individuals, but they are secure in their uniqueness

9. *Confident people enjoy being tested because they are prepared.* Because they are prepared, they feel that challenges will bring out their best and that they will likely succeed.

10. *Confidence usually grows best when it is cultivated gradually, patiently, and with warmth.* There are two basic training models. On tries to overwhelm and eliminate the weak. We find this model used in many elite special operations training programs, like the Army Rangers and Navy SEALS. These programs start with the cream of the crop and weed out many of the candidates through exposure to grueling conditions. Those who remain standing know that they can trust both themselves and their teammates in virtually any situation.

    A second model aims to strengthen and build—challenging, but not overwhelming individuals. For example, British Commando training adapts a more paternalistic approach wherein trainers train alongside trainees, offering encouragement and support. They make the training increasingly challenging, but never exceed individuals' readiness and capabilities. Trainers view each trainee as a valuable asset that they don't want to lose. Rather than leading by fear and criticism, leaders try to inspire and allow trainees to learn from their mistakes through natural consequences.[1] The Outward Bound program employs a similar training model. Participants are gently encouraged to perform at their best, say by pushing past their fears to complete a challenging ropes course. Then participants gather around the supportive leader, who praises their effort, and asks them how they were able to perform as well as they did. The leader might also ask what they learned from their experience. This model tends to draw out and build upon existing strengths. People who are so trained tend to have less fear and do tend to persevere and perform better under pressure. This model usually works best for most workplaces, families, and schools.

11. *To be confident is to have the confidence to "fail."* Mortals will always be fallible, meaning we are imperfect and make mistakes. When we reframe failure as efforts toward success or as falling short of our goals, then "failure" becomes less intimidating. Without judging or condemning ourselves, we simply examine our efforts for ways to improve. With experience, we aim to improve performance, as this poem by Danish poet Piet Hein advises.

The road to wisdom? Well, it's plain
And simple to express:
Err
And err
And err again
But less
And less
And less.

How To Build Confidence

The above principles suggest a number of approaches to build confidence. If you are not already, you might engage in an exercise or sports program. You might regulate arousal by practicing abdominal breathing, relaxation, and mindfulness. Look for every opportunity to gain expertise and experience through reading, taking classes, training, and real-life experience. The rest of this chapter will explore mental preparation for everyday life challenges. Chapter 30 will address physical training considerations.

Activity: Bringing Confidence Forward

In psychological research, this approach, known as covert modeling, has been shown to improve performance and reduce anxiety. It can be used to enhance confidence related to a daunting challenge that you face at work, home, or sports. Try following these steps:

1. *Identify your daunting challenge* (e.g., taking an important promotion test, tackling a difficult assignment, or having a potentially difficult discussion with a family member or boss).
2. *Break your daunting challenge into a staircase of items, such that each step represents one of one- or two-dozen chronological steps.* Thus, for an important promotion test, the staircase might be:
   - Studying three months before
   - Studying two weeks before
   - Discussing the test with co-worker a week before
   - Studying the night before
   - Reviewing the morning before
   - Driving to the test site
   - Walking into the testing room
   - Taking a seat
   - Receiving a copy of the test
   - Reading the first question
   - Reading a question I can't answer
   - Leaving the test
3. *Create a list of past successes and achievements.* Write down four or five events from your life where you behaved capably and felt good about your performance. Perhaps it was an event where you were challenged to perform well—perhaps you felt some anxiety, but you persisted and performed competently. For each event, describe the circumstances in detail, noting your surroundings (weather,

distractions, etc.), what you did (e.g., see yourself persisting and performing well), and how you felt during and afterwards (e.g., determined, satisfied, energized). This step alone lifts the mood and confidence by remembering positive events from your life. Perhaps you can think of a past achievement that relates to your present challenge. For example, having success as a bicycle rider might transfer to learning to ride a motorcycle. However, this is not critical. Any success experience will work. Select one that is especially pleasant to remember.

4. *Start with the first item on your staircase.* Visualize it for a few seconds and experience it fully and in detail for about a minute. Then recall the selected success/achievement experience fully and in as much detail as possible. Immerse yourself fully in the recall. Then superimpose this image over the image of your daunting challenge. Sit with this experience until you feel confidence associated with this step on the staircase.

5. *Repeat this process for each step on the staircase, perhaps taking two or three steps per day.*

The power of this strategy rests on the fact that your success/achievement image comes from your real experience and uses your genuine feelings of confidence to counter any negative feelings associated with your challenge. Note that you can also use this staircase in other ways. You can experience and then pair each step with relaxation, mindfulness, rational self-statements, humor, or success or rebounding imagery (success and rebounding imagery are described below).

Activity: Success (Mastery) Imagery

In this strategy, you'll strengthen neural pathways in the brain associated with successful execution through mental rehearsal. It is best to try this strategy in combination with physical practice. We'll use an example from sports. However, this strategy could be applied to any situation at home or work. The key to success is to keep imagery vivid. Imagine and experience all the details of this exercise—what you see, hear, smell, touch, and taste. Most of your awareness will be from the perspective of what you are seeing and sensing from the inside. Perhaps only 25% of your awareness will focus on what you would see from the outside, as if you were watching yourself through a video camera.

1. *Lie down or sit comfortably.* Start by spending about five minutes to relax and compose yourself. Use abdominal breathing, relaxation, or mindfulness (such as the body scan).

2. *Imagine yourself succeeding—coping and performing effectively—for about fifteen minutes.*
   - Start by seeing yourself in a pressure-packed situation. You notice that your breathing is calm and regular. Though you are perspiring, your thinking is clear and your body is relaxed and fluid. Your body is moving with confidence and poise. Sense that inside your body.
   - You see yourself executing your task effectively—smoothly, almost effortlessly, with great concentration. You notice with great clarity what you are focusing on. You sense all parts of your body moving extremely effectively. You enjoy

the fun of being in the flow—fully absorbed and meeting each challenge with relaxed efficiency and power.

3. *Practice this exercise frequently so that the mentally rehearsed execution comes naturally when it matters the most.* It is usually best to rehearse one movement or aspect of successful performance frequently before moving on to another aspect of the game. Eventually, you might put the pieces together, as Spencer Wood, Ph.D., (2003) has done in this success imagery for golf.[2]

> You are at one of the biggest golf tournaments of the year. The time is near for you to tee off and you are looking forward to your opening drive even more so than usual. You are at your very best and you are really enjoying your great form. Take some time to really enjoy your surroundings. Take a deep breath. Relax. See the green fairways, the carefully sculptured hills and bunkers. You can hear the distinctive swish of the clubs being swung as they cut an elegant path through the air. You hear the solid connection of the golf ball and club head. As you address the ball of your opening drive you feel an incredible sense of power, and energy, and joy for the game you love. You love competition and you love competing in this, one of your favorite things to do in the world, play golf. You are so composed, relaxed, and poised. Your concentration and focus is at its very best, and you feel supremely confident. You are committed to doing your best and you are performing at your very best. You have a great swing. You are accurate and powerful. Your strokes are smooth, fluid, effortless, and accurate. You feel confident, energized, and your positive body language shows it. Your concentration is amazing. You are in a relaxed, comfortable shell of concentration. External distractions such as weather conditions, opponents, or crowd noise do not affect your great composure, concentration, and confidence. You are putting with incredible form and accuracy. You love sharing your putting skills with the crowd. Your short game is just as accurate as your long game. You are at your very best.
>
> Take a deep breath. Relax. Feel free to stay in this warm and comfortable state of relaxation for as long as you wish. You are relaxed and fully refreshed.

Activity: Rebounding (Coping) Imagery

Rebounding (or coping) imagery is mental rehearsal that adds the skill of recovering from common states that interfere with performance, such as excessive anxiety, tension, negative thinking, or faulty execution. It begins with five minutes of relaxation as success imagery does. You vividly imagine the pressure-packed situation. However, this time you notice yourself experiencing one or more of these common negative states. With calm awareness and without judgments, you simply see yourself correcting these states, as shown on the next page. This type of imagery is often preferred since slipping and then recovering is more typical of real-life situations.

For this state....	You see yourself.....
Anxiety	Pausing to mindfully accept the feeling without judgment, let awareness of the anxiety dissolve, and then return your concentration to proper execution.
Tension	Stopping to calm your breathing and relax your muscles.
Negative thoughts, such as.... • Oh, no, what if we lose! • I can't • I'm too anxious to execute. • I must do this perfectly.	Calmly thinking... • I love doing my best. • I can. • I enjoy concentrating and competing. • I keep my focus on the moment-to-moment process.
Fatigue, perspiration, elevated heart rate	Thinking, "I feel so relaxed."
Making a mistake	Regaining composure and concentration quickly, and executing the next movement successfully.

Then you complete the steps of success imagery as described previously.

Follow-up Self-Talk

Remember your follow-up self-talk, which affects confidence in the future. If you did reasonably well, reinforce your success. You might think, "Good job"; "All in all, not bad"; or "It felt good to prepare and succeed." If things didn't go well, you might think, "This was a tough situation; next time I'll prepare differently," or "It's water under the bridge, and now I'll move on."

Chapter 29

Creativity & Flexibility

In the beginner's mind there are many possibilities. In the expert's mind there are few.
Zen saying

In times of war or uncertainty...We demand discipline. We expect innovation...[in protecting the lives of my teammates and completing the mission, utilizing all skills and attention at my disposal].
U.S. Navy SEALs Creed

In the Civil War, Lt. Colonel Joshua Chamberlain led Maine's 20th Regiment. Chamberlain had turned down a prestigious commission in order to study the art of warfare thoroughly before later accepting one. Chamberlain led his men on an arduous 100-mile march to Gettysburg. Upon arrival, he was commanded to hold the Union Army's left flank at all costs. With only fifteen minutes before the battle started, Chamberlain quickly emplaced his soldiers, as he studied the terrain in anticipation of dangers. During the battle, it became evident that the Confederate Army was about to envelope the flank. So Chamberlain innovated a new battle drill under fire. He moved half of the original line of soldiers at an angle of ninety degrees to wall off the left flank, successfully blocking the envelopment. Soon, his regiment was about to run out of ammunition. Again innovating under fire, Chamberlain commanded his regiment to fix bayonets. He ordered the newly formed half of the line to charge, swinging around like a gate. When they were abreast of the original line, he stepped in front to lead the entire regiment in a bayonet charge, routing the stunned veteran Confederate regiments. Chamberlain's creative leadership in this pivotal battle changed the outcome of both the battle and the entire war.

Creativity means coming up with something new and useful. Often creativity is merely seeing what is already there, rearranging it or giving it a new twist, and making something wholly or partly new. What we come up with might be an invention, strategy, idea, or product that improves our lives—health, performance, mood, or leisure.

Historically, creativity has resulted in many useful inventions. For example, the invention of the ingenious, ubiquitous zipper around 1900 has saved countless hours. The bicycle was around for seventy years before someone thought in 1861 to add a chain and gears to the pedals, resulting in a more useful recreational vehicle and mode of travel. Creativity has also led to important solutions to problems. In WWII, the Allied invasion at Normandy was stalled. Over the centuries, the farmers of Normandy had created small rectangular fields, surrounded by steep banks of earth, stone, and thick vegetation. The mounds, called hedgerows, were up to ten feet wide and eight feet high. Between the hedgerows were narrow roads. If American tanks moved down these roads, they were blasted by the Germans' pre-planned fire, blocking tanks behind them. If the tank drivers tried to climb the steep banks, they exposed the unarmored underbelly to anti-tank fire. While officers debated what to do, Sergeant Curtis G. Culin took scrap metal from German roadblocks and welded teeth onto the front of the American Sherman tanks. These so-called Rhino tanks could then punch through the walls of the hedgerows and allow other tanks to pass through and fan out. This simple invention saved countless lives. Ironically, Culin's creation used what was already there—steel beams provided by the Germans.

Today, creativity is a basic survival tool that is vital to optimizing performance and coping in a complex, rapidly changing world. Creative people are more resilient. They experience less stress and mental illness when under adversity because they see more options when old ways are not working.

Most people erroneously assume that:
- Creativity is only found in the arts.
- You must be genetically favored with extraordinary brilliance to be creative (i.e., creativity exists at birth; either you have it or you don't).
- Creativity always comes in sudden bursts without having to work hard.
- You must come up with an astounding finished product in order to be creative.

In truth, creativity is standard issue. Everyone has creative potential that can be cultivated through hard, disciplined work. The generally accepted rule is that it takes at least ten years of immersion in a field before one can make a distinctive mark in that field. For example, Einstein labored for ten years on relativity before the theory came together. Many people who don't have school intelligence are creatively intelligent. If you don't get perfect or complete final results, you can still enjoy the creative process and find satisfaction in drawing closer to the final goal and in strengthening your creative skills.

Creativity appears and can be nurtured in many ways. Because of brain plasticity, neural pathways that are strengthened in one creative area of life can be used in other creative endeavors. The following inventory helps to reveal how creativity is already being manifested in your life, and helps to dispel the myth that only artists are creative.

The Creativity Checkup

The following are ways that people can be creative. Rate each from 1-10, where 10 means that you are exceptionally creative, as creative as humanly possible. Zero means you are never creative to the slightest degree.

_____ Finding ways to do things in the simplest way possible
_____ Finding short cuts, saving time, making a job easier
_____ Making good decisions after considering different options
_____ Communicating ideas in different ways
_____ Organizing (e.g., a room, an event, a mission)
_____ Talking your way out of a jam
_____ Telling stories
_____ Amusing others (e.g., children, friends)
_____ Amusing yourself
_____ Writing
_____ Cooking (e.g., tweaking recipes, making something from scratch)
_____ Cleaning
_____ Motivating or encouraging people
_____ Resolving conflict

_____ Strengthening relationships
_____ Planning dates
_____ Dancing
_____ Playing sports
_____ Entertaining
_____ Acquiring money (to meet basic needs, buy things needed to create, etc.)
_____ Putting others at ease
_____ Inventing games (or giving old games a new twist)
_____ Telling jokes
_____ Bargaining with a salesperson
_____ Making others feel good or smile
_____ Explaining or teaching things simply, clearly, or in an amusing way
_____ Solving problems
_____ Expressing feelings
_____ Raising children
_____ Spotting weaknesses, anticipating problems, and making plans to improve
_____ Finding ways to calm yourself and maintain focus in crisis
_____ Experiencing positive emotions under stress and quelling negative emotions
_____ Turning life's negatives into positives
_____ Gardening
_____ Turning mistakes or guilt into growth
_____ Making family memories
_____ Seeing another's viewpoint; seeing different sides
_____ Beautifying a space, making it attractive
_____ Making new designs, processes, ideas, programs
_____ Changing yourself
_____ Feeling fully alive by using your strengths
_____ Integrating ideas (e.g., putting them together in a new way)
_____ Giving order to chaos or confusion
_____ Getting others to behave constructively
_____ Getting yourself to change for the better
_____ Creating joy or friendliness
_____ Improving relationships
_____ Building teamwork
_____ Seeing many options before deciding
_____ Finding meaning during difficult times
_____ Learning new skills
_____ Questioning conventional methods and imagining new ones
_____ Encouraging others to be creative
_____ Making an environment that encourages creativity in self or others
_____ Looking at situations in ways that encourage solutions (e.g., "My boss isn't a tyrant, he's frustrated")
_____ Finding enjoyment in difficult situations
_____ Turning complex ideas into simple ones
_____ Making a satisfying, meaningful life

You'll probably notice that some creativity is already being manifested in numerous ways in your life. While few people realistically record tens, it is likely that there are few if any zeros—suggesting that creative potential is already being utilized and is ready to be developed further. For areas with low ratings, you might simply think, "This is an area that hasn't been developed *yet*."

The Creative Process

Creative people pay attention. They are aware of what is going on outside of them. They see the entire situation—problems and opportunities, available resources, barriers to success, and what is needed. They also pay attention to what is going on inside of them—inner resources, hunches or intuitive promptings of the mind, and ideas that bubble up. Then they go to work. In reality, it is usually more accurate to say that they usually go to play, because creative people typically immerse themselves in what they love to do, and enjoy the process.

When under stress, most people narrow their focus, running in old ways and missing new possibilities. Creative people, however, step back and open their minds to new possibilities, breaking through presumed limits to do something new, perhaps something that had been thought impossible.

The Creativity Model

This model, consisting of six parts, describes the typical creativity process, whether of a brilliant inventor or an everyday person wrestling with a problem.

1. *Present reality.* Most see the world as it is, and don't question limits defined by "experts." For example, the advisory panel to Ferdinand and Isabella said that there couldn't possibly be new lands of significance to discover. However, creative people, like Columbus, see the world with a sense of curiosity and challenge, and are open to new possibilities.

2. *Preparation.* Creative people look deeply into the problem or challenge. They fill their minds with information and relationships. They learn and gain the tools needed to innovate, knowing that creativity usually builds on knowledge previously acquired. Perhaps experts are consulted. Perhaps different options are considered. The left brain tends to take in and explore isolated pieces of information, so this is mostly a left-brain process.[1]

3. *Barrier.* We often reach a sticking point, where it is difficult to see the world in a new, more useful way and find a solution to the problem.

4. *Inspiration.* This is sometimes called the "Aha" or "Eureka" moment where a new vision comes to awareness. The right brain puts together the pieces in a way that is uniquely yours. This new vision transcends the old rules and replaces them with new ones. This new insight often comes after the problem has been put away for a while, allowing ideas to percolate and connect in the mind. This incubation period may last minutes to years. For example, after Archimedes had struggled with how to determine whether or not a crown was truly gold, he was relaxing in his bathtub. As his mind spun free, it came to him that just as his body displaced its volume in water, a crown would also displace its volume in water. Dividing the crown's weight by its volume would reveal its density, and thus tell if it were truly

made of gold. He then exclaimed, "Eureka, I have found it." The aha can come all at once, as in this case, or it can evolve gradually in small bits and pieces.

5. *Implementation.* The creative person now takes the new idea and applies it, usually writing it down (so that the details can be remembered and described to others) and experimenting to see if the idea works or needs to be improved.

6. *A new reality.* The creative outcome becomes a part of the real world.

How To Nurture Creativity

- *Relax and trust the creative process.* The creative process usually takes time and patience until pieces fall into place. Intense pressure to meet unreasonable deadline stifles the creative process. Conversely, a reasonable timeline can keep us on task. Trust that solutions will usually bubble up if we do our part, even when needed resources are lacking.

Creativity in the North Vietnam Prison Camps

In the Hanoi Hilton, the creativity exercised by American prisoners or war helped many to survive. Larry Chesley (1973) relates that he and his fellow prisoners set up an educational program, with each of forty-eight prisoners teaching a subject area: American history, psychology, sociology, physiology, religion, languages, trigonometry, dance (this was taught by a former Arthur Murray instructor), and so on. They even had music lessons on an imaginary piano keyboard, drawn on the floor with a piece of brick. Each man was given a key and a pitch. The prisoners played simple tunes by hopping on and off keys. They were taught chords by having three or four stand on their respective keys simultaneously. Evening programs included discussions of hobbies, special interests (ranging from skeet shooting to auto racing, travel sites, movies, and books), and how to be better husbands and fathers. Chesley memorized poems such as Henley's "Invictus" and Kipling's "If" that lifted his soul, along with the Twenty-third Psalm, which made him conscious that God had not forgotten them.

- *Reframe a problem as a challenge and an opportunity for growth.* Approach challenges with a welcoming attitude of curiosity, rather than negativity. Curiosity fans the creative fires, whereas negativity dampens them.[2]
- *Observe.* Be mindful. Without judging or attaching to any particular outcome, simply notice the situation (What is going on? In what context is this happening? What might help? What resources are available—what is lacking?). Notice your inner feelings about the situation. Pay attention to your hunches. Watch with interest and curiosity.
- *Get started early.* Early activity permits time for ideas to incubate. Procrastination doesn't. Although most people share the illusion that pressure promotes creativity, the pressure caused by procrastination usually constricts creative thinking[3] and results in a poorer product. The exception to the rule occurs when a prepared person is fully engaged in a flow state—where one gives

273

full attention to a meaningful task where capabilities are not overwhelmed. This was the case with Lt. Colonel Chamberlain.

- *Have the courage to persevere.* In studying scores of the most creative contributors in various domains, Mihaly Csikszentmihalyi, Ph.D., (1996, p.1) concluded, "A genuinely creative accomplishment is almost never the result of a sudden insight, a lightbulb flashing on in the dark, but comes after years of hard work." Creative contributors don't necessarily have higher IQs, but they do persist. Be willing to work long and hard. Expect to make a meaningful contribution. Stay motivated by writing down why your efforts matter to you. Remember, a cause such as bettering the world or helping others is usually more motivating than causes that are primarily materialistic.

- *Fill your mind from many sources.* Keep your mind open to new ideas. Pick the brains of the best thinkers you can find. Attend conferences in the field, and sometimes in unrelated fields, to get different perspectives to draw from. Study other disciplines and cultures, and past contributions. Visit museums. Study how people around the world solve problems. Such efforts might pay off for you later, as you integrate ideas or adapt them to your particular challenge. Gain experience through training and experimentation.[4]

- *Give your mind time to spin free.* After focused effort, give the mind a break. This allows you to step back, see things afresh, and give the right brain time to connect disparate thoughts. Long walks, bike rides, swimming, or other forms of exercise have been used by the likes of Benjamin Franklin, Thomas Jefferson, Albert Einstein, and other highly creative people. Try meditation. Paradoxically, emptying your mind of cares promotes creativity.

- *Do something daily to lift your mood.* Growing evidence indicates that positive emotions promote creative, flexible thinking and problem solving, and adaptive coping. Remember to apply the skills of part VI, especially when under stress, when the need and benefits of emotional uplifts are greatest. Downplay mistakes. Everyone makes them as we attempt new strategies. After mistakes, calmly ask yourself, "Next time, what could I do differently?"

- *Replace destroyer thoughts.* Certain negative thoughts stifle creativity. Beginning below are common limiting thoughts and their constructive replacements:

Limiting Thoughts (Expert's mind)	Empowering Thoughts (Beginner's mind)
I'm not creative.	Everyone is creative. Perhaps I'm not very creative in this area yet.
That can't be done. It won't work.	That's what scoffers said about flight, breaking the sound barrier, breaking the four minute mile, walking on the moon, regulating the immune system, the telephone, laptops, and countless other innovations.[5]
I can't.	As Richard Bach said, "Argue for your limitations, and sure enough, they're yours." Maybe I can. Maybe a way will appear.

274

I must find the right way and follow the rules.	The *tyranny of ors* says there is a right way or a wrong way. In fact, there are many useful ways to solve a problem. I'm willing to take some risks—even risking "failure"—in order to learn and grow. Some solutions might toss out old ways and replace them with new ways. Others preserve and refine old ways.
Past failure means I won't succeed.	The past isn't prologue. Dr. Seuss failed art in high school. His children's books took about a year to complete, yet he did succeed. *Peanuts* creator Charles Schultz's drawings were rejected from his yearbook.
My ego is on the line. I must not fail.	My productivity doesn't equal my worth. I'll approach this with a more playful attitude.
I must do this fast.	Rushing usually degrades the thoughtfulness required for creativity. People who think they are performing best under the gun often are not.
We've never done it that way.	Perhaps there's a better way. I'm open to new possibilities. I'll give it a try.
I must be certain before risking.	As Supreme Court Justice Oliver Wendell Holmes said, "Life is the art of making decisions in the absence of sufficient information."
We tried that way before.	What exactly was *that way*? Perhaps there's a way to improve that approach.
I can't leave my comfort zone. I won't change.	My survival may require my willingness to change. Is this worth it to resist? I have a range of options, ranging from no change, to some change, to radical change.
We must do it my way.	Perhaps there's a better way I'm not seeing yet. What have I got to lose by being open-minded?

- *Ask questions to stimulate the creativity process.* Creative people frequently ask questions such as: "What would happen if...?"; "What if we tried it this way?"; "Why not try it this way?"; "What would it take to do this?"; "Why didn't that past attempt work?"; "What would I (or others) like to see happen?"
- *Go back and forth between extremes.* Csikszentmihalyi (1996) notes that creative people flexibly alternate between extremes as the occasion requires, such as alternating between:
  - Discipline and play
  - Extroversion and introversion

- Wholesome humility (I don't know everything) and wholesome pride (I'm confident)
- Periods of rest and idleness and times of great energy and concentration
- Realism/practicality and being imaginative (seeing possibilities)
- Convergent thinking (homing in, focusing in the present) and divergent thinking (stepping back, seeing the big picture, generating ideas)
- Ambition/aggressiveness (including the willingness to sacrifice one's own comfort to get the job done) and selflessness/cooperation
- Appreciation, understanding, and respect for culture and old rules versus willingness to break with tradition and take risks (if one is only conservative there will be no change; if one is only rebellious one's work is rarely constructive or appreciated)
- Passion for work and objectivity (passion keeps interest alive during adversity; objectivity keeps judgment alive and controls emotions)
- Pain and enjoyment. Pain springs from criticism (people don't always appreciate novelty) and the sacrifices needed to produce. Enjoyment comes from flow—the wholehearted involvement in valuable work, which is enjoyable for its own sake.
- Tolerance of ambiguity (I acknowledge what is) and intolerance of ambiguity (I seek a better way)
- *Maximize time and energy.* Csikszentmihalyi notes that creative people have efficient habits that help them focus, reduce distractions, preserve energy, and minimize time wasting. These include working during their most productive times of the day and dressing simply or in the same way each day. They get plenty of sleep, which pays off in more productivity the next day. They use an efficient retrieval system, such as filing cabinets, to reduce time wasted in searching. They turn off passive, mentally fatiguing entertainment such as TV and computer games. And they create a workplace that is free of unwanted distractions. In addition, they tend not to divide their focus by multitasking.
- *Access the synergy of others.* The best ideas rarely come from lone individuals. Pick the brains of friends, family, children, cabbies, or anyone else with whom you rub shoulders. Most people like to share ideas and opinions.
- *Make a creative environment.*
  - If you are a leader, create a culture where people feel safe to experiment and take risks without fear of excessive criticism or competition. Encourage people often with comments such as: "Good work"; "Tell me about your idea"; "Why don't you try that out!" Then step back and let your people create.
  - Seek mentors and a team that is supportive, respectful of new ideas, and unified in its goals.
  - Structure the physical environment so that it is most conducive to creativity. You might prefer a quiet, more Spartan environment, free of distractions. Others like music and soft furniture.
  - Enrich your marriage. The most creative contributors tend to have stable and satisfying marriages, according to Csikszentmihalyi.
- *Write down ideas as they come or you'll forget them.* File them so you can easily access them when you have additional ideas.

The Steps of Creativity

A twenty-four-year-old Frenchman named Philippe Petit created quite a stir when he tight-roped between the tops of the twin towers in New York City in 1974, a distance of forty-three meters, eight times in forty-five minutes. He started with a goal of doing something that would defy the bullying of fear. He invested six years in the planning, and had the help of a large group of New Yorkers who helped him secretly haul a ton of equipment. He began by shooting an arrow with fine filament fishing line across the gap between the towers. The fishing line was used to pull a thicker cord across the gap. This was followed by a rope, and then the steel cable that he used to traverse between the towers.

How many of the creativity principles can you spot in this brief story?

Finding Creative Strategies for Difficult Situations

Creativity is not always needed or desirable. Sometimes old ways are working well and efficiently. At times, such as when there isn't time to innovate, we fall back on methods we are trained to implement. Think, for example, of the chaos that could ensue should a member of a highly trained SWAT team begin to innovate on his own. However, in difficult, real-life situations, especially when the old ways are not working, a process called creative problem solving can often uncover a workable strategy. Creative problem solving is a skill that is teachable. People who are skilled in creative problem solving generally have better mental health (e.g., less depression, substance abuse, anxiety, hopelessness, and hostility) because they can devise more coping options. Rather than passively worrying, this strategy teaches one to actively solve problems. The strategy is particularly useful for complex problems that keep us stuck. The steps to creative problem solving follow:

1. *Identify a problem you would like to solve.* It could be conflict with a boss, co-worker, or family member. It might be excess weight, poor sleep, or hating your job. Naming the problem creates an opportunity to improve your life. We can't solve what we are not aware of, and the more we run from problems, the worse we feel. If you can't identify a specific irritant, identify cues of discomfort—such as feelings of sadness or anxiety, or troubling behaviors, such as drinking.

2. *Describe the problem from many different perspectives.* The more ways we can view the problem, the more likely we are to find new solutions. So spend considerable time describing the problem in writing from many angles. The following are ways to approach this step:
   - *See if you can come up with a range of explanations.* Why is this happening (think of as many causes as possible)? What's really going on? See it from different angles. Try the reverse formulation strategy (Csikszentmihalyi, 1996). Let's say you feel you've been denied a raise because the boss dislikes you. Reversing the explanation might yield, "I dislike the boss." Other possible

277

explanations: I've been distracted by problems at home. Maybe I was more concerned with prestige than doing a good job. Maybe I didn't give the boss what she wanted.

- *Describe the problem from multiple perspectives* (Michalko, 2001). First describe it from your own point of view. Then from at least two others (such as someone who is close to the problem, a government leader, an entrepreneur, a wise counselor, a spouse, or a reporter). Then synthesize the descriptions. If you are working with others, ask each participant to come up with his own personal perspective of the problem and the ideal solution.

- *Journal the problem and describe your entry with one word.* For example, Don, a cop, is feeling overwhelmed by the strain of having two jobs to support his family, getting too little sleep, and having problems at work. He watches too much television, exercises too little, and eats poorly. Lacking social skills, he has few friends in law enforcement and even fewer outside of the force. He feels tempted to overuse alcohol to calm his nerves. He is doubting his abilities. The word that he selects, *inadequate*, will eventually suggest a number of possible solutions. Michalko (2001) suggests that further defining the word from the dictionary, thesaurus, or by providing your own meaning might also help to trigger more solutions.

- *To jolt your usual thinking, create a metaphor, analogy, or symbol and describe how the problem is like that.* For example, negotiating a contract with that client is like talking to a brick wall. Eventually, a solution is suggested, for a brick wall can be dismantled gently, one brick at a time (Biech, 1996).

- *Use word play to change your focus.* Change, delete, or add words to your problem description. For example, the original explanation, "My boss is Satan—immoral, judgmental, an underachiever with no leadership ability who must be stopped!" shifts to, "He is unhappy and in need of help."

- *Formulate a question that captures the problem, and then change the question.* For example, Toyota employees were asked how they could become more productive. The question got little response. After rewording the question to "How can you make your job easier?" the executives were inundated with ideas (Michalko, 2001, p.33). Try word play with the verb to see what that triggers. For example, "How can I increase sales" might become "How can I attract (repeat, extend, etc.) sales."

- *Ask and respond to questions*, such as:
  - Is the obvious irritant part of a larger problem that needs addressing (e.g., low self-esteem, poor social skills)?
  - How bad is it? How bad will it be years from now? Is it possible that it's not a big problem in the grand scheme of things?
  - What would happen if I do nothing? What is the cost of doing nothing?
  - How might I be a cause of the problem?
  - What barriers are blocking progress?
  - Is there something beautiful or interesting I can find about this problem (Michalko 2001, p.48)?

- *Try describing the problem through artistic expression* (painting, drawing, sculpting, etc.). This can yield insight that verbal expression doesn't.

3. *Gather information from as many sources as possible.* Seek understanding, advice, and possible solutions from books, the web, people you know, experts, and so forth.

4. *Conceive the outcome.* Can you imagine what you'd like to see happen? What would be an acceptable outcome? What would be the ideal? Clarifying the outcome can suggest pathways to reaching it. The following strategies can facilitate this step:

   - The famous psychotherapist Milton Erickson suggested contemplating this statement: "I would be happy to understand how to _____" (state the desired outcome, such as work well with the boss or increase my friendships). This encouraging, upbeat statement invites a positive approach to the problem solving process and increases the likelihood of a solution unfolding.

   - Visualize the problem solved. Suppose you went to bed tonight and when woke up something had happened so that you realized a change had happened. You've gotten over or around the barrier. What would be the first thing you'd notice? What other pleasant physical and emotional reactions would you notice? How would life be better for yourself and others? Attaching pleasant emotions to the problem solving process facilitates the process (Echterling et al., 2005). Sometimes simply changing the way we look at the problem, or our feelings toward the problem, is the most workable strategy, since some situations can't be "fixed."

   - Draw, paint, or sculpt what the desired outcome feels and looks like. Again, artistic expression can generate insights that verbal expression may not.

5. *Generate a range of possible solutions.* Insanity is doing the same thing repeatedly and expecting different results. When the old way isn't working, the idea is to come up with as many new possibilities as you can. The more problem solving strategies you can conceive, the more likely you are to find the best possible option.

   - Brainstorming is a process for generating as many solutions as possible. Although individuals can do this, this process works best in a team, where the ideas and support of many can be tapped. Each person is considered an equal colleague who holds a key to solving the problem, or a piece of the puzzle. All contributions are respected, and the atmosphere is friendly. A week or two before the brainstorming session, ask each team member to think about and bring ideas for solving the problem. This allows time for ideas to percolate. At the brainstorming session all ideas are listed, say on a white board. To this list, everyone adds additional solutions that bubble up spontaneously. This is a freewheeling process where anything goes. All ideas are recorded without evaluation, discussion, judgment, or criticism, which stifle the creativity process. One idea might piggyback on another—even unlikely ideas can suggest more ideas. Try to keep this session light and moving. When ideas stall, try saying something like, "The stock market will crash if we don't come up with five more solutions." Be on the lookout for ways to blend suggestions. Thus, one might learn to like the boss, pay more attention to his needs, focus more on intrinsic motivations for working, retool for a new job, accept the way things are, and find more satisfaction outside of work.

- Other strategies for generating solutions include:
  - Play with the opposite. Suppose you want to improve your relationship with the boss. Now, think of ways you could estrange yourself from her (e.g., ignore her or be aloof, forget assignments, look disdainful). The list will paradoxically suggest solutions to the original problem.
  - The scaling technique (Walter & Peller, 1992) can sometimes help identify solutions. Where on a 1-10 scale is the situation, where 10 is the ideal solution? What would be happening differently as you get to a higher number? At what number would you feel you're in control? What would your next step be?
  - Ask, "What would_____ (someone who is skilled or respected) do?"

6. *Evaluate the options.* Once possible solutions have been generated, each is evaluated. Weigh the pros and cons of each. Ask questions, such as: How would that help? Why? How might this be a bad idea (thinking like your adversary might help you tweak the solution)? You might allow incubation time to allow team members to further evaluate the options, and how they might be implemented.

7. *Select the "best" plan (or combinations of plans), implement it, and evaluate your progress.* In making an action plan, consider questions such as who, what, where, when, and how. Write down the specifics. Calendar a time to check on your progress, being open to the need for adjustments in your plan.

Reflections on Creativity

- Creativity is not optional equipment. It's a built-in potential, a seedling planted deep in the human personality. And like any other human possibility, creativity can be helped to grow and flourish. (Thomas Kinkade)
- We are either victims or creators of reality. (Anonymous)
- We are all artists by birth, realists by training. (Anonymous)

Drills

- Contemplate yourself surrounded by the conditions you intend to produce, as Wayne W. Dyer, Ph.D., has taught. In other words, visualize your life turning out as you want because you have taken the necessary action.
- Take an everyday object, like a rubber ball or a brick. Think of six uses that are unrelated to its usual use. Think of how it's form and function teaches about resilience. For example, a rubber ball or brick can prop open a window on a spring day, allowing fresh air in, much like an open mind allows new ideas in. A ball is resilient in that it bounces back when it hits a wall. It creates fun just by being itself. A brick is stronger after being heated.
- To expand your usual way of "seeing" the world and to slow down and play with ideas, take a color, such as orange or blue. What does that color taste like? Sound like? What is its temperature, texture, and smell? What emotions go with it? Imagine

280

the taste of _____ (e.g., chocolate). Imagine it changes to the taste of _____(e.g., an orange).

Flexibility

Creativity requires mental flexibility, or the ability to adapt to changing situations. Peak performers can shift gears when standard procedures aren't working. Let's suppose you have made a good plan. You are mindfully aware of how things are going, and you realize that the plan isn't working. What do you do? Will you be flexible?

The Flexibility Checkup

This scale shows the degree to which you have cultivated flexibility. Rate each from 1-10, where 10 means that you are exceptionally flexible, as flexible as humanly possible. Zero means you are never flexible to the slightest degree.

_____ I usually have a plan, but I don't "fall in love with" my plan (i.e., I'm not rigidly attached to a plan that isn't working).
_____ I constantly think of alternate routes to success.
_____ I always have a back-up plan (a plan B).
_____ I willingly and rapidly adapt to changing situations.
_____ I know when to change course and devise a new strategy.
_____ I can accept defeat (to "live to fight another day" when a goal is unachievable); I know when to cut my losses.
_____ I know that I can't solve every problem, but I am willing to take action based on my best judgment.
_____ I have a nimble mind; I think well on my feet.
_____ I see when change is needed and welcome it.
_____ I will consider and take risks that are appropriate.
_____ When under stress, I'm willing to try something new.
_____ I don't let my mental maps (seeing the things as I want or expect them to be) stop me from seeing things as they really are. I am open to all new evidence.
_____ I accept what can't realistically be changed or controlled, but think of many ways to cope even with such situations.
_____ I roll with the punches when things don't go as planned; I don't get bent out of shape.
_____ I quickly adapt, but I don't hurry into things about which I'm not reasonably certain.
_____ I don't always have to be right.
_____ I go along with conditions as they are.

Effective copers are usually securely rooted in self, values, and methods that work. But they can bend when bending is called for. The opposite of flexibility is inflexibility or rigidity. Those who are always the same might lose their advantage in changing circumstances. For example, a pitcher who always throws a fastball, no matter how fast, will eventually get hit if he doesn't switch speeds or location.

Coping Flexibility

The Australian military has begun resilience training for recruits. Past studies have shown that coping strategies such as avoidance, self-blame, and denial predict distress and failure in basic training. However, during basic training—when recruits have little control—acceptance, seeking social support, and positive appraisal are often more effective than active problem solving. So recruits are taught to distinguish when control is realistic or not. If they determine that outcomes resulted from something controllable (e.g., "I used the wrong method" or "I didn't try hard enough"), then they are encouraged to problem solve. If results were due to uncontrollable factors, then they were encouraged to accept the outcome, talk to supportive people, distract through relaxation, or replace negative thoughts (e.g., "I failed because it was a difficult situation, not because I'm stupid"). This flexible approach resulted in less psychological distress, greater positive states of mind, less self-blame, and less pessimistic thinking (Cohn & Pakenham, 2008).

What is the take-home message? There is wisdom in knowing what we can control and what we can't, and in having fluid strategies for coping with either situation. The broader the coping repertoire, the better is one's functioning and mental health.

Emotional Flexibility

Some people, especially those in high-risk groups (e.g., cops, firefighters, and the military) are trained to be tough during adversity. Messages such as "suck it up, carry on, don't quit, ignore yourself and your own needs, and deny pain" help them function in the short term. However, these messages, rigidly applied, might not work well when they come home—especially if their mental resources have been stretched to or beyond the breaking point.[6]

Many of our heroes are unwilling to admit the need for help, when the truth is that they need to be flexible, to stop, admit needs, and replenish the "water in their emotional wells." Competent treatment for PTSD or other stress-related disorders processes and heals emotional wounds. Burdens are lightened, enabling survivors to carry on better and be fully available for their buddies and loved ones. Treatment is like training in coping skills that were never learned or under-learned. Therapists are like coaches or trainers. Yet most of our high-risk group members with PTSD are not diagnosed, so they don't get the healing help that is needed. Others are diagnosed, but don't seek help.

The evidence that treatments for PTSD work is unassailable. It is wise to know when to suppress pain, when to rely on yourself, and when to allow others to help. Traumatic memories do not typically resolve with willful suppression. However, effective treatment can teach many new ways to lessen emotional suffering.

Additional Flexibility Principles

1. "'Winners never quit and quitters never win.' Not quite. There comes a point, if a goal is implausible, when it's smarter to give up and switch to a new target, evidence suggests. The key is adaptability, explains psychologist Carsten Wrosch [of Concordia University]...Those who don't or won't disengage in the face of

repeated failure are at risk of physical and emotional suffering, including skin, stomach, and sleep problems and even diabetes, heart disease, and osteoporosis." Inflammation is higher in those who have trouble letting a goal go, probably because of cortisol, which increases with frustration. If the nut won't crack, seek a different goal. As W.C Fields said : "If at first you don't' succeed, try, try again. Then quit. There's no point in being a damn fool about it." Focus on enjoying the process and let the outcome go.[7]

2. Don't over-rely on past training and experience. And don't assume training has totally prepared you. It takes years to become an expert, and experts usually outperform novices. But if something happens to change the rules, the differences shrink. Many overconfident, complacent experts perish in the outdoors. They might rely on old habits and miss new developments. Pay attention. Continue to learn. Don't be imprisoned by your old paradigm (the old way of looking at things).

Reflections on Flexibility

- There is no sin punished more implacably by nature than the sin of resistance to change. (Anne Morrow Lindbergh)
- Blessed are the flexible for they shall not be bent out of shape. (Anonymous)
- When you discover you're riding a dead horse, dismount. (Bill O'Hanlon)
- But change will come, and if you acknowledge this simple but indisputable fact of life, and understand that you must adjust to all change, then you will have a head start. (Arthur Ashe)
- If digging the same hole deeper isn't striking oil, try digging elsewhere. (Anonymous)
- Plan the flight and fly the plan, but don't fall in love with the plan. Be open to a changing world and let go of the plan when necessary so that you can make a new plan. (Laurence Gonzales)

Flexibility Drills

- To stimulate flexibility in your life, try something new outside of your job (e.g. a new hobby, instrument, language, kind of community service, way to clean or do chores, club to meet new people, restaurant, recipe).
- On the job look for adjustments that might improve outcomes.

Visual Flexibility Exercise

In sports and other action settings, vision can become rigidly locked (tunnel vision) to the point that we fail to see the whole picture. Westerners tend to prematurely zoom in on a detail, and in the process miss the context and surroundings. Ideally, a police officer would see a perpetrator with a gun (narrow focus) and also screen the surrounding area for armed accomplices (broad focus). Individuals can be trained to flexibly shift between a broad and a narrow focus. To improve your ability to fluidly shift between broad and narrow focus, try this exercise described by athlete trainer Spencer Wood, Ph.D., (2003).[8] This can easily be adapted for various professions:

- Line up five objects, such as plastic cones, horizontally over a distance of about ten feet. Step back about five feet.
- Without shifting your head and eyes, look at all the objects at once (broad focus) for about ten seconds.
- Holding the eyes and head still, shift to narrow focus, looking intently at one object. Notice all the details of the object: contour, color, shadows, and so forth. Pretend you have a zoom lens on a camera that focuses further in on a small detail.
- Every ten seconds shift back and forth, like a zoom camera. Vary your narrow focus. For example, one time you might zoom in on two objects. Another time you might zoom in on a different object, and a different detail on that object.
- For realism, you can add distractions—such as noise, waving arms in the background, or flashes of light—to improve your ability to focus.

SPECIFIC RESILIENCE TRAINING FOR HIGH-RISK POPULATIONS

PART VIII

CRISIS PREPARATION

Chapter 30

Pre-Crisis Job Performance Training

We are never [totally] prepared for what we expect.
James A. Michener, *Caravans*

So far, we have explored many skills that are universally useful to people in all stations of life, whether they be combatants, parents, teachers, or children. In this part of the book, we will explore skills and principles that are of specific interest to high-risk populations, such as the military, police officers, firefighters, and other emergency service providers who are most likely to encounter crises. A crisis is a dangerous event that can potentially overwhelm our usual coping skills and emotional stability. While no amount of training and experience can make us completely invulnerable, intelligent training can prepare us as much as is humanly possible.

The goal of this part of the book is to equip high-risk groups with two specific skill sets, both of which are essential to resilient living in highly-stressful environments: (1) Job performance skills, and (2) Additional emotional coping skills for during and after crises. Although this part of the book will specifically benefit high-risk groups, the principles and skills will also benefit anyone, since we all are likely to encounter extremely distressing events in our lives.

High-performing individuals anticipate challenges. Instead of getting stuck in "What if...." thinking and worries, they think, "If or when X happens, then I will..." In other words, they think ahead and train for crises. In this and the next chapter we will explore skills related to job performance and the emotional challenges of the job—skills that help crises just seem like the job you were trained to do. We'll start with job performance skills by looking at two well-conceived training programs. Both aim to expose individuals to the types of hazards they are likely to face, make them realistically aware of their present skills levels, challenge them without overwhelming them, and over-train to increase skill and confidence. This chapter will conclude with two strategies for conditioning our bodies for peak performance.

Hi-Reliability Training Program

"The more you sweat in training the less you bleed in battle."
Irwin Rommel, respected German field marshal, WWII

Israel has an effective graduated training program for elite security officers. The candidates are male military combat veterans. The training imitates the type of stress the candidates are likely to face. It starts with a dangerous obstacle course, under the assumption that physical fitness and high-level motor performance confer clear psychological benefits, including confidence. Under the assumption that it is the unexpected stressors that create the most stress, candidates gradually learn to overpower armed terrorists, shoot at lawbreakers, return fire, and control mobs.

Stress is gradually incorporated into the training in the form of loud noises, jump-up targets, smoke grenades, the use of weapons, and physical attacks. Training is frequently stopped to allow for analysis, discussions, and the drawing of conclusions by participants and trainers.

Researchers (Zach, Raviv, & Inbar, 2007) noted that stress impairs performance only on complex tasks. At the start of the program, performance under low stress was better than under high stress. However, the training program significantly improved physical and psychological performance under stressful conditions. It appeared that improved performance was linked to improved physical fitness, hardiness, and reductions in anxiety.

They concluded that when properly prepared for the "unexpected," individuals can better focus on performing without being unduly distracted by or concerned with stress. Alternatively, proper functioning becomes so ingrained with training that individuals can better attend to coping with stress.

The Five-Step FBI Training Program

An enlightened training program has been used at the FBI Academy to train law enforcement officials from around the country. The program emphasizes realistic awareness of skills and overtraining (Printz & Wrangnert, 1999).

Step 1. *Honest, non-judgmental awareness of skill level.* Participants undergo increasingly difficult challenges in order to let them see the point at which they fail to perform well. For example, 90% of shots fired at close-range pop-up targets under pressure miss their mark. Participants become aware of their false confidence, learning that their shooting skills are not as good as they'd assumed. Neither are the skills of their buddies, whom they trust for backup. This step promotes awareness of needed improvement and the importance of calling for backup. Said one veteran, "Training humbled me. It will keep me from repeating mistakes in the future."

Step 2. *Flexible Mindset.* This step reinforces the beginner's mind. Participants are taught to be friendly, but flexible, ready to switch gears in a split second. Many police who were killed were well liked and hard working. They looked for the good in people, and dropped their guard when they thought an offender showed a good quality. So participants learn not to overgeneralize; not to assume people are all good or all bad. The latter can make a police officer paranoid and more likely to overreact. When participants go home, they are encouraged to drop the suspicion.

Step 3. *Task Mastery.* Participants repetitively practice basic skills until they are almost second nature. Under controlled conditions, participants encounter gradually more difficult real-life scenarios with real equipment and conditions. Like the Israeli security training program, participants are inoculated to stress: they start with small doses and gradually work their way up to more stressful situations.[1]

Step 4. *Train Mentally.* Mental imagery training powerfully reinforces physical training. In fact, in several studies, mental practice is as effective as physical practice. Anything can be imagined, while physical training might be limited by budgetary or safety restraints. Mental practice can be done anywhere. Start by getting very relaxed (e.g., by abdominal breathing and progressive muscle relaxation). Imagine in detail a stressful situation you are likely to encounter. Then visualize your effective response. See yourself performing well, with calm pulse and breathing rates. Rehearse split-second decisions. For example, a cop must overcome reluctance to shoot a perpetrator in a lethal encounter. In mental rehearsal, the police officer imagines quickly appraising the situation, considering the options, and then shooting. Then he imagines the outcomes (e.g., seeing the disabled perpetrator, administrative leave, distressing emotions afterwards).[2]

Step 5. *Off Duty Balance.* This includes physical exercise, recreation (including time with family and worship), meditation, and other distractions from job strain— all of which are essential for mental health and peak performance.

Pulse Rate Conditioning

A low resting pulse rate predicts general mental health years later. Recall, also, that pulse rate under pressure also correlates with performance. The best performers strive for a low resting pulse rate that can rise quickly, but not too high, and can recover quickly. Remember that at about 140 beats per minute there is good thinking, memory recall, and physical reactions. However, beyond 145 beats per minute we see deterioration in performance. As fear and anger elevate the pulse to about 180 beats per minute or above, tunnel vision is likely to occur and officers do foolish things (e.g., throwing their gun away and rushing an armed perpetrator).

Training at the FBI Academy has conditioned pulse rate flexibility through aerobic conditioning coupled with recovery conditioning as follows: Jog for 80% of the time at a level that makes speaking difficult. For 10% of the time, jog at a level where you can barely speak, and for 10% of the time jog at a low intensity, such that you can speak with ease. Thus, for a thirty minute jog, twenty-four minutes would be at a level where speaking is difficult, three minutes would be at a level where you can barely speak, and three minutes would be at a comfortable level for speaking. Participants are encouraged to build up slowly, starting with walking.

Mental Rehearsal for Flexible Pulse Rate

See yourself responding properly to a crisis situation. Your pulse appropriately increases, and decreases quickly after the crisis (mastery image). Alternatively, practice rebounding imagery. See yourself getting overly aroused in a crisis situation, but you remember to do your tactical breathing to quickly lower your pulse rate to the ideal range (around 140 beats per minute or less), while you tell yourself, "It's normal to become aroused; just calm the breathing and focus on the task."

Activity: Using What You've Learned

With co-workers, brainstorm to identify as many crises as you can that you are likely to encounter. Then develop a training program that readies you for these situations, using the principles and skills of this chapter:
- Physical agility, strength, and endurance training
- Realistic, non-judgmental awareness of skill level

- Training for, and in conditions that imitate, real life crises—gradually introducing more and more real-life stressors
- Mindfully observing the situation; having a flexible mindset
- Stopping to process (to reinforce successes, make needed adjustments, anticipate contingencies)
- Thorough, repetitive practice of needed skills, including mental rehearsal following physical rehearsal
- Pulse rate conditioning
- Off-duty balance

Chapter 31

Preparing Emotionally for Crisis

Hope for the best, prepare emotionally for the worst.
Anonymous

...every time I kill someone I feel farther away from home.
Tom Hanks' character in *Saving Private Ryan*

Emergency service providers are typically well trained to carry out the *tactics* of their mission. However, they are typically not prepared for the strong emotions they are likely to encounter as a result of crises. For example, a firefighter was prepared to rescue people. He didn't realize how difficult it would be to arrive at the school cafeteria and find so many children killed by a tornado. Dicks (1990, p.33) chronicled the psychological surprises experienced by Vietnam vets, who said, "All the training I'd had hadn't prepared me for this." They weren't prepared for the smell of dead or burned flesh, for seeing their comrades bleeding, or for hearing them scream in pain. They weren't prepared to see a four-year-old child with a sparkling smile unwittingly carrying a bomb booby trap on his back, and want to kill in revenge even the children who'd killed his comrades. A peacekeeper in Rwanda, Lt. General Roméo Dallaire (2003, p.512), poignantly described how difficult it was to watch dogs eating children's corpses, the "throwaway young lives" whose pleas for help were unheeded by the world. The exquisitely trained Navy SEAL, Marcus Luttrell (2007), couldn't rescue his best friend, whom he'd sworn to protect, because of the murderous enemy fire that pinned him down. He wasn't prepared for the feeling of helplessness as he heard him plea, "Please help me, Marcus."

Sometimes leaders try to shield their people from the difficult emotional aspects of their jobs, erroneously thinking that they will become too fearful to perform if they really know what to expect. Such an approach woefully underestimates people's abilities to prepare themselves. If people know what to expect, and how to deal with what they expect, they will perform better, not worse. So we must trust people's abilities. We must say, for example, "Expect this, and prepare for it. Focus on your job and don't act in revenge." Emotional preparation must be just as rigorous as physical preparation. We can hope for the best, but prepare, especially emotionally, for the worst. How is this done? The overarching principle is to gradually expose individuals to increasingly troubling emotions—challenge but don't overwhelm—in order to build emotional confidence.

Study Similar Experiences

Minimize emotional surprises by reading books or watching movies that realistically depict the emotional challenges of your profession. A few good books are:
- *Lone Survivor* (Marcus Luttrell)
- *Two Wars* (Nate Self)
- *I Love a Cop/Fire Fighter* (Ellen Kirschman)

- *Deadly Force Encounters: What Cops Need to Know to Mentally and Physically Prepare for and Survive a Gunfight* (Alexis Artwohl and Loren W. Christensen)
- *Blood Lessons: What Cops Learn From Life-or-Death Encounters* (Chuck Remsberg)
- *From Vietnam to Hell: Interviews with Victims of Post-Traumatic Stress Disorder* (Shirley Dicks)
- *With the Old Breed* (E. B. Sledge)

Some excellent movies are: *Blackhawk Down, We Were Soldiers,* and *Saving Private Ryan.*

Incorporate Emotional Processing into Training

When you pause to process training performance, you might ask individuals: "What would you feel if.... (e.g., your best friend were shot or commits suicide, you shoot a civilian by mistake, you shoot a terrorist)?"; "What would get you through this?"; "What would you do?"; "What resources, external and internal, would help (remember resources such as using a journal to facilitate the grieving process, accepting emotions non-judgmentally, normalizing strong emotions, and using distress regulation skills)?" Have some ideas, but you needn't have all the answers. Simply posing such questions can stimulate a constructive anticipatory thought process and fruitful discussion. Gradual exposure to troubling emotions helps to emotionally inoculate individuals.

If time permits, you might ask a comrade prior to a difficult mission, "What are you feeling? What will you do?" (as U.S. Coast Guard chaplain Jim Ellis[1] did with divers shortly before they entered the water to retrieve bodies from the Egypt Air 990 disaster). Such questions can normalize strong emotions and then prompt one to focus on the mission.[2]

Remember Why You Are Doing This

Recall that concentration camp survivor Viktor Frankl said that people can endure almost anything if they have a reason to. A deep sense of meaning and purpose is an anchor. In your journal, describe why you have chosen this profession. Perhaps you are fighting to protect the freedom, safety, or future of loved ones, neighbors, or friends you'll never meet.

Anticipating the Worst Case Scenario: Emotional Inoculation Exercise

This exercise ties together emotions, thoughts, and behaviors. It spurs people to consider: (1) what they will likely encounter; (2) where they stand in terms of present coping ability; and (3) the options they have for coping, including those they have not yet considered. It also helps people to mentally rehearse for troubling future events.

This can be done individually, but it works best with a partner. Both partners respond individually to six questions, then discuss their responses.

Instructions

First, identify an emotionally stressful event. It has been suggested that anyone could be pushed to the breaking point. Think of the most stressful event that you could possibly face. Perhaps you have already experienced such an event, or can imagine it. The event could involve death, ill will, personal fallibility, and/or suffering. Partners then share their responses and select one event they'd like to consider together. Next, respond individually in writing to the following six questions.

1. *Describe the objective <u>facts</u> of the event.* For example, after a long standoff, police officers rush the man who is holding a child at knifepoint. They shoot and kill the perpetrator, and soon realize that an errant shot has also killed the child.
2. *What feelings attend this event?*
3. *Given your present thinking, how would you <u>likely</u> <u>respond</u> to this event?*
   - Fully describe your behaviors and coping attempts.
   - Explain in detail the <u>thoughts</u> that underlie your feelings and behaviors—before, during, and after.
4. *How would <u>most people</u> in your profession respond to this event?* Describe thoughts, feelings, and behaviors before, during, and after the event.
5. *What would you consider an <u>ideal</u> response to this event?* Discuss thoughts, feelings, and behaviors before, during, and after the event.
6. *How would you feel if your response were less than the ideal?*

Finally, process what you have written. Exchange your written responses as each partner reads the other's responses.
   - Discuss your observations about what the other person has written.
   - Share what you have learned from your partner's writings.

Comments

This exercise is very effective, for at least four reasons:
1. *The events are personally relevant.* Thus, involvement is great.
2. *A wide range of coping options is explored.* For example, one police officer commented that his partner opened his eyes to coping ideas he'd have never thought about. Sergeant Sergio Falzi of the Calgary Police Service related that a male called 911 and stated that he'd just killed his wife. Upon arriving at the apartment, police officers saw a lone male covered in blood, holding a knife in a threatening manner. The officers gave him verbal commands to drop the knife. When he refused, the senior officer discharged Taser probes. Only one probe hit the man and had no effect. While the officer was reloading a second cartridge the male raised the knife and walked toward the officers. At this point, the second officer shot and killed the male. Afterward the senior officer became upset, believing himself a coward for not drawing his side arm immediately. The officer that was forced to use his side arm complimented the first officer for his calm composure during the incident and for thinking to use the Taser first before

transitioning to lethal force. He told the senior officer that he was braver than himself for trying to use non-lethal force first.[3]

3. *The exercise begins the process of dealing with emotional pain and fallibility.* This could save an individual's life—physically *and* emotionally. Said one police officer, "I gained an appreciation and compassion to realize that even strong colleagues are still uncertain of their coping ability. Yet I realize we can mature to reach our capacity. We practice shooting to get better. Why should we assume we're automatically good at emotions?"

4. *Teamwork is developed on an emotional level.* Trust grows as teammates realize that fallible people can persevere and conscientiously work to improve their coping abilities.

Anticipation Hierarchy Exercise

This can be done as a useful homework exercise. Develop a hierarchy of difficult future events you are likely to encounter. That is, make a list such that events are listed from least distressing to most distressing. For example, finding victims alive in a collapsed building might be less distressing to a rescue worker, while finding dead children might be most distressing. For each event:

- *Use emotional success (mastery) imagery.* That is, see yourself keeping your emotions in check, thinking adaptively, and performing well.
- *Use emotional rebounding (coping) imagery.* That is, see yourself getting very distressed during an event. Then see yourself calming yourself by modifying your thoughts, controlling your breathing, and normalizing and accepting all emotions (recall mindfulness)—and then performing well.

Killing

In the course of their duties, certain high-risk professionals—such as military, law enforcement, and security personnel—are called upon to kill another human being. As the world becomes more violent, the likelihood of their having to kill becomes greater. Researchers are finally acknowledging that killing is a strong predictor of PTSD, depression, violence, functional impairment, and alcohol use (e.g., Maguen et al., 2009). Curiously, soldiers might freely talk about their losing a limb to a roadside bomb in Iraq, but become eerily quiet when the discussion turns to killing.

We train combatants to kill. Tragically, we rarely prepare them for the emotional aftermath of killing. Thus, military leaders rarely mention the word killing, instead using euphemisms such as *neutralizing* the enemy or *eliminating* the target.[4] By shielding combatants from the moral and psychological aspects of killing, we also prevent them from fully preparing emotionally.[5] We can't adequately prepare for what we avoid. As the acknowledged expert on killing, Army Ranger and former West Point psychology professor Lt. Colonel Dave Grossman, says, "Denial has no survival value." Grossman explains that those who train to kill must reconcile with the reality of killing, *or suffer more afterwards.* Elite fighters who kill, for example, experience lower rates of PTSD, compared to reservists and police officers who kill. Perhaps the latter groups hope that they'll never have to kill another, and are caught emotionally less prepared when they must do so. As the saying goes, hope is not a strategy. With permission, we will summarize Grossman's main points on killing.[6]

1. *Killing is traumatic.* In all wars since WWI, there have been more psychiatric casualties than deaths from enemy fire.[7] Cops are more likely to suicide than to be killed on duty. Killing is a major contributor to PTSD. As combatants are being better trained to overcome their natural reluctance to kill, PTSD rates are likely to increase if training methods don't change.

2. *Most Americans find killing repugnant.* They would rather befriend and build than harm others.[8] Even enemy soldiers are viewed as fellow warriors and humans. This is healthy. It is normal, then, to feel revulsion and guilt after killing. These feelings, however, can destroy one emotionally, unless one has thought through killing.

3. *In the Judeo-Christian culture, people have been taught, "Thou shalt not kill"* (Ex. 20:13). However, in nearly all Bible translations, the original Hebrew word *ratzach* is more correctly translated as "murder." Murder is the unlawful taking of life with malicious intent (e.g., for personal gain). Thus, it is not killing that is prohibited, but murder. In fact, the Bible frequently mentions war, killing, and soldiering without condemnation. Ecclesiastes states that "To everything there is a season, and a time to every purpose under heaven: A time to be born, and a time to die...a time to kill, and a time to heal...a time of war, and a time of peace...He hath made every thing beautiful in his time (3:1-8, 11). God favored honorable warriors who slayed many, such as Joshua, David (until he *murdered* Uriah), and Gideon. In the New Testament:
   - Jesus taught, "Thou shalt do no *murder* (Matt 19:18, emphasis added).
   - Jesus said, "He that hath no sword, let him sell his garment, and buy one" (Luke 22:36).
   - Jesus said of the Roman centurion (a military leader of the Roman Empire): "I have not found so great faith " (Matt 8:10).
   - Cornelius, the devout Roman centurion, was the first non-Jewish Christian. Peter baptized him and never once condemned him for being a soldier (Acts 10).
   - [Those authorized to administer the law] "beareth not the sword in vain" (Romans 13:4).

   Honorable warriors commit and prepare to fight violence: to defend those who can't protect themselves, to defend the country against those who seek to destroy it, and to protect society's most cherished values. They are commissioned by their government to lawfully use even lethal force for these purposes. They commit to sacrificing their own lives and to use lethal force when needed.

   The warrior who is prepared to legitimately use deadly force decisively and without hesitation—with assurance that his cause is just—can better live with killing afterwards. If he has worked through in advance the moral, spiritual, and emotional aspects of killing, he is less likely to be traumatized afterwards. Notice how the creed of the elite Navy SEALs reflects these considerations:

In times of war or uncertainty...a special breed of warrior [stands] ready to answer our Nation's call...to serve his country, the American people, and protect their way of life...always ready to defend those who are unable to defend themselves...I voluntarily accept the inherent hazards of my profession, placing the welfare and security of others before my own...If knocked down, I will get back up, every time...We train for war and fight to win. I stand ready to bring the full spectrum of combat power to bear in order to achieve my mission and the goals established by my country. The execution of my duties will be swift and violent when required yet guided by the very principles that I serve to defend.

Grossman's Five Stages of Killing

Preparing to kill for a just cause takes determination and effort. It begins with stopping avoidance and fully facing the issues involved. Lt. Colonel Grossman's Stages of Killing is a very useful place to start.

1. *Self-questioning.* The combatant asks, "Am I capable of killing? What if I freeze and let my buddies down?" Killing is often more frightening than the fear of being killed. Being a coward and letting one's buddies down is another of combatants' biggest fears.
2. *The actual killing.* The warrior does what his is trained to do, often automatically and under the influence of a surge of adrenaline.
3. *Exhilaration.* The warrior has hit the target, executed his combat duties, and saved lives. He often feels euphoric, exhilarated, and relieved, knowing that he performed well and has survived. He might be in the state of denial—saying that he is fine, while manifesting the 1000-yard stare.
4. *Aftereffects.* The magnitude of killing hits. One might feel like a destroyer who has committed the ultimate sin, the taking of life. Perhaps the act seems even worse as the combatant approaches the fallen enemy and finds pictures of family, or hears the dying enemy cry, "Mom!" At this stage, remorse is common. Perhaps the combatant feels guilty for feeling satisfaction. Here he must distinguish between satisfaction from doing his duty (which is healthy) and satisfaction from killing (which is not). I once interviewed a hunter whose family needed the meat that he provided. He felt satisfaction in providing food for his family, but always felt queasy about taking the deer's life, even though he felt it justified. A similar, albeit more intense, conflict is typical among warriors who kill. The surviving warrior might typically ask, "Where do I stand before God?" and might feel that innocence and joy have been lost. Nausea, sleep disturbance, flashbacks, depression, anxiety, and dissociation (see chapter 32) are commonly experienced. After killing, police officers often feel as if they are hovering above the scene of the killing or feel that the scene is happening to someone else. A third of them have distorted memories about the killing. Some feel bad for freezing, even though this is sometimes prudent to prevent the premature killing of another, or understandable when the officer is taken by surprise by a perpetrator and is uncertain of what to do. They might shake to realize they could have been killed (Miller, 2006).[9]

Negative aftereffects are minimized if the warrior has worked through killing beforehand, remembering:

- Joy comes from preserving life and freedom, not killing.
- "I'd chose not to kill, but the enemy (perpetrator) makes the decision as to whether or not I use deadly force."
- "I'll do what the government trains me, equips me, authorizes and empowers me, and expects me to do."
- "God won't reject me for lawfully killing when necessary." (Alvin York, the most decorated soldier in WWI, was a conscientious objector for religious reasons at the beginning of the war. After an officer explained to him, from a Biblical perspective, the need to use lawful killing to stop tyranny, York became a committed, noble warrior.)
- Other thoughts to remember:
  - A warrior deters evil and ultimately saves lives.
  - I'm prepared to confront people who hurt others.
  - The enemy intends to kill my friends and me, and will do so if I don't take decisive action.
  - I think I'm going to have to kill this guy. He thinks he can take on the might of my government.
  - A criminal who'd resist a police officer has no respect for the rules of decent people.

5. *Rationalizing and Acceptance.* If one hasn't worked out killing beforehand, this might be a long process. As Grossman says, "Combat kills enough people. It's madness to let it destroy me mentally, too." Honorable warriors have sworn to fight evil. They are motivated by profound love. Cops who kill usually do so in the context of trying to protect others (Miller, 2006). This stage is completed when the warrior realizes that sometimes the enemy (or criminal) needs to be killed for the good of society; force was justified and necessary. If the surviving warrior feels guilty that a comrade fell in battle, the warrior remembers that warriors accept that unavoidable risk; the fallen comrade would want you to go on and live joyfully. It is helpful if elders remind the warrior who has killed, "You did the right thing. Welcome to the club." If a police officer's gun must be taken to satisfy administrative policy, this is best done in private and with dignity, so the officer does not feel needlessly shamed.

The Story of A Prepared Mother

Her son was soon to serve on a destroyer in the Gulf. He had volunteered to be part of a boarding party, which meant he might have to kill.

Before departing for the Gulf, he came home for three days of leave and seemed only to want to hang out at home. One day, just before leaving, he asked his mother if they could have some coffee. He said, "I'm trained to kill without a weapon. What if I have to kill?"

She said, "You have sound judgment...You wouldn't kill without a good reason. What would it feel like if you had to? You are my son, and I'll never desert you. This is what warriors are called to do. What are your options? Do you have buddies to cry with? Crisis intervention? There's even the option not to serve."

How fortunate for a son to have a mother who is willing to mindfully confront the emotional side of crises without judgment and with compassion.

Training Considerations

A hallmark of PTSD is avoidance. The opposite of avoidance is acceptance—which is fully facing reality. Prepared warriors learn to come to terms with the necessity of lawful killing. They learn to approach war with determination and confidence, not avoidance. Grossman's training considerations can help:

1. *Make targets as human as possible.* This helps combatants adjust to the idea of pulling the trigger on another human being when required to do so.

2. *Mentally rehearse killing the enemy.* In today's violent world, the enemy might be children who have been programmed to hate, or terrorists dressed as civilians. Visualize the scenario before, during, and after killing. Include details such as remembering the morality of the fight, picking a point to aim at, seeing the mortally wounded enemy, walking off the adrenaline afterwards, and remembering helpful thoughts. As uncomfortable as this may seem, it is better to mentally rehearse than to be caught unprepared and overwhelmed.

3. *Expect to handle killing better with training and experience.* Seasoned veterans are so called because they have years of experience that help them maintain grace under pressure and bounce back emotionally. It is normal to find killing repulsive, especially at first. Eventually, the warrior accepts killing as a necessary action that duty requires. With determination, experience, and training, an area that is feared and avoided becomes an area of confidence.

4. *The honorable warrior accepts the world in a balanced way.* He accepts that there is evil in the world. Without honorable warriors, evil would prevail. He knows that if he is prepared to do his duty, he will do so with little panic. He will function better—being less likely to be killed himself and more likely to support his buddies who depend on him.

5. *Use modern technology to prepare.* Police departments in New York and Denver have trained with rapid response software, which resulted in a 50% reduction in shootings, but a doubling of hits on perpetrators. In other words, software training helps police officers make better judgments as to when lethal force is needed, and then apply it more effectively.

Reflections on Being a Warrior

- The true goal we seek is far above and beyond the ugly field of battle. When we resort to force, as now we must, we are determined that this force shall be directed toward ultimate good as well as against immediate evil. We Americans are not destroyers—we are builders. (President Franklin D. Roosevelt, December 9, 1941, Fireside Chat)

- Those who don't approach war with determination are those who are more likely to be debilitated by it. (Lt. Col. Dave Grossman)

- I asked a World War II veteran why he fought. He said, "I was 18 years old. I knew the difference between right and wrong. I didn't want to live in a world where wrong prevailed...so I fought." (Steven E. Ambrose, Ph.D., remarks at the dedication of the National D-Day Museum, June 6, 2000)

- The only thing necessary for the triumph of evil is for good men to do nothing. (Edmund Burke (1729-1797), British statesman and philosopher)

- Except for ending slavery, genocide, Fascism, Nazism, and Communism, war has never solved anything. (Anonymous)
- If there must be trouble, let it be in my day, that my child may have peace. (Thomas Paine (1737-1809))
- If you must kill, do so out of a sense of duty and justice, never with hatred. Hatred carries a heavy price. (Anonymous)

On Being Wounded

Grossman explains that warriors can be trained to keep going without panicking, despite being wounded. For example:
- Police officer Jennifer Folfer took seven bullets but kept firing, killing two perpetrators. She said that her training with plastic bullets taught her to keep firing and survive. Often real life situations are less stressful than rigorous training.
- LAPD officer Stacy Lim encountered carjackers as she came home one night. After being shot in the heart, she drew her gun and fired. Remaining conscious, she stumbled into her apartment, where her roommate called 911. Six months later, she was back on the job.
- After being shot in the eye, another police officer put eight bullets into the perpetrator. When asked by investigators why he used so many bullets, he replied, "That's all I had."

Grossman gives the following guidelines for surviving gunshot wounds:
1. *Take cover.* Get out of the line of fire, and shoot back. Mentally rehearse shooting back after being wounded.
2. *Don't panic.* Knowing you are alive after being wounded is a good sign. It means you can still think and function. Think of the reasons why you want to survive. You stay calm and focused because you are trained to do so.
3. *Tap adrenaline.* One cop who'd shot a perpetrator five times before he stopped advancing reasoned that he could still carry on despite being wounded. Tissue wounds might not hurt. Bones that are hit hurt, but the wounds are not life threatening. Forty percent of one's blood can be lost without losing consciousness. Expect that your heart will race, your mouth will be dry, and your palms will be sweaty after being wounded. Yet you carry on.
4. *Resolve that you will live.* Determination gets resilient copers through crises. Resolve that no one will take your life without a fight. You will probably live if you are stable enough to be transported.
5. *Afterwards, expect stress symptoms.* It is normal to experience anxiety, nightmares, and flashbacks. Remember the skills you've learned to reduce stress, such as calm breathing, thought field therapy, eye movements, and writing in your journal. If you feel guilt for surviving when your buddies didn't, remember that warriors die in war—it is the price warriors sometimes pay. Your buddies would want you to carry on and live a good life. The enemy wins if survival guilt takes out another honorable warrior.

War Zone Integrity

Abuse no one and nothing, for abuse turns the wise ones to fools and robs the spirit of its vision.
Tecumseh, Shawnee Warrior

No man, deep down in the privacy of his own heart, has any considerable respect for himself.

Mark Twain

Committing and witnessing atrocities has been found to predict PTSD, suicide, and guilt in combat vets upon returning home.[10] Atrocities—cruel, brutal, or evil behaviors—include:

- Unlawful violence: killing, torturing, or humiliating civilians or enemy combatants who have surrendered or been captured.
- Stealing from civilians or the enemy.
- Rape, which cheapens the perpetrator's sexuality and makes it more difficult to experience wholesome intimacy.[11] Rape also typically traumatizes the victim for decades (PTSD, sexual disgust, fear of intimacy, and a range of physical symptoms including pelvic pain, gastro-intestinal disorders, and headaches are common).

Atrocities, whether committed by Nazis or prison guards at Abu Ghraib, embolden the enemy. In addition, they haunt and corrupt the spirit of the perpetrator. Moral wounds are typically accompanied by shame, self-loathing, and loss of inner peace. Some returning vets incite brawls, demanding from others the respect they don't feel for themselves. Or they engage in a "frenzied search for calm" through work, sex, or drugs (Shay, 2002, p.39). Numbness might alternate with anger, depression, and anxiety. Conversely, right actions strengthen one spiritually, resulting in self-respect, spiritual wholeness, and confidence.

Paths to Inner Peace and Self-respect

The wise warrior will think through the moral aspects of the war zone in advance in order to prevent long-term scarring of the soul. Remember the two pathways to inner peace and self-respect:

1. *Decide in advance to live morally—then do so.* Determine what you will and won't do. Previously developed codes might aid this process. For example, in their creed, Navy SEALs pledge to "Serve with honor on the battlefield... Uncompromising integrity is my standard. My character and honor are steadfast. My word is my bond...The execution of my duties will be...guided by the very principles that I serve to defend." Let your actions be guided by justice and duty, never hatred or vengeance. This will minimize regrets. Beware of gradual entrapment, or seduction by degrees, regarding your conduct. For example, the seemingly harmless belittling of the enemy might eventually lead to treating them inhumanely. Respect the enemy's humanity and intelligence, if not his cause.

> ## The Warrior's Code of Honor
>
> - I will always act in ways that bring honor to me, my comrades, and my cause.
> - I will use lethal force when duty requires without hesitation—and only when duty requires.
> - As much as humanly possible, I will show concern for innocent human life and the welfare of enemy combatants who are no longer a threat.
> - I will speak the truth, knowing that lies in battle cost lives.
> - I will distinguish between right and wrong, choosing the harder good over the easier wrong.
> - I will be motivated by loyalty to my comrades, duty, and the justice of my cause, and not revenge.

2. *When you err, have a system in place for righting wrongs.* Humans will always be imperfect, and will always make mistakes. The *U.S. Army Combat Stress Control Handbook* (Department of the Army, 2003) states that misconduct stress behaviors can be committed by good, even heroic, soldiers under extreme combat stress. Try to live beyond reproach. If you slip, remember that no one is beyond redemption. Most world religions have a method for making peace with wrong actions: Admit the wrong, make amends when possible, acknowledge mitigating circumstances, reconcile with Deity (e.g., allowing God to take away the burden), resolve not to repeat the misconduct, and forgive self for being imperfect (releasing the desire to punish yourself and be burdened by regrets).

Reflections on War Zone Integrity

- Great individuals make great teammates. (John Wooden)
- Every atrocity strengthens the enemy and potentially disables the service member who commits it. (Jonathan Shay)
- Do the right thing when you are out there. (Vietnam vet struggling with PTSD, imploring his buddies)
- The steady trigger finger kills a lot more enemy than the one that trembles with hatred. (Lt. Col. Dave Grossman)
- A peace above all earthly dignities, a still and quiet conscience. (Shakespeare)
- What stronger breastplate than a heart untainted! (Shakespeare)
- A person of good character feels moral pain after doing something that caused another person suffering...even if entirely accidental or unavoidable. (Jonathan Shay)
- Somewhere, at this very moment, there is a Soldier in training...who is preparing for war and expects a leader of character... The American Army is a force for good—each of you will be a force for good. (Lt. Gen. William B. Caldwell, IV)
- We should neglect no honorable means of dividing and weakening our enemies. (Robert E. Lee)
- No one has the right to do wrong, not even if wrong has been done to them. (Viktor Frankl)

The following essay, based on the writings of Dr. Edward Tick,[12] captures many of the themes and challenges of trying to be an honorable warrior. Please read it, and then complete the activity at the end.

On Being an Honorable Warrior

Dr. Edward Tick is a psychotherapist who has treated many war veterans. In his book *War and the Soul: Healing Our Nation's Veterans from Post-Traumatic Stress Disorder* Dr. Tick asserts that PTSD is best understood as an identity disorder and soul wound—with moral pain being a root cause of PTSD.

The soul (*psyche* in ancient Greek) is deeper than the intellect. The soul reasons and rises above instincts. It yearns and searches for meaning, ethics, beauty, love, harmony, and order. The soul dreams; it chooses between good and evil. War, however, can trigger uncivilized aspects of our nature—unkind and brutal instincts which may as yet be unrestrained. It can shatter our sense of goodness and innocence, and leave one feeling like someone different, separated from the soul.

Universal Warrior Themes

In nearly every generation and culture there are recurring themes centered around war, warriors, and conflict—and their potential for good and bad. For example, the Greek pantheon had two war gods: Athena used war rationally and reluctantly in order to protect civilization, resulting in spiritual triumph. She did not delight in war's horrors. Ares, on the other hand, the god of slaughter, was bloodthirsty, undignified, and unrestrained.

Saint Augustine reasoned that war should only be used for good intentions, "securing peace, punishing evil-doers, and uplifting the good" and never motivated by "the passion for inflicting harm, the cruel thirst for vengeance, an unpacific and relentless spirit,...or the lust of power."

The Ideal Warrior

Most cultures depict honorable warriors as being on a spiritual journey, embodying the finest virtues of humankind, despite war's violence. Honorable warriors are servants of civilization, defending and protecting causes they consider dearer than self or personal gain.

Preparing for war is a rite of passage that can, as William James wrote, propel one constructively into adulthood by building toughness, maturity, discipline, tolerance for discomfort, and higher functioning. Among Native Americans, capable warriors earned respect and recognition, while those who didn't pass the test honorably felt alienated and unproven as men.

Having faced death, honorable warriors understand how fragile life and happiness are, and thus strive to preserve peace. They will try to avoid conflict unless their homeland and cherished values can be protected in no other way. They will not profane life or dishonor the dead, but will treat others with dignity and respect.

Honorable warriors direct their abilities actively, persistently, and bravely, with mind and body in harmony. They rise above the warrior's shadow traits—avoiding malice, cruelty, impulsivity, emotional unsteadiness, rage, and sadism, which can be unleashed in war. Thus, they do not kill with hatred or vengeance, but only as duty requires. Dr. Tick notes that the North Vietnamese veterans have much lower rates of PTSD than American soldiers suffered. Significantly, Ho Chi Minh told his people not to hate or blame American soldiers, but to only consider them as victims of their leaders' decisions.[13]

War Wounds and the Warrior's Soul

In order to go to battle with the whole heart, the warrior must believe the threat to be a real threat to his homeland, loved ones, and/or most-cherished values—one that can only be resolved through armed conflict. False pretenses lead to moral wounding.

However, even in a war considered just, the warrior's soul can still be damaged. "No man in battle is really sane," said William Manchester, a WWII Marine vet in the Pacific. War requires one to be violent, perhaps to kill another person who in another time or place could have become a friend. Veterans commonly ask, "Am I good or bad? Did I murder? Will God forgive me?"

Even in wars whose cause is considered suspect, warriors might feel respect for enemy soldiers slain in a fair fight and experience no guilt. However, random killing of innocent civilians or the committing of atrocities (e.g., torturing prisoners of war, raping, stealing, or destroying property) leads to regrets and deeper, lingering moral pain.

Also, witnessing the carnage of war can cause one to become numb or indifferent to the suffering of others, which is contrary to the ideals of the honorable warrior.

Rejecting the Warrior Identity

The reality of war's horrors can lead warriors to deny, disown, shun, or squash their warrior identity. The warrior might feel different since returning from the war, or separate from his or her soul. The soul might feel diminished, shattered, lifeless or wounded. But rejecting this part of the soul also disconnects us from the power for good of the warrior's soul.

Reclaiming the Honorable Warrior

Veterans are not necessarily warriors just because they have been to war. To become an honorable warrior, one learns to bring forward war skills into present life in a mature way.

In peacetime, the honorable warrior uses acquired wisdom and vision to build and protect life, rather than to destroy it—dissuading people from the use of violence, unless it is absolutely necessary. Honorable warriors fearlessly keep sanity and kindness alive in their homeland.

As they did before the war, they stand for life, justice, and beauty. They cultivate character, kindness, compassion, honesty, decency, cooperation, and sensitivity to the suffering of individuals.

They accept and affirm conflict and war's hardships. Their souls become big enough and loving enough to contain these.

On the battlefield, they show restraint and resist dehumanization. That is, they do not mix the violence of war with hatred, cruelty, and impulsivity. They treat prisoners and the wounded humanely. After the war, they hold no grudges, but are forgiving so that they can live in the present. In contrast, dishonorable warriors are insecure, still trying to prove themselves. They remain hardened to the suffering of others and thus prone to cruelty. They are unable to control their aggression, and are hostile and impatient with imperfect or weak people.

After war, honorable warriors apply their skills in the service of humanity, perhaps becoming police, firefighters, or politicians. They see themselves as belonging to the human race, and not a tribe. Thus, they might return to war-torn countries to rebuild schools or hospitals, or to provide medical supplies or assistance. They view former enemies as brothers and sisters who now share a common experience.

The mature warrior distinguishes murder (which is unauthorized, vengeful, hateful, or malicious homicide) from killing in battle. For example, in the Judeo-Christian tradition, waging war for power or personal gain is considered wrong, but fighting to preserve the survival of loved ones is not.

Conclusion

Moral wounds can worsen the wounds of PTSD and keep them festering. From the standpoint of prevention, therefore, it is wise for each potential combatant to:

- Be clear on why you are fighting and reconcile to the necessity of the conflict and violence.
- Determine in advance to only do what you consider to be good behavior, and to refrain from doing bad in order to minimize regrets that can plague your conscience.
- After the war, use your warrior skills for the betterment of humankind.

ACTIVITY

As you consider the virtues of the honorable warrior as described above, please list five behaviors you will do during war/combat, and five behaviors you will not do. Then list five ways that you will use your warrior skills and wisdom in the service of humanity after returning from war.

Chapter 32

Preparing for Post-Crisis Stress Symptoms

Most people facing crises remain remarkably resilient most of the time. Be realistically confident in your coping ability. Expect to cope well with stress. However, no one, not even the most resilient or highly trained individual, is invincible. Anyone's resilience can be worn down by sufficient exposure to traumatic events—such as combat, death, wounding, and witnessing intense human suffering—or even by stress overload or accumulation of lesser stressors. For example, repeated deployments put our military service members at greater risk for combat-operational stress reactions and injuries, while the relentless nature of police work can at times stretch officers to the breaking point.

Hopefully, the growing number of resilience skills you've been practicing will keep your breaking point well above the fray. Remember, however, that stress symptoms are normal as the body gears up for difficult challenges. Pay attention to stress symptoms, calmly and without judgment. When they become excessive, view them as a warning sign. Just as resilient warriors are well prepared with a tactical plan, so are resilient individuals prepared with an action plan for possible post-crisis stress symptoms. These symptoms include:

- Feelings of sadness, anger, guilt, pressure, anxiety, or being out of control
- Cynicism or distrust
- Sleep problems
- Difficulty concentrating or remembering
- Exhaustion
- Arousal (e.g., racing or pounding heart, rapid pulse, elevated blood pressure)
- Breathing difficulties
- Headaches or bodily pain (often accompanied by chronic muscle tension)
- Overuse of drugs and alcohol
- Agitation, inability to relax
- Troubling dreams
- Diarrhea, constipation, nausea, or indigestion
- Loss of confidence or self-esteem
- Relationship problems[1]
- More serious stress symptoms, such as dissociation and PTSD

It is natural to assume that you are strong, that it's the other guy who will get wounded physically or psychologically. This assumption might keep you functioning on your job in the short run. Eventually, however, stress symptoms can accumulate—degrading your ability to perform and enjoy life, and making recovery harder. Eventually, overconfidence and the myth of invincibility are shattered, which can leave us feeling stunned, dazed, and stuck. Denial leaves us unprepared for coping with, and recovering from, these symptoms.

Part of resilience is knowing that you can recover if and when post-crisis symptoms arise. If you are well prepared, you will anticipate such symptoms and have an action plan for restoring balance. Remember that stress symptoms are normal. These symptoms are not a sign of personal weakness. They simply signal the need to take care of yourself: to take time to recover, replenish your emotional reserves, and build (or rebuild) coping skills. Take that time. Don't compare yourself to others who may appear to be coping better.

Concern vs. Worry

Yale psychologist Irving Janis (1977) conducted intriguing research in the 1950s relating fear in patients who were anticipating surgery to their post-surgery recovery. Janis found that patients could be divided into three types. The first type, the "under-worriers," were like John Wayne, thinking, "Surgery is no big deal; I'll recover easily and quickly." This group asked no questions and didn't think much about the surgery or recovery. The second group, the "over-worriers," avoided in a different way. Patients in this group mentally obsessed about the surgery, asking constant questions, refusing to be distracted from thinking about it, and trying to avoid the surgery. In intellectually worrying, they didn't face their fears nor plan for post-surgery discomfort. The third group, whom I call the "concerned group," realistically anticipated the surgery, asking sufficient questions, mentally rehearsing a plan (e.g., "If or when pain is intense, I'll roll over and take deep breaths or pain medication"). Then they could be distracted. As you might expect, it was this last group that fared best in terms of post-surgery recovery. This group needed the least pain medication, recovered the fastest, and showed the least anger compared to the other two groups—who fared equally worse. The moral of this study is that people can usually best prepare for distress by realistically expecting it, mentally rehearsing their coping plan with realistic optimism (not worry), seeking helpful information, and then allowing their attention to shift to other things. This is a very useful model to add to our resilience repertoire.

The reality, however, is that many high-risk groups are taught to ignore their feelings on the job in order to function. To a degree this makes sense. The problem, however, occurs after the crisis is over and they still don't deal with their feelings, as though doing so were a sign of weakness. It is as though they try to stuff their feelings in an imaginary sack, hoping they'll go away, and try to quickly "get back to normal." Perhaps they try to drown the pain with alcohol, drugs, or various risky behaviors. Perhaps they numb their feelings and become uncommunicative and aloof. Unfortunately, buried feelings don't go away, but cry out for attention. If they don't get it, they will likely show up as psychological and physical distress symptoms. Eventually, the person is likely to snap. The idea is to go toward the distressing emotions, not away from them, just as elite special operations forces go toward the physical battle.

The Reality of Trauma

Trauma is a double-edged sword. On the positive side, those who survive trauma (such as combat or prison camps) often report greater happiness, sense of purpose, and appreciation of life than those who have not. They frequently say that they were strengthened by their struggles, learning to control their fear, gain confidence ("If I survived this, I can survive anything"), stand up to wrongdoers, discover strengths and abilities they weren't aware of, be loyal to comrades and a just cause, and increase hope and spiritual faith. These strengths are often parlayed into satisfying career accomplishments. The more severe the challenge, the greater are the potential benefits, provided one is not completely overwhelmed by the traumatic event.

On the other hand, a significant percentage of trauma survivors also experience multiple negative results, sometimes co-existing with the positive results. The possible negative consequences of trauma exposure include: unhappiness, intimacy troubles (e.g., divorce and impotence), mental and physical symptoms, spiritual numbness, loss of faith, and loss of confidence (e.g., feeling shame for being helpless or unable to control symptoms).

The resilient individual is realistically optimistic about the gains resulting from facing trauma, while being realistically prepared for the negative consequences. Some people seem less vulnerable to stress than others by virtue of genes, life experience, and training. However, we can all move up the resilience staircase from whatever step on which we presently stand. A crisis is not an endpoint, but a turning point, an opportunity to acquire new skills. Stress symptoms signal the need to restore balance so that the learning can continue. It is wise to pay attention to these symptoms.

How to Prepare for Post-Crisis Symptoms

The formula is to anticipate symptoms, recognize them, and be prepared for them. Symptoms can be managed *before* the crisis (through prevention and training programs), *during* the crisis (through coping skills), and *after* the crisis (through coping skills and treatment) according to the following principles:

- *Anticipate symptoms.* Cohen and colleagues (1987) have described the four phases of disaster response. A disaster is a catastrophe, man-made or natural, that jeopardizes the health, safety, and/or functioning of many people, and includes terrorism, earthquakes, tornados, and flooding. These phases are viewed as normal, and have much in common with responses to other crises. It is helpful to know what to expect, and to realize that it is best if one has time to recover before another stressor hits.[2] In phase 1, survivors experience strong initial emotions, such as fear, disbelief, confusion, and numbness. During this phase, people tend to cooperate, and heroic deeds are not uncommon. In phase 2, lasting from a week to several months, denial alternates with intrusive symptoms. Anger, irritability, apathy, and social withdrawal are common, as are increased visits to doctors for physical complaints. In phase 3, lasting up to a year, resentment is felt when expectations of aid and restoration are disappointed. The sense of community weakens as individuals refocus their energies on personal concerns. Phase 4, reconstruction, may last for years as people gradually rebuild their lives. Recovery occurs through reappraisal, finding meaning, accepting the "new normal," and developing a new self-concept. The point is that recovery is not always instantaneous, and that it is often mixed with distressing symptoms.
- *Know what kind of traumatic events are worst.* These are more likely to result in stress symptoms, and include (Ursano, Fullerton, & Norwood, 1995):
  - The threat of death or injury
  - Physical injury to self
  - Exposure to grotesque scenes (such as carnage or mutilated bodies)

- Intentional injury/harm to people, such as 9/11 or the Oklahoma City bombing
- Causing death or severe harm to another (this includes accidents, atrocities, and authorized killing)
- The sudden, violent loss of a loved one—including friends, family, and especially children
- Witnessing or learning of violence to a loved one
- Disaster that disrupts the community, the source of support
  Note: Any kind of abuse, especially sexual abuse (including rape and even the threat of sexual abuse), at any time in one's life is a risk factor for serious stress symptoms if it is not resolved.
- *Know who comprises high-risk groups for disaster.* These include (Ursano, Fullerton, & Norwood, 1995):
  - All emergency service workers, including rescue workers
  - Heroes (who may not be afforded, or expected to need, the time to grieve or take care of themselves)
  - Those who are injured
  - Children (who may become quiet, agitated, or sad; exposure to dead bodies often triggers an aversion to meat)
  - Adults who lose children
- *Recognize PTSD-like reactions.* These are understandable following exposure to a traumatic event. A partial list of these symptoms include:
  - Troubled sleep, nightmares. Recall that Marcus Luttrell (2007, p.4) awakened nightly, hearing his friend scream, "Help me Marcus. Please help me."
  - Feeling like the soul is irrevocably shattered, broken, or trampled (Note that this is a feeling, not a fact.)
  - Trouble concentrating
  - Forgetting aspects of the trauma, or general forgetting
  - Haunting, intrusive memories—thoughts, images, emotions and/or sensations; flashbacks
  - Attempting to avoid remembering because remembering is so stressful (e.g., trying not to think about, talk about, or look at anything that reminds you of the trauma; avoiding people that make you remember or feel)
  - Hypervigilance (being constantly on guard, not feeling safe, anticipating a catastrophe when one is unlikely)
  - Angry outbursts, irritability
  - Feeling different or estranged from "normal" people (e.g., "Nobody understands me.")
  - Easily startled, unable to relax, wound up
  - Shaking
  - Withdrawn, disinterested in your usual pastimes
  - Emotionally numb, flat affect, no feelings, dead inside, difficult to love or feel happy
  - Feeling that you won't have a normal future (e.g., career, family, or long life)
  - Fear, anxiety

- Chronic guilt, shame
- Depression
- Lowered self-esteem, feeling like a different person
- Cynical, pessimistic, generally distrustful of others
- Questioning the meaning of life or cherished values; loss of spiritual faith
- Excessive fatigue
- Increased use of alcohol and/or other drugs
- Troubled relationships
- Hurting self or loved ones
- Dissociation (see below)
  Note: Notice medical symptoms that can signal the presence of emotional stress or PTSD, such as pain (headaches, backaches, pain around an injured or abused area), gastrointestinal disturbances, skin problems, eating disorders, obesity, high cholesterol, hypertension, allergies, and fainting.

What to Do About Post-Crisis Stress Symptoms

Fortunately, you have many resources to help reduce the symptoms of excessive stress.

1. *Remember to use your basic countermeasures.* Especially during times of excessive distress, remember to get sufficient sleep, exercise, and nutrition, and to keep your life in balance. Remember also the strategies for managing distress: calm breathing, progressive muscle relaxation, meditation, heart coherence, thought field therapy, eye movements, defusing, and dream management. Ease emotional pain by writing in your journal, using a daily thought record, or talking things over with a supportive person. Challenge the common myths: "No one could understand what I've been through" or "I can't talk to anyone—especially my family." Another person doesn't have to share your exact experience to be empathic and supportive. Avoid avoidance—escaping your pain through drugs or alcohol, withdrawing, or addictions (e.g., excessive work, gambling, shopping, or risky behaviors). Turning to these, while understandable, does nothing to change the memories of the crisis. Instead turn toward the pain. Accept it mindfully and process it by, say, journaling or getting treatment from a mental health professional. Take time off to recharge your emotional batteries.
2. *Learn to distinguish guilt from shame.* Guilt is feeling bad about a specific behavior—either acting wrongly or failing to act rightly. Shame is feeling bad as a person, worthless to the core. Guilt is healthy insofar as it motivates constructive change. Then it is best released. Shame is not healthy. Crisis survivors might feel guilty for:
   - Feeling glad that they survived; relieved that it was someone else who didn't
   - Feeling undeserving to live (e.g., "Why did Joe die when he was such a better person?")
   - Performing below their training level (due to fatigue, uncertainty, confusion, fear, and so forth)
   - Falsely believing they can prevent all injury or loss of life in a crisis
   - Being unable to control their symptoms

For one's emotional survival, shame must be replaced by guilt, and guilt must be realistic. The best response to guilt is compassion, forgiveness, and determination to live well. Veterans Administration counselor Raymond Scurfield, Ph.D., (1994) explained that veterans often carry unrealistic guilt. He cites an example of a Vietnam war veteran, tired and resting from unloading supplies, who said nothing as he watched a killing unfold. A silhouetted enemy sniper—whom he assumed was an American—approached an American sentry and shot him. The veteran assigned nearly 100% of the blame for the sentry's death to himself. Through skillful questioning, Scurfield helped the vet to see that the sentry, the sentry's buddy, the skilled sniper, the sentry's leaders, the politicians who placed the sentry in the field with insufficient support, and others shared responsibility for the death. The veteran could then deal with the realistically lowered percentage of the blame. What can you do with the realistic guilt that remains? You can confront and process it with compassion and forgiveness. For example, veterans counselor Ed Tick, Ph.D., brings guilt-laden soldiers back to Vietnam. There, former enemies welcome their comrades in battle, who share a common history, with forgiveness and kindness. War wounds and war stories are shared and respected. Former enemies part as newfound friends. Some soldiers return to former war-zones and build hospitals and schools, replacing old symbols of destruction with new symbols of healing and building. Religious rites might be accessed for penance. Survivors might realize how truly difficult it is to make cool decisions under conditions of uncertainty, fear, fatigue, and pressure. We can forgive ourselves, accepting that humans are fallible, but never worthless or incapable of growth. We can start anew and go on, knowing that our fallen comrades would want this for us.

3. *Anticipate relationship challenges.* Those who develop PTSD following a crisis are more likely to experience marital and parenting problems and divorce. It might be more difficult to trust and be intimate. If you have PTSD symptoms, consult a skilled mental health professional for evaluation and treatment. Expect to need extra practice and help with couples and family skills. As the SEALs expect to be always learning, it is wise to always be improving social skills—finding needed help when necessary. Stay away from drugs, which greatly increase the likelihood of violence.

Preparing for Dissociation

PTSD is strongly predicted by:

1. *Peri-traumatic dissociation.* This is dissociation that occurs during or immediately after the traumatic event. It is a common reaction to severe stress. For example, fifty percent of police officers in deadly force encounters dissociate (Artwohl & Christensen, 1997), while 96% of Army soldiers in military survival training report peri-traumatic dissociation symptoms (Morgan et al., 2001).

2. *Avoidance of emotions and thoughts related to the trauma.*

Dissociation and avoidance tend to co-occur. In dissociation we tend to mentally flee what we tell ourselves is unbearable. As we mentally drift away from the stressful reality, we don't function as well in the present because we are no longer fully present.[3]

310

Future symptoms also tend to persist, or even increase, unless the traumatic memory material is processed and settled.

Making Sense of Dissociation

Dissociation is a rather complex term with many meanings. Let's try to make sense of this term, since a clear understanding of dissociation explains and normalizes many PTSD symptoms. A simplified picture, Figure 32.1, explains how associated and dissociated memories are stored in the brain. To the right of the walled-off traumatic memory material are normal, *associated* memories. These memories are stored in an organized, chronological order, much like files in a filing cabinet. We can pull up a memory and put it away, more or less at will and with appropriate emotions. Lessons from one memory connect to other memories. Thus, one with generally positive memories of adults from childhood might view the world as generally safe. Across all memories is the sense that you are the same person. Your awareness can be directed so that you can be fully focused and present in any given moment.

Figure 32.1
AWARENESS AND MEMORY (Reprinted from Schiraldi (2009))

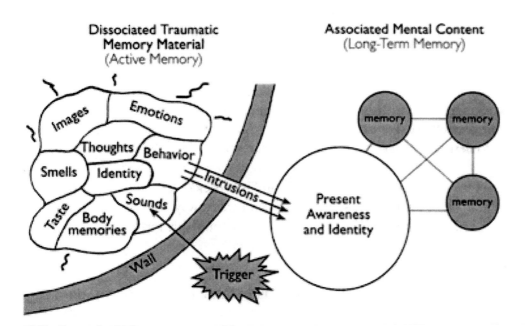

A traumatic memory, however, is stored quite differently. First, the walled off memory is stored in the forefront of awareness, easily triggered by a reminder of the trauma. It is not securely filed in long-term memory. Thus, a veteran driving down a highway starts to feel that he is back in Iraq, vulnerable to an improvised explosive device. Like a leaky dam, the wall allows memories to intrude into awareness unbidden, often against one's will. The dissociated memory material is highly emotional and relatively non-verbal.

While normal memories are rather logically processed before they are stored in memory, traumatic memories are stored before they are completely processed. Thus, they are highly emotionally charged and accompanied by unchallenged or unspoken distortions. So the veteran driving down the highway after coming home thinks, "I'm not safe," because the thoughts locked in the dissociated memory don't connect to the thoughts in associated memories, which might say, "I'm generally safe."

Not only is the traumatic memory dissociated from helpful associated memories, but the different aspects of the traumatic memory are dissociated from each other. Thus, a trigger might not bring the entire memory into awareness, but only certain aspects. For example, a veteran might smell food at a barbeque that reminds her of Iraq. She might unaccountably feel intense sadness and nausea, but not associate these reactions to coming upon children who died in a bombing in a marketplace.

In response to dissociated memories, trauma survivors might mentally drift away to avoid the painful intrusive memories (much like the cop whose awareness seems to float above the dead body), or become completely pulled into the memory (such as one who relives a flashback). In either case, survivors are not able to fully focus on the world around them.

A final aspect of dissociation is that the trauma survivor often feels like two different people (e.g., "The person I was before the trauma and the person I am now").

Why are traumatic memories stored as they are? The likely mechanism is that the hippocampus is impaired by the strong emotions and chemical changes in the brain due to overwhelming traumatic events. The hippocampus would normally help the brain to make sense of a memory and store it with appropriate emotion in a logical, integrated way. Instead, the amygdala becomes overactive as the hippocampus becomes under-active, resulting in the dissociated memory material.

Since dissociation can degrade performance, prevention and treatment of dissociation are of paramount important. The goal of treatment is to fully process the dissociated memory material—integrating the memory fragments, neutralizing the strong emotions and distortions, and then storing the memory alongside the other memories in long-term storage. Now the traumatic memory is experienced as just one memory on file, and not the one memory that constantly dominates awareness. Because this can be a challenging process, treatment is best provided by a trauma specialist skilled in treating dissociation.

Recognizing Dissociation

The common signs of dissociation are:
- Depersonalization—mentally leaving the body and looking down on self or another victim to avoid suffering (e.g., "I was on the ceiling watching myself be raped.")
- Spacing out or drifting away (missing a conversation, being unresponsive to others, losing track of what's happening, withdrawing, falling asleep)
- Derealization—"I'm not here"; "It feels as though I'm in a dream"; foggy feeling; distorted sights/sounds; things move in slow or fast motion; feeling out of touch with surroundings; familiar places seem strange; not recognizing yourself in the mirror
- Flashbacks (suddenly and vividly experiencing the traumatic memory, or parts of the memory, as if it were recurring in the present)
- Numbness to pain or feelings

- Body becomes still or stiff
- Twitching, grimacing
- Attempts to self-soothe and stay grounded—rocking, jiggling leg, stroking chair
- Eyes stare downward or blankly (1000-yard stare), dart anxiously, or blink/flutter rapidly
- Disorientation
- Feeling split, like a different person since the trauma
- Sudden strong, unexplainable emotions or physical sensations
- Intrusive memories—especially when trying to relax or sleep, when stressed, or when drinking or using drugs
- Forgetting all or parts of the trauma, or portions of your life
- Experiencing different personality states (or alter egos, one or more of which may be attempting to contain distressing trauma material)[4]

Strategies to Manage Dissociation

Dissociation is more likely to occur when the crisis is experienced with extremely intense emotions (such as fear, anger, guilt, shame, or intense grief), distortions, and unresolved traumatic memories from earlier life experience. As a general principle, we aim to view painful circumstances as calmly as possible—neither fleeing, fighting, nor otherwise resisting the emotions, and thus giving the memories undue emotional charge. The general goals are:
- Treat unresolved traumatic memory material (those with dissociative symptoms before a crisis are more likely to dissociate during or after the crisis)
- Prevent dissociation from occurring
- Should dissociation occur, accept it calmly until it passes

The following specific steps are useful:
1. *Treat unresolved past trauma.* Remember that those who enter crisis situations with unresolved trauma are more likely to develop PTSD and dissociate.
2. *Desensitize the nervous system.* PTSD is characterized by a dysregulation of the autonomic nervous system. Many of the strategies we've already discussed reduce sympathetic nervous system arousal, including exercise, yoga, calm breathing (hyperventilation can induce dissociation), meditation, heart coherence, and cognitive restructuring.
3. *Optimize brain health.* All the steps that improve memory and cognitive processing theoretically reduce vulnerability to dissociation: exercise, diet (remember especially to increase intake of omega-3s, fruits, and vegetables, and to reduce saturated fats and sugar), adequate sleep (REM sleep helps to process traumatic memories; animals deprived of REM show dissociative symptoms), avoid harmful medications and drugs (including smoking, stimulants, and heavy or binge drinking), and regulate blood pressure.
4. *Manage panic.* The progression that often occurs following exposure to traumatic events such as rape, terrorism, or injury is:

OVERWHELMING FEAR → PANIC ATTACK (extreme emotional and physical arousal)[5] **→ DISSOCIATION → PTSD**

This progression is interrupted by applying skills to deal with panic that might occur. Calm panic as follows:

- Pre-plan and practice inoculation statements for *before* the crisis (e.g., "This could be rough, but I'll focus on my job."), *during* the crisis (e.g., "Fear is normal. Relax, take deep breaths and focus on what I need to do."), and *after* the crisis (e.g., "All in all, I did pretty well."; "It's OK to feel distressed; I'll mindfully walk it off or sit with the emotions").
- Calm your body. Relax your muscles and use calm breathing. Adapt a special approach to panic: Rather than tensing, which worsens panic, say, "Hello, fear." Bend with the panic attack like a reed blowing in the wind until the panic attack runs its course (usually within ten minutes). Focus on the job at hand and staying alive and functional. Calmly flow with, rather than trying to escape, the fear. In other words, let the fear in, if it comes, with a warm, accepting heart. Avoid smoking, which greatly increases the risk of panic attack.
- Should dissociation occur, say in the form of depersonalization or derealization, accept that without judging or fighting it.
  - Think, "Dissociation is just the mind trying to protect me from pain. Thanks. Nevertheless, I'll bring awareness back to the task at hand."[6]
  - Ground yourself. You can ground in your body by mindfully noticing clenched muscles and reminding yourself that this is normal. Relax with low and slow breathing. Rub something tangible (such as fabric, your elbow, a tool, or weapon), wiggle your toes, or press your feet down—movement helps to expend stress. Also try mindfully walking off adrenaline or doing progressive muscle relaxation. You can also ground yourself in your surroundings. To prevent your mind from drifting away, describe five objects that you see around you in detail. Then describe five sounds you hear. Then physically handle five objects and describe what you feel.
  - Talk to your buddies. Putting words to the experience helps to integrate traumatic memories.
  - If additional help is needed, try eye movements or thought field therapy.
5. *After the critical incident is over, allow time to decompress and calm down if possible to restore psychological order.* If traumatic memories intrude or you experience other symptoms of dissociation, ground yourself (Baranowsky, Gentry, & Schultz, 2005):
- *In symbols of the present.* These remind you that the crisis is passed. Look at recent photographs, birthday cards, newspapers, or your driver's license.
- *Verbally.* Tell yourself:
  - "This is a memory from the past talking—old stuff. It will pass."
  - "My feelings are understandable. They come and go."
  - "I'm safe now."
  - "That was then. This is now. Today is_____. The time is _____."

314

- "I'm here now."
- "This is the same me—before, during, and after the trauma."

- *In your posture.* Notice when you dissociate that you slouch, your face shifts, and you feel emotions such as fear, sadness, anger, and vulnerability. Exaggerate that posture, facial expression, and emotions. Now stand with a strong, confident posture and facial expression. Alternate back and forth between the negative and confident stances. Notice that you are in control.

You can also journal the facts and feelings to defuse and integrate the traumatic memories. Some find that debriefing (discussing the various aspects of the crisis in a peer group setting) helps reduce the impairment resulting from peri-traumatic dissociation.[7]

In *Waking the Tiger*, Peter Levine, Ph.D., (1997) suggests emotional first aid following a crisis. Animals in the predator's jaw will freeze (or dissociate), as though dead. Should the predator drop its prey and go away, the animal will kick, twitch, and shake to restore equilibrium—and then run to safety. In a similar way, allow yourself to shake and tremble after the crisis. This is the body's way to release stress and counter the freeze state of unspeakable terror. One or two days after the crisis, try recounting the trauma. Ground in your body if the emotions become too intense. Allow yourself to tremble and shake, as this is normal. Try to complete and discharge the movement that was frozen during the trauma. Perhaps you see yourself moving differently and performing better. Thus, if you froze before an oncoming car struck yours, this time allow yourself to turn the steering wheel to the right. If you froze while being raped, this time forcefully push the perpetrator away, perhaps with the aid of a strong resource person. If you froze in an uncertain lethal force encounter, this time see yourself squeezing the trigger as you were trained to do.

Know Thyself Activity

Make a list of the post-crisis stress symptoms you have encountered or would likely encounter. List the actions you will take to manage those symptoms.

Chapter 33

Early Treatment

I'm a better general because I got some help.
General Carter Ham

Following crises, a substantial minority of high-risk groups experience mental disorders serious enough to require professional help. For example, in recent wars, ten to twenty percent of combat veterans have experienced PTSD. This is undoubtedly an underestimate, and PTSD symptoms typically increase in the year after combat veterans return home. When we add other serious stress-related psychological problems, such as depression, anxiety, substance use disorders, anger, sleep disturbance, and relationship problems, this percentage of veterans who could benefit from professional treatment greatly increases.

Resilient individuals are masters at rebounding from stress. They are also wise enough to: (1) know that no one is immune to PTSD and other stress-related mental disorders; and (2) know when they need help to rebound. There is indeed "a time to kill, and a time to heal" (Eccl 3:3). Rather than worrying about *appearing* strong, they are concerned with *healing* (becoming whole again), so that they can be the best possible resource to themselves, their friends, and their families. Resilient people actively seek needed help, rather than passively waiting and hoping that time will heal emotional wounds.

Why Is Early Treatment Important?

PTSD is the most complex of the stress-related mental disorders. One who understands the nature and treatment of PTSD also understands much about the nature and treatment of the other stress-related mental disorders. So we will henceforth focus on the early treatment of PTSD. It is critical to understand the following facts about PTSD:

1. *Chronicity is high in PTSD.* Many people do not spontaneously recover with time, and needlessly suffer decades after the crisis has past. Cortisol acts like battery acid on the hippocampus. The damage that it causes seems to be reversible in the short term. The longer PTSD persists, the more difficult it might be to modify traumatic memory networks.
2. *PTSD is a highly co-morbid disorder.* PTSD is bad enough in terms of human suffering. However, those with PTSD are also highly likely to suffer from other medical and psychiatric problems (such as depression, anxiety, substance abuse, anger, hostility, cardio-vascular disease, cancer, diabetes, gastro-intestinal problems, headaches, chronic pain, skin problems, autoimmune diseases, suicide, accidents, higher medical utilization, poorer lipid profiles, greater unhappiness, and greater overall mortality, to name a few). Those with PTSD typically cause strain on family members, who feel like they are walking on eggshells and who might take on similar symptoms. In short, PTSD impairs happiness and performance across many domains of life.

3. *Early treatment works.* Respected VA researchers Friedman, Keane, & Resick (2007, p.318) state, "There is sufficient evidence to recommend cognitive-behavioral therapy [standard treatment for PTSD] as an early intervention for trauma." For severe symptoms, seek treatment within one month following the crisis. Early treatment can prevent post-traumatic stress symptoms from becoming PTSD.

   Even late treatment, though perhaps more challenging, is better than none. A study in Australia (Creamer et al., 2006) provided standard treatment decades after the war to Vietnam vets, a group that is usually considered resistant to treatment. The vets participated in twelve weeks of small-group treatment. The treatment was comprehensive cognitive-behavioral therapy consisting of: education about PTSD; symptom management; discussions of their traumas; managing addictive behaviors; relationship, communication, and problem solving skills; physical health and lifestyle instruction; and relapse prevention. This was supplemented with individual treatment. The treatment resulted in impressive improvements in PTSD symptoms for most vets.[1] Anxiety and depression also significantly improved.

   When the full battery of PTSD treatment options are used, recovery from PTSD is very likely. As there are over 150 treatment strategies (see Schiraldi, 2009) the picture is very hopeful.

4. *When you are healed, you are better prepared for the next crisis.* Treatment can bring you back to 100%. As commandant of the Marine Corps, General James T. Conway, said, "If you are not at 100%, you're not there for your buddies."[2] On CNN national television, two courageous generals talked openly about seeking counseling for PTSD in hopes of reducing the stigma of getting professional help. General Carter Ham, one of only twelve four-star generals in the Army, saw twenty-two soldiers, sailors, and civilians killed when a suicide bomber blew up a mess tent near Mosul, Iraq. He repeatedly asked himself what he could have done differently to save them. Upon returning home, he could not relate to his wife, who said, "All of him didn't come back." After getting help, he said, "I'm a better general because I got some help. You need somebody to assure you it's not abnormal…to have trouble sleeping, to be jumpy at loud sounds…to find yourself with mood swings at seemingly trivial matters." Brigadier General Gary S. Patton watched a soldier die before his eyes. Upon his return, he still felt the blood, smelled the battlefield, had a metallic taste in his mouth, and awoke from sleep because of noises that he thought were explosions. He said it was healing just to talk with others who had experienced the same symptoms.[3]

   Once you recover from PTSD, traumatic symptoms are less likely to pull you away from performing in the present.[4] You will have learned additional coping skills that can help you and those with whom you associate. You will likely have greater empathy and compassion for those you serve with. With confidence in the recovery process, you can urge others who need help to get it. Lt. Col. Dave Grossman (2009) related that a Marine Gunney who'd served four tours in the Middle East said to his comrade, "I had a low spot in my life and got help. Yours is falling apart. Go get help."

318

Regarding treatment, then, we must be flexible, changing from the crisis mode of "press on, suck it up, don't quit, deny pain," to the healing mode of "stop and admit needs, unburden and heal emotional wounds, and replace the water in the well so you can carry on better." Performance won't degrade with treatment; it will improve. Some will respect the fact that you sought help. There is no shame in this.

The Healing, Recovery, and Growth Process

Life is not linear (see Figure 33.1). Each person starts with an upward reach, the inclination to fulfill one's potential. But all of us, to one degree or another, are derailed by stressors ranging from overload to crises. Overwhelming traumatic events can seriously thwart our progress and ability to enjoy life, throwing us, as it were, into a dark valley. Although PTSD feels like a shattering of the soul that will never heal, the reality is that one is not broken, but just temporarily derailed. The healing process begins, often with needed treatment—often two steps forward and one step back. With time, patience, and effort—and at a pace that you control—recovery is very likely to occur. Although we are never completely the same, we can generally return to the point we were in terms of functioning and ability to enjoy life. From the point of recovery, we can again proceed with the journey of growth—equipped with new skills, learned from the recovery process, that facilitate the growth process. Pain can be turned into a positive.

Figure 33.1
HEALING, RECOVERY, AND GROWTH (Reprinted from Schiraldi (2009))

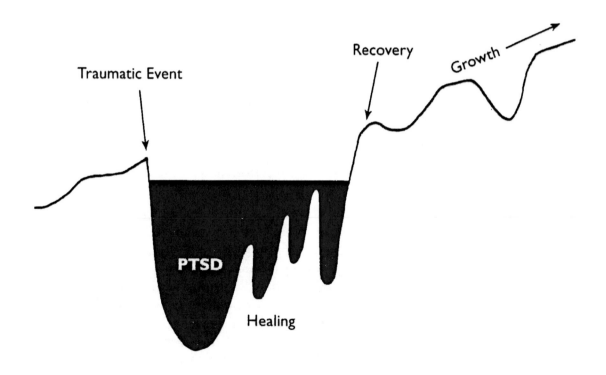

Treatment of PTSD usually involves helping the survivor to: stabilize and manage symptoms; confront, neutralize, and properly store traumatic memories; and restore balance in life. It is helpful to think of the trauma specialist with whom you might choose to work as a coach who is helping you improve your coping skills, much like a golf coach would help you improve your game. Traditional psychological treatments might be complemented with spiritual or cultural approaches to healing. Become an expert by reading about the nature of, and treatment options for, PTSD. This will help you gain more from the treatment process, and will help you be a more effective resource to others who also experience PTSD.

How Will I Know When I Have Recovered?

There are a number of indications of recovery. These are adapted from Dr. Mary Harvey (1996):
- You'll be able to recall or dismiss the traumatic memory consciously (with minimal intrusions, nightmares, or flashbacks)
- The feelings associated with the memory can be named and tolerated
- Other symptoms (e.g., depression, anxiety, grief, or sexual dysfunction) diminish and/or are well tolerated
- A sense of self worth, enjoyment, and meaning in life are restored
- You are comfortable with all feelings—positive, negative, and neutral
- You are committed to your future

The Myths and Distortions that Complicate Recovery

Sadly, most people with PTSD do not get proper treatment and thus suffer needlessly for years. Many others whose symptoms do not rise to the level of a formal diagnosis of PTSD nevertheless suffer from troubling PTSD symptoms and could benefit from treatment. So many people don't obtain critically needed treatment for several reasons. Some don't know where to find it. Others fear that treatment might jeopardize their career or reputation. And others are blocked from seeking help by common myths and distortions. The most common of these are listed below, along with their counterarguments:
- *Those who seek treatment are weak and dependent.* It is strength to recognize areas in which help would benefit us. An intelligent treatment plan encourages greater self-reliance, and healing helps us reach this. Healing PTSD also helps to improve the co-morbid psychological conditions that block our progress.
- *I should be able to "soldier on" alone.* Why? Is it written somewhere that one must never get assistance from others? If help ultimately strengthens us, is it weakness to ask for it, or is it strength and wisdom?
- *If I show that I have feelings I will lose control.* Actually, people are more likely to lose control by bottling up feelings in an unhealthy way. It is liberating to realize that we can show human emotions like grief, fear, and pain, and even shed tears, such as at a funeral—and then return to full functioning. With emotional flexibility, we are less likely to snap. It is only by acknowledging vulnerability in

certain areas that we can strengthen those areas. As the saying goes, we have to feel it to heal it.[5]

- *I should only be tough and mean.* Many war heroes are also tenderhearted. Most people would prefer to serve beside strong individuals who also have a heart. It is OK to show and ask for warmth and affection.
- *I must always be on guard and never relax.* A rubber band that is constantly stretched will snap. Be vigilant when needed, then take a breather when it's safe so that you can function better.
- *These symptoms will go away with time.* They might, but if they are severe they likely won't.
- *I'll lose it and never recover if I start talking about the trauma. I couldn't stand the pain of talking about the trauma.* Verbalizing helps to integrate and neutralize the traumatic memory. Talking about the trauma might be uncomfortable initially, but usually becomes easier with each repetition—especially when we choose the proper setting. A skilled trauma specialist will help you do this at a pace that is acceptable to you.
- *Talking about the trauma makes it worse.* See the comments above.
- *Denying my feelings will make the pain go away. Distancing or drinking will get me through.* Ignored pain tends to accumulate until it erupts, often destructively.
- *I shouldn't have to suffer. I shouldn't have to work at healing.* Why would that be when everyone suffers? Perhaps you could adopt a softer, more accepting response to suffering as you work to solve your problems.
- *I should not request time to recover.* When time is needed to recover, have the courage to ask for it.
- *I must appear strong so no one thinks I'm weak. I should be ashamed for having symptoms.* This keeps many from getting help, and causes many to self-medicate to disguise the symptoms. Would you rather *look* strong, or invest the effort to *be and feel* strong inside?
- *I should be over this by now.* Recovery takes time—as long as it takes. Often, the slower you go in treatment, the faster the recovery.
- *All problems can be resolved with willpower and getting back to work.* Obviously this doesn't work well in many cases of PTSD, since many symptoms can persist for decades until new approaches are tried.
- *Mental health professionals are useless, touchy feely incompetents who can't relate to what I've been through* (Artwohl & Christensen, 1997). Like any profession, some trauma specialists are effective and some are not. Some trauma specialists have worked in high-risk professions, or have worked hard to experience the challenges of these professions. Some have a capacity to care and help even though they have not experienced what you have. Nevertheless, shop until you find one you can respect, relate to, and work with.
- *I'm irrevocably bad for what I did. I'll never get over this.* Would a truly bad person feel the remorse that you do? Humans are able to listen to guilt, make needed changes, and then release it. Eventually, the guilt subsides.

Activity: Finding Needed Help

Fortunately there are many useful resources for helping those with PTSD (see Appendix 9). The Sidran Institute, for example, helps one locate a trauma specialist in one's geographic area. (When looking for a mental health professional, it is best to find a trauma specialist, since the complexities of treating PTSD require an exceptional degree of expertise in PTSD.) The *Post-Traumatic Stress Disorder Sourcebook* (Schiraldi, 2009) explores the nature and treatment options of PTSD in a clear and comprehensive way. This book also contains an extensive resource list.

If symptoms have persisted or are disrupting any area of your life, and self-management strategies are insufficient, you might consider finding a trauma specialist with whom you can comfortably work. Prepare by reading as much as you can about PTSD. Discuss the specialist's approaches to treatment beforehand, so that you know what to expect.

Chapter 34

Summary: Putting it All Together

Each person already has within the seeds of remarkable resilience. In our journey together we have explored many skills to help you grow this resilience. As with any other skill, resilience skills take time to acquire, and practice to maintain. Perhaps you will incorporate some resilience skills into your daily life without much conscious thought. Other skills might require that you deliberately set aside some time to practice.

Go back from time to time to practice valuable resilience skills. When life throws you a curve that sets your resilience back somewhat, remember to refer to this book and practice the skills that are meaningful for you. If resilience can be grown once, it can be grown again.

Like any other important health practice, resilience building and maintenance is an ongoing process. Fortunately, once they have taken root, resilience skills become almost second nature and, therefore, easier to apply in times of distress.

To summarize and reinforce your most important skills, as well as to serve as a quick reminder during difficult times, please review the entire book, and list below and on the next page those ideas and skills that you most want to remember. You might also write down the page numbers for easy reference.

Ideas I Most Want to Remember

Skills I Most Want to Remember

Activities

- Make a year's plan for weekly practice of the skills you find most meaningful.
- If you are working with a group or team:
  - At the end of training, ask, "What will you take away from the training?" This is a very effective way to summarize and review the most important points of training in participants' own unique words. (Allow time for review. A few days before asking this question, ask individuals to review the entire book to identify the most useful principles and skills.)
  - Organize follow-up in-service or booster training. The best way to learn is to teach. So ask individuals to take a piece of the training and create a practical lesson. You might have the group or team practice, say, one skill per week or month. During the training, you might ask questions, such as: "How would you apply this skill on the job?"; "At home?"; "How would you use it to help a buddy in distress?" These questions prompt individuals to think through the application of skills, reinforce learning, and make it more likely that the skills will actually be used when needed. Trainers might also create a high-risk crisis situation. They then ask participants what they will think and do before, during, and after. This requires synthesis, or the putting together of many principles and skills.[1]

Going forward, you indeed have many strengths, skills, and resources to draw upon. May you be confident, ever learning, and a rich resource to those you care about.

Appendix 1: Small Groups

Objectives & Benefits
- Learn small group skills; increase interpersonal effectiveness
- Enjoyment: friendships, team building, empathy
- Clarify thinking, problem solving, understand self and others better

Small Group Norms
- Respect and sensitivity (listen, only one person has the floor at a time, empathize, avoidance of racist or sexist language, try to see another's viewpoint)
- Participation
- Willingness to experiment with different strategies
- Responsibility (which includes consideration for how one's actions affect others in the group)
- Openness (share insights, disclose, give feedback, willingness to risk and be known—because others might learn from your experience and like you if he/she knows the real you)
- Punctuality (a type of consideration for others and their time)
- Willingness to absorb feedback before defending self or cutting off the speaker
- Freedom to pass when disclosing is not comfortable (this happens less and less as trust builds)
- Confidentiality and trust
- Freedom to be fallible
- Freedom to probe (i.e., seek more information)
- Freedom to think and disagree respectfully
- Freedom to show honesty and emotions
- Leadership can change; we sit in circle to reinforce the concept of equality

Disruptive Roles
- Sarcasm
- Complaining/negativity
- Aggressing/hostility
- Competing
- Dominating
- Withdrawing
- Status seeking
- Blocking
- Horsing around
- Special pleading

Expectations
- It usually takes three meetings to make a group functional and to build trust and comfort.
- It is best not to change group membership after the training has begun (if new members are added all members must be re-acquainted).

Appendix 2: The Promise and Possibilities of Primary Prevention

Primary prevention aims to stop problems before they occur. Preventive efforts that address risk factors for psychological dysfunction are vitally important and feasible, as the following quotes indicate:

- Resilience "...vivifies an emerging paradigm shift in mental health, built around the intriguing possibility that psychological dysfunction can be better approached through prevention than by struggling, however valiantly and compassionately, to undo deeply-rooted damage." (Cowen, Wyman, Work, & Iker, 1995, p.248)

- "The concept of prevention as it is used in public health has been taken seriously in the mental health field only in the last few decades....There is a need for both universal interventions to promote health in broad populations as well as for interventions targeted at high-risk groups." (Panel report to National Prevention Conference sponsored by NIMH, Coie et al., 1991, p.1013)

- "We must recognize the fact that no mass disorder affecting large numbers of human beings has ever been controlled or eliminated by attempts at treating each affected individual. This is not only sound public health doctrine, but it is as applicable to the field of mental health as it is to the field of public health." (Albee and Gulotta, 1986, p.217)

- "Earlier successes of prevention in areas of physical health—notably the positive benefits of improved nutrition, better sanitation standards, and the eventually successful efforts at inoculation against communicable diseases—offered great hope that similar victories might be gained in the area of mental health." (DeArmond and Marsh, 1984, p.671)

- "Prevention offers the potential for avoiding widespread human suffering, as well as saving costs associated with treatment and lost productivity. Further, preventive intervention trials provide a strong test of causal theory: the successful modification of processes and mechanisms hypothesized to cause adverse outcomes, and subsequent avoidance of these outcomes, helps investigators to discern a causal relationship." (Muehrer and Koretz, 1992, p.109)

- *Mental Health: A Report of the Surgeon General* calls mental illness a critical need that the Nation must address, and calls for prevention efforts that consider risk and protective factors (DHHS, 1999).

References

Albee, G. W., & Gulotta, T. P. (1986). Facts and Fallacies about Primary Prevention. *Journal of Primary Prevention, 6* (4), 207-218.

Coie, J. D., Watt, N. F., West, S. G., Hawkins, J. D., Asarnow, J. R., Markman, H. J., Ramey, S. L., Shure, M. B., & Long, B. (1993). The Science of Prevention: A Conceptual Framework and Some Directions for a National Research Program. *American Psychologist, 48,* 1013-1022.

Cowen, E. L., Wyman, P. A., Work, W. C., & Iker, M. R. (1995). A Preventive Intervention for Enhancing Resilience Among Highly Stressed Urban Children. *The Journal of Primary Prevention, 15* (3), 247-260.

DeArmond, M. M., & Marsh, K. F. (1984). Preventive Psychiatry on the College Campus. *Psychiatric Annals, 14,* 671-678.

Department of Health and Human Services. (1999). *Mental Health: A Report of the Surgeon General.* (DHHS Publication No. ADM 01702401653-5), Washington, DC: U.S. Government Printing Office.

Muehrer, P., & Koretz, D. S. (1992). Issues in Preventive Intervention Research. *Current Directions in Psychological Science, 1,* 109-112.

Appendix 3: PTSD Risk Factors

Severity of Exposure
- Physical injury, perceived life threat, exposure to multiple or chronic trauma, threat of recurrence, intentional human cause (sexual, military sexual, threat of rape, childhood sexual or physical abuse, battering, witnessing domestic violence), combat (intensity, killing, repeated deployments, committing or witnessing atrocities), medical trauma (illness of child, life-threatening accident, pediatric or pre-verbal surgery)
- Life stressors and environmental hassles are risks for PTSD above and beyond traumatic exposure (work stressors, shift work, lack of supervisor support, etc.)

Instability in Family of Origin
- History of mental illness, early separation from parents, severe punishment, poor functioning, drugs, suicide, violence, less parental support (especially from fathers as regards global self-worth and PTSD in Vietnam vets), post-traumatic symptoms in parents stemming from child's trauma

Individual Factors
- Psychiatric history—previous anxiety, depression, substance abuse, personality disorder, hostility
- Mental and physical health status before combat
- Prior trauma/neglect—especially child sexual abuse; combined childhood physical abuse and rape are especially potent; childhood physical or sexual trauma render individuals more vulnerable to adult PTSD (e.g. in police, soldiers). Males are more distressed by sexual abuse than females in some studies.
- Poor adjustment & emotional intelligence
    - High trait anger
    - Difficulty experiencing positive emotions, high negative emotionality, difficulty remaining calm under stress, self critical, poor impulse control, negative attitudes about emotional expression, closed to new experiences
    - Negative global beliefs, self-criticism, negative self schemas, negative appraisals about self (accounted for 25% of PTSD variance in fire academy recruits), catastrophizing, rumination, self-blame
    - Poor memory recall (perhaps suggesting impaired hippocampus)
- Poor quality sleep
- Substance use (smoking, drugs, problem drinking)
- Biology
    - Hyperactive nervous system (chronically high nor-epinephrine), low DHEA
    - Low cortisol levels (DHEA/cortisol ratio inversely correlated to dissociation in elite special operations soldiers)
    - Smaller hippocampus

Peri-traumatic Reactions
- Dissociation (in police, trait dissociation is also associated with PTSD). Tonic immobility (paralysis, tremors, analgesia, suppressed vocal behavior, fixed and unfocused stare, periods of eye closures) is strongly related to peri-traumatic dissociation and might promote self-blame. Hyperventilation might induce this.
- Strong negative emotions/reactivity—guilt, self-blame (common in vets, battered women, sexual abuse survivors), anger, hostility, panic

- Hyper-arousal—e.g., emergency room heart rate strongly predicts dissociation and PTSD
- Avoidance/passivity—denying, minimizing, unwilling to believe it happened, escaping to daydream/drugs, trying to forget, blocking out, social withdrawal rather than active planning and problem solving

Post-Traumatic
- Lack of social support has a strong effect (e.g., perceived negative homecoming)
- Difficulty expressing feelings
- Avoidant coping (substance use, social withdrawal, wishful thinking, attempts to forget/block out memory)
- Additional life stressors
- Co-morbid depression, anxiety, substance use disorder
- Shame (perceived core badness, self-blame)
- Persistent dissociation

Miscellaneous
- Gender—females generally become more aroused and express themselves more (which might explain their better treatment response). However, sexually assaulted men have equal or higher PTSD rates.
- Small effects for lower age, socio-economic status, education, intelligence, ethnicity
- Genes—up to 30% of variance may be genetically determined
- Left-handedness—in a small but robust study

Appendix 4: Resilience Training Model (Components & Goals)
~Adaptive functioning amidst adversity~

I. Resilient Brain. Peak brain function through critical health practices that optimize "brain hardware."

II. Emotional Intelligence (EI). Comfort with feeling and expressing emotions. One can perceive, name, and understand emotions. Not hijacked by strong emotions—can suppress and deal with them later. Can handle and regulate strong negative emotions and loss of control. Can experience positive emotions.
- Calm under pressure; calm concentration/focus (turn fear into focus)
- Calm and rational thinking
- Resolve /manage distress (disturbing thoughts and emotions)
- Ego strength = sense of personal autonomy, self-esteem, self-protective, stable sense of self amidst changing circumstances, understands strengths, securely attached (securely attached children become more resilient). Ability to think, "Abuse happened to me, but it doesn't define who I am."

III. Adaptive Coping
- Active—not passive, avoidant, or frozen; realize actions make a difference (e.g., people in World Trade Center milled around)
- Confident
- Flexible—not surprised by turn of events in life; can adjust to changing circumstances, alter plans, know when to change self or strategies; resourceful
- Creative problem solving—curious, consider options then act, engaged, assess one's capacity to act, know what can and can't be done (realistic control), go inside to imagine something better
- Persistent, persevere, determined (to be different, build better life, do best, tolerate fear and still perform), courageous, self-disciplined, makes goals and plans, hard working
- Not afraid to risk and "fail"
- Elastic (stretch, return to original, some bounce back stronger, rise above, changed in good way)
- Training & experience that challenges, but doesn't overwhelm

IV. Mental Conditioning ("Brain Programming")
- Happiness, gratitude, optimism ("keepers of the dream")
- Intrinsic religious faith, spirituality, religious practice
- Meaning and purpose—reasons to survive, belief that what one is doing is meaningful (e.g., civil rights workers)
- Moral courage/integrity (honest and authentic, behavior conforms to values, respect, fair play); trustworthiness. Minimal regrets/baggage. Morality = "being holy in an unholy world"
- Love/altruism—separates self from suffering
- Humor

- Long view of suffering—willing to endure, especially when there is a reason; suffering is not personal; no catastrophizing

V. Social Involvement & Balanced Living

- Variety of fulfilling and healthy social, physical, intellectual, recreational, and cultural pursuits (e.g., hobbies, education, social activities)
- Social competence (social/attachment skills, marriage enrichment, conflict resolution, interpersonal relating, willingness to converse, willing to seek out support/comfort while still being independent and self-reliant, validating, empathy, altruism, closeness to others, team player, commits to relationships, identifies and relates to positive role models; "I don't have to go it alone" attitude)
- Family practices (family as team ethic, family evenings, one-on-one interviews, family councils)
- Pleasant events scheduling
- Unit cohesion and pride—good leadership and training, bonding with others, shared positive experiences

VI. Crisis (e.g., "war zone") Preparation

- Prepared to face events and symptoms realistically and non-judgmentally (e.g., wounded buddies, fear, disgust, hatred, psychological wounding)
  - Prepared for real life scenes through realistic training and use of media
  - Aim high, accept imperfect performance, recognize what is realistic
  - Prepared for post-crisis symptoms
  - Become an honorable warrior, reconcile to killing, war zone morality
  - Appreciate treatment opportunities

Appendix 5: U.S. Navy SEALs Creed

SEALs Creed	Resilience Qualities
In times of war or uncertainty there is a special breed of warrior ready to answer our Nation's call. A common man with uncommon desire to succeed. Forged by adversity, he stands alongside America's finest special operations forces to serve his country, the American people, and protect their way of life. I am that man.	Humility, purpose, determination, confidence, camaraderie, service
My Trident is a symbol of honor and heritage. Bestowed upon me by the heroes that have gone before, it embodies the trust of those I have sworn to protect. By wearing the Trident I accept the responsibility of my chosen profession and way of life. It is a privilege that I must earn every day.	Moral strength, trustworthiness, responsibility, active
My loyalty to Country and Team is beyond reproach. I humbly serve as a guardian to my fellow Americans, always ready to defend those who are unable to defend themselves. I do not advertise the nature of my work, nor seek recognition for my actions. I voluntarily accept the inherent hazards of my profession, placing the welfare and security of others before my own.	Loyalty, altruism, purpose, humility, intrinsic motivation, realism
I serve with honor on and off the battlefield. The ability to control my emotions and my actions, regardless of circumstance, sets me apart from other men. Uncompromising integrity is my standard. My character and honor are steadfast. My word is my bond.	Integrity, emotional intelligence
We expect to lead and be led. In the absence of orders I will take charge, lead my teammates and accomplish the mission. I lead by example in all situations.	Leadership, teamwork, responsibility
I will never quit. I persevere and thrive on adversity. My Nation expects me to be physically harder and mentally stronger than my enemies. If knocked down, I will get back up, every time. I will draw on every remaining ounce of strength to protect my teammates and to accomplish our mission. I am never out of the fight.	Perseverance, optimal mind/body fitness, bounce back, resolved, active, optimism
We demand discipline. We expect innovation. The lives of my teammates and the success of our mission depend on me—my technical skill, tactical proficiency, and attention to detail. My training is never complete.	Discipline, flexibility, creativity, skilled, focused, beginner's mind, life-long learning
We train for war and fight to win. I stand ready to bring the full spectrum of combat power to bear in order to achieve my mission and the goals established by my country. The execution of my duties will be swift and violent when required yet guided by the very principles that I serve to defend.	Prepared for use of violence within authorized rules of engagement
Brave men have fought and died building the proud tradition and feared reputation that I am bound to uphold. In the worst of conditions, the legacy of my teammates steadies my resolve and silently guides my every deed. I will not fail.	Connection to others and meaning, determination, expectation of excellence

Appendix 6: Health Planning Sheets

Sample Menu for a Week of Meals

Write down what you plan to eat and drink each day, and amounts of food/liquid.

	Mon	Tue	Wed	Thurs	Fri	Sat	Sun
Breakfast							
Snack							
Lunch							
Snack							
Dinner							
Snack							

Sleep plan:

I'll get ____ hours of sleep each night (a little more than you think you need), retiring at _____ and waking at _____ (strive for regularity as much as possible, altering your times by no more than 1 ½ hrs. from one day to another).

Exercise plan (describe below what you'll do each day of the week):

An Initial Fourteen-day Commitment

Keep a record to see how well you stick to your plan for fourteen days. Throughout the fourteen days make whatever adjustments you need, and then continue the plan as you read the rest of the book.

Day	Date	Exercised (minutes)	Number of meals eaten	Sleep		
				Hours	**Time to bed**	**Time out of bed**
1						
2						
3						
4						
5						
6						
7						
8						
9						
10						
11						
12						
13						
14						

Appendix 7: Breakfast Nutrition

This breakfast shake is formulated to meet the nutritional needs of adults. For convenience, ingredients can be put in a blender, refrigerated overnight, and blended just prior to drinking it. Most find that it tastes good and satisfies hunger very effectively, resulting in fewer calories consumed throughout the day. There are no unhealthy ingredients.

Adding fruits and vegetables to one's diet promotes weight loss, and protects against heart disease, cancer, and other diseases. This shake provides five servings of fruit, which meets the total requirement for the day. One only needs 5 servings of vegetables during the rest of the day to meet recommendations for fruits (4) and vegetables (5). Adding a serving of carrots does not appreciably alter the taste. The shake also provides two servings of dairy (2/3 of the daily requirements for most adults). Those who are lactose intolerant might substitute soymilk.

Item	Amount	Calories	Some Benefits
Milk, skim [can substitute soymilk a/o low-fat yogurt]	2C	180	• Low-fat dairy reduces risk of cardio-vascular disease, hypertension (which is linked to dementia), diabetes, metabolic syndrome (improves insulin sensitivity; may reduce body fat), curbs appetite, and quickly reduces oxidative stress and inflammation (which is linked to a wide range of diseases from heart disease to gout & depression) • Calcium cuts risk of colon cancer. 2000 mg/day linked to longevity.
Orange juice	1C	110	Lowers blood pressure
Healthy cereal, such as *Nature's Path Optimum Power* with flax, soy, blueberries	1/4C	50	Fiber, antioxidants, omega-3s. Whole grains lower the type of body fat linked to metabolic syndrome, heart disease, and diabetes.
Wheat Germ	1Tbsp	30	Fiber, B vitamins. Whole grains lower the type of body fat linked to metabolic syndrome, heart disease, and diabetes.
Rolled oats	1Tbsp	25	Fiber (glucan) lowers cholesterol, blood pressure, and insulin resistance. Antioxidants also relax blood vessels. Whole grains lower the type of body fat linked to metabolic syndrome, heart disease, and diabetes.
Soy protein powder	1Tbsp	33	Provides 8g of high-quality protein. Isoflavones protect against cancer and possibly heart disease. Protein at breakfast is linked to lower calorie intake during rest of the day.
Walnuts	1/8C = 1Tbsp	100	Fiber and heart-healthy fat protect against heart disease. Antioxidants reduce inflammation.
Banana	1	90	Potassium in a single banana daily helps prevent stroke
Cantaloupe	1/8	40	Rich in antioxidants & vitamins. Blueberries improve memory, increase insulin sensitivity, and, in animals, prevent hardening of the arteries.
Strawberries, fresh or frozen	1/2 C	50	
Blueberries, fresh or frozen	1/2 C	80	
	Total Calories	About 800	

337

Notes

- Vanilla can be added for flavor, and fruits can be alternated for variety.
- Adding 1/2 tsp cinnamon helps to lower blood LDLs, triglycerides, and sugar.
- Frozen fruit can be as nutritious as fresh fruit. Adding frozen fruit just before blending gives the shake an ice-cream-like texture.
- Apples (called the "new fish" because they have antioxidant properties in the brain, slow the aging process, and improve brain function) and grapes (resveretrol) are particularly good fruits to use.

Other Benefits

- You usually won't feel hungry for hours after drinking, so you can have a smaller lunch. A number of factors work together to reduce the appetite for hours:
  - Bulk and liquid fill the stomach.
  - Protein, fiber, fat, and acid slow the emptying of the stomach, keeping blood sugar levels more constant.
  - The shake provides four cups of liquid. When properly hydrated, we feel better and less hungry, and retain less water and fat.
  - Alternatively, one can divide the shake into portions to drink throughout the day.
- Magnesium, found in nuts and whole grains (also in vegetables and legumes) might improve brain function and prevent cognitive decline.
- The shake is brain-, heart-, and cancer-healthy because it is low in unhealthy fat and high in fiber and antioxidants.
- Consuming more than 1/3 of one's daily caloric intake at the beginning of the day might favor weight loss.

Pre-Mixed Ingredients for Multiple Servings

For convenience, mix in a plastic container enough dry ingredients for multiple servings, refrigerate, then just spoon out ½ cup and add to blender, along with other ingredients, to make one serving.

Dry Ingredients	1 Serving	16 Servings
Cereal, *Nature's Path Optimum Power* with flax, soy, blueberries	1/4C	4 C
Wheat Germ	1Tbsp	1C
Rolled oats	1Tbsp	1C
Soy protein	1Tbsp	1C
Walnuts	1Tbsp	1C
Cinnamon	½ tsp	8 tsp = 2 2/3 Tbsp

Appendix 8: The Optimism Questionnaire

Optimistic Thoughts. *Think about a difficult time you experienced. Place a check beside any optimistic thoughts that went through your mind. When finished go back and circle the number of an item if it seems like a thought you could choose for a difficult situation in the future.*

1. I'll improve upon my past.
2. I find something to enjoy or appreciate each day, no matter what.
3. I expect the future to be better (not perfect, but better).
4. I am committed to making my life count.
5. What I choose to do will make a difference.
6. Though I might feel sad sometimes, I won't give up or give in to despair.
7. I think about what's the best thing to do.
8. I am committed to making my future more pleasant.
9. There's a connection between what I do and what happens to me.
10. What I do today will affect the ways things turn out in my life.
11. I'll shake off the effects of setbacks and become wiser and stronger.
12. I'll bounce back well.
13. Though I might fall short in some ways, I know I am still capable in other ways.
14. I enjoy challenges for the strengths they call forth. They're not stumbling blocks, but steppingstones to growth.
15. I believe that things will generally improve.
16. When having a tough time, I notice my strengths as well as the things I'd like to improve.
17. I believe I will rise above any adversity and live well.
18. I can improve upon my bad habits.
19. I enjoy difficult challenges—I view them as a test of my skill level, not my worth as a person.
20. All in all, things will probably turn out well.
21. I generally see myself as capable.
22. I choose reachable goals and am confident of achieving them.
23. I am inclined to think, "I can do this."
24. I believe in myself.
25. I am equal to the task.
26. I generally think my efforts are effective.
27. I am open to new ways of thinking, new ideas, and new evidence.
28. I don't stew over things that are beyond my control.
29. There's no use crying over spilled milk; today's setbacks will be water under the bridge tomorrow.
30. In most situations, I can devise solutions and feel in control.
31. If I do my best, things will turn out as favorably as possible.
32. I remain hopeful and determined in difficult times.
33. Setbacks are temporary.
34. I'll learn and improve as long as I live.
35. Rather than blaming or condemning myself, I focus on what steps I can take.
33. Others [specify]:_____

Optimistic Actions. *Check those that generally apply. Then circle those that you could apply in a difficult situation in the future.*

1. I persevere as long as it is reasonable to do so; I generally don't give up when things get difficult.
2. I seek help from others when I need it.
3. Problems get me going—I either do something, or let go of the worry.
4. I arrange things so that a good solution will likely happen.
5. I set realistic and specific (not vague) goals for myself.
6. I initiate attempts to improve my performance.
7. When a problem presents itself, I usually come up with at least a couple of things to do about it.
8. I make a plan of action to solve problems and then follow the plan.
9. I work at having good friendships and other social relationships.
10. I actively solve problems when I can.
11. I accept situations that I can't change without undue upset.
12. I try to make small changes and improvements when big ones are impossible.
13. I work toward good outcomes and try to avoid bad ones.
14. I gain inspiration from wherever I can (e.g., wholesome entertainment, worship, nature, literature).

Active Coping Style. *Optimists tend to be active, rather than passive. Check those that generally apply to you. Then circle those that you'd wish to cultivate.*

1. I take a breather in order to perform better over the long haul (e.g., a break, vacation, recreation, warm drink, exercise, sleep, medical exam, nutritious meal, fresh air and sunlight, put aside worries, make a plan).
2. I set realistic, specific goals (not vague "do-your-best" goals), then take steps to meet them.
3. I come up with several different solutions to a problem.
4. I'm prone to exert effort, rather than wanting to sit back and relax all the time, knowing that this:
    • Strengthens me in the long run and leads to emotional fitness
    • Keeps me emotionally conditioned
    • Stretches me (when balanced with rest) so that I'll be more ready when the hour of need arrives
5. I follow the problem solving method.
6. I don't stew over what's wrong, but focus on what I *can* do.
7. I manage time so that time doesn't manage me.
8. I seek counsel when needed (e.g., from friends, families, experts).
9. I am inclined to take rational action (e.g., gather needed information, make a plan, take action, take small steps forward when I can't do it all at once, seek help).
10. When people do things that upset me, I talk it over with them, and perhaps negotiate, compromise, offer to bend, or accept them as they are.
11. I constructively acknowledge feelings—write them in a journal, talk it out, garden, etc.

12. I take responsibility for what I *can* control or improve (my thoughts, my feelings, my actions).
13. I acknowledge external factors that play a role in my performance (fatigue, overload, task difficulty, situation)—there's often a fine line between making excuses and acknowledging mitigating circumstances.
14. I accept myself—self-regard is an active choice, not something that is automatic or inherited.
15. I commit myself (my energies, talents, time, efforts) to worthwhile causes (i.e., I stay invested and involved in worthwhile activities).
16. I try to change the source of the problem, or, if impossible, change myself. Changing the self is called secondary control, which mitigates depression. It can include:
    * Changing my point of view
    * Accepting what is
    * Learning lessons
    * Developing character
    * Accepting that God has a plan and a hand in this
    * Becoming more flexible, realizing I can survive when things don't go my way
    * Finding meaning, faith in God
    * Recognizing that it is possible to experience pain while simultaneously feeling great hope and joy
17. I am flexible:
    * If I see that I can't change the situation, then I accept it—being passive can sometimes be appropriate (e.g., "Live to fight another day").
    * I am open to new ways of thinking, new ideas, new evidence, and new solutions.
    * I try for small changes when large changes are not reasonable (e.g., I ask myself, "What small victories are possible?"; What is wise to accept?")
18. I seek to understand my feelings.
19. I try to empathize with others, to understand their viewpoint and feelings.
20. I seek out other people for support or encouragement.
21. I try to figure out why things go wrong and adjust—not stewing but focusing on possible solutions.
22. I see the bright side.
23. I remember to play the "Well, at least...." game ["Well, at least_____ (I learned what's important in life; I know I can survive almost anything; I don't have to see that nutty boss anymore, etc.")].
24. I use warm, accepting humor to help me cope and soften self-condemnation.
25. I persevere when it is reasonable to do so [As W.C. Fields said: "If at first you don't succeed, try again. Then quit. There's no sense being stupid about it."]
26. I work at being healthy.
27. I take precautions to safeguard my health (e.g., optimists get checkups, don't engage in frivolous or unsafe sex).
28. I work at having good friendships and other social relationships
29. I strive to be aware of shortcomings and improve upon them.
30. I help others out of concern for them.
31. I participate in hobbies.
32. I proactively anticipate and prevent bad outcomes.

33. I can shift gears, or change my thinking and focus, so that I don't stew over spilled milk

Passive Coping Style. *Pessimists tend to use these. All of these reflect denial of reality. Check those that generally apply to you. Then circle the items you'd wish to improve. For each item circled, list more constructive actions.*

1. I tend to avoid confronting my troubles, so that they don't get solved.
2. I isolate myself.
3. I tend to deny that troubles exist (e.g., "I don't have a problem"; "It really doesn't bother me").
4. I complain, brood, or blame self or others—which keeps things the same.
5. I allow myself to feel bad without doing anything constructive [e.g., I think, "That's awful!" or I feel guilt, despair, sadness, overwhelmed, or pessimism but don't do much about it.]
6. I give in to discouragement, apathy, helplessness, or passivity.
7. I daydream to escape my problems.
8. I will often think about ways to make the situation better instead of acting.
9. I use drugs or other forms of sedation to escape (e.g., excessive eating, sleeping, shopping, sex, gambling).
10. I allow myself to be bored and never satisfied.
11. I am resigned to Murphy's Law (If something can go wrong it will).
12. I rationalize my being passive.
13. I believe that nothing I do really makes a difference.
14. I stay housebound or in bed, I don't fix up my living quarters, or I expect others to do things for me.
15. I don't try to improve a bad relationship.
16. I give in to depression, anxiety, anger, hostility, pessimism, or worry.
17. I withdraw, avoid, give up, freeze, or do nothing.
18. I placate others, ignoring my own needs because it's easier to give in than to take a stand.
19. I make excuses for my poor performance.
20. I take all the blame for my poor performances.
21. I am a fatalist. (I deny the cause/effect relationship—e.g., "I'm going to die anyway, so I'll smoke.")
22. I don't knock myself out about much.

Appendix 9: Resources

General Resilience

- Ashe, A., & Rampersad, A. *Days of Grace*. New York: Random House. Retaining inner peace and optimism, despite tragedy. By the dignified tennis champion who innocently contracted AIDS from open-heart surgery.
- Frankl, V. *Man's Search for Meaning*. Boston: Beacon. The classics work on discovering meaning in one's life out of suffering. Written by the Holocaust survivor who founded Logotherapy.
- Geisel, Theodor. *Oh, the Places You'll Go*. New York: Random House. Part of the Dr. Seuss series; a clever, humorous treatise on human growth and fallibility.
- Gonzales, L. *Deep Survival: Who Lives, Who Dies, & Why*. New York: Norton. Survival skills that transfer to everyday life include surrender to the situation, reasoned action, calmly take responsibility, and persistence.
- Hanh, T. N. *Peace is Every Step*. New York: Bantam. A peaceful monk's practical ways to cultivate inner peace, joy, serenity, and balance.
- Herriot, J. *The Best of James Herriot: Favourite Memories of a Country Vet*. Pleasantville, NY: Reader's Digest. Uplifting and humorous stories about animals and their owners.
- Kushner, H. S. *When Bad Things Happen to Good People*. New York: Anchor. A rabbi's profound insights on suffering.
- Lewis. C.S. *A Grief Observed*. New York: HarperCollins. Insights on enduring and recovering from the crushing loss of a loved one.
- Linehan, M. M. *Skills Training Manual for Treating Borderline Personality Disorder*. New York: Guilford. Specific skills that are useful for functioning populations as well, including mindfulness, interpersonal effectiveness skills, emotion regulation skills, and distress tolerance skills
- Marx, J. *Season of Life*. New York: Simon & Schuster. Inspired by Viktor Frankl, former NFL star Joe Ehrmann now teaches highly successful young athletes that manhood is not found in athletic prowess, sexual exploitation, and materialism, but in love and meaning.
- McCain, J., with M. Salter. *Why Courage Matters*. New York: Random House. As Mother Teresa noted, everything lies in having courage for whatever comes in life. Provocative insights rooting courage in love.
- Morgenstern, J. *Organizing from the Inside Out*. New York: Henry Holt. Reduce stress at work and home by organizing, beautifying, and developing a retrieval system.
- *Mother Teresa*. DVD documentary by Ann & Jeanette Petrie (Petrie Productions). Powerful modeling and universal messages of unconditional love, forgiveness, and faith.
- Opdyke, I.G. *In My Hands*. New York: Anchor. Stirring story of the courageous Holocaust rescuer who remained tender inside, despite incalculable suffering.
- Roberts, M. *Join-Up: Horse Sense for People*. London: HarperCollins. Gentle leadership from the "horse-whisperer." For those who work with youth, including parents.
- Seligman, M.E.P. *The Optimistic Child: A Revolutionary Program that Safeguards Children Against Depression & Builds Lifelong Resilience*. New York: Houghton Mifflin. Using cognitive therapy to immunize children at risk for depression by building resilience. See *Penn Resiliency Project* on the web to learn more.
- Schiraldi, G. R. *World War II Survivors: Lessons in Resilience*. Ellicott City, MD: Chevron. Forty-one combat survivors explain how they preserved their sanity and the ability to function under many forms of extreme duress. Their lessons are applicable to all of us today.

- Schiraldi, G. R. *The Self-Esteem Workbook*. Oakland, CA: New Harbinger. Based on the successful "Stress and the Healthy Mind" course, University of Maryland. Detailed instructions for many effective skills.
- Schiraldi, G. R. *Ten Simple Solutions for Building Self-Esteem*. Oakland, CA: New Harbinger. Combines cognitive behavioral, mindfulness, and ACT strategies. Based on the effective "Beyond 9/11: Stress, Survival, and Coping" course, University of Maryland.
- Schiraldi, G.R., & Kerr, M.H. *The Anger Management Source Book*. Chicago: McGraw-Hill. "A must for those who are serious about managing their anger more effectively." (R. J. Hedaya, M.D., Clinical Professor of Psychiatry, Georgetown University Hospital).
- Schiraldi, G. R. *Conquer Anxiety, Worry and Nervous Fatigue: A Guide to Greater Peace*. Ellicott City, MD: Chevron. From hyperventilation to worrisome thoughts. "The best book for anxiety we've ever seen" (Sidran Institute).
- Ten Boom, C., with Sherrill, E., & Sherrill, J. *The Hiding Place*. Grand Rapids, MI: Chosen. Imprisoned in the German concentration camps for rescuing Jews, this remarkable woman tells of living with compassion and courage in a world of hatred.
- Vaillant, G. E. *Aging Well: Surprising Guideposts to a Happier Life from the Landmark Harvard Study of Adult Development*. New York: Little, Brown. Warm and powerful insights for adults of all ages on thriving mentally, physically, and socially. From what is generally considered the finest longitudinal study of lifetime development. Also by Dr. Vaillant are *Adaptation to Life* and *Spiritual Evolution: A Scientific Defense of Faith*.
- Wooden, J., & Carty, J. *Coach Wooden's Pyramid of Success: Building Blocks for a Better Life*. Ventura, CA: Regal Books. Wooden, who died at ninety-nine, was an extraordinarily successful and beloved athlete and coach, who masterfully applied the principles of positive psychology. Also, Johnson, N. L. *The John Wooden Pyramid of Success*. Los Angeles: Cool Titles. More moving principles and wisdom.

Resilient Couples and Family Skills

- Markman, H., Stanley, S., & Blumberg, S. L. *Fighting for Your Marriage: Positive Steps for Preventing Divorce and Preserving a Lasting Love*. San Francisco: Jossey-Bass. From conflict resolution to increasing fun. Practical. Based on solid research.
- Prevention and Relationship Enhancement Program: Resources for a Loving Relationship, Denver, Colorado (Tel: 800-366-0166). *Fighting for Your Marriage* and other books. Four excellent, practical DVDs to help develop communication skills, solve problems, and promote intimacy. The PREP program is well researched and respected.
- Lundberg, G., & Lundberg, J. *I Don't Have to Make Everything All Better*. New York: Viking Penguin. Treasure chest of methods for relating to people. Learn how to walk alongside people emotionally (validating), rather than arguing or criticizing.
- Lundberg, G., & Lundberg, J. *Married for Better, Not Worse: The Fourteen Secrets to a Happy Marriage*. Another down-to-earth treasure for creating a satisfying marriage.
- Latham, G. I. *The Power of Positive Parenting: A Wonderful Way to Raise Children*. No. Logan, UT: P&T ink. Useful and thorough guide to steady, consistent, and peaceful parenting.
- Garcia-Prats, C. M., & Garcia-Prats, J. A. *Good Families Don't Just Happen: What We Learned From Raising Our Ten Sons and How It Can Work For You*. Holbrook, MA: Adams Media Corporation. Principle-based skills, starting with respect between spouses.
- Eyre, L., & Eyre, R. *Teaching Children Joy*. Salt Lake City, UT: Deseret. When we can teach it to children, then we have learned it.
- www.foreverfamilies.net. For those who prefer to work off the web, this has been found to work as well as workshops. Instructions for many exercises on all aspects of strengthening

marriage and family. Spiritual bent, but anyone can apply the useful skills independent of orientation.
- All Family Resources (www.familymanagement.com). Rich range of topics from parenting to dealing with crisis.

Physical Fitness
- To find lists of certified fitness instructors go to the American Council on Exercise (www.acefitness.org) or American College of Sports Medicine (www.acsm.org).
- For exercise guidelines, go to www.health.gov/paguidelines (or google ACSM exercise guidelines).
- *Flow Motion: The Simplified T'ai Chi Workout.* DVD by C. J. McPhee & D. Ross. Los Angeles: Lightworks Audio & Video. Gentle beginner's workouts in tai chi, which has been found to lower blood pressure and improve fitness.
- Christensen, A. *Easy Does It Yoga.* New York: Fireside. Instructions for gentle postures for the aged, injured, or inactive. Many can be done desk-side to relax and increase energy and flexibility, and are thus useful for all.

Nutrition
- USDA's www.ChooseMyPlate.gov helps you make an eating plan that is tailored to your needs. Based on solid research, this user-friendly site offers a wealth of useful information.
- USDA's database of antioxidants in hundreds of foods lists the ORAC (oxygen radical absorbance capacity), which is one limited measure. Google USDA ORAC.
- A user-friendly website to count calories in everyday and restaurant/fast foods is http://nutritiondata.com.
- DASH diet Plan at www.nhlbi.nih.gov/health/public/heart/hbp/dash. Free to view, $3.50 to get hard copy. The DASH eating plan has been found to improve cardiovascular health.

Sleep
- American Academy of Sleep Medicine lists hundreds of accredited centers and board certified sleep specialists (www.aasmnet.org; www.sleepeducation.com)

Heart Coherence
- Institute of HeartMath, Boulder Creek, CA (Tel: 800-711-6221; email info@heartmath.com; www.heartmath.org; www.Heartmathstore.com). Contact for books, videos, music, and other products related to heart coherence, as well as to purchase emWave products that enables one to monitor heart rhythms in real time as one practices HeartMath skills.

Thought Field Therapy
- Thought Field Therapy founder Dr. Roger Callahan's website www.TFTrx.com
- Association for Thought Field Therapy (La Quinta, CA 92247; www.ATFT.org)
- Robert L. Bray, Ph.D., TFT Center of San Diego, 5959 Mission Gorge Rd. Ste 106, San Diego CA 92120 (619-283-1116). Author, trainer, psychotherapist.

Positive Psychology
- Harvard Medical School. *Positive Psychology: Harnessing the Power of Happiness, Mindfulness, and Personal Strength.* Boston: Harvard Health Publications. Very effectively and succinctly traces the evolution of positive psychology, outlines major findings, and presents many practical skills.
- Values in Action Inventory of Strengths (Peterson's VIA-IS, www.viacharacter.org/surveys/surveycenter.aspx; also see www.positivepsychology.org).

Assesses core character strengths that are related to happiness. VIA takes 35 minutes; rank orders strengths from top to bottom and gives norms.

- University of Pennsylvania Positive Psychology Center (www.authentichappiness.org). Free scales that measure signature strengths, optimism, happiness, gratitude and more. Find ways to use signature strengths in daily life—love, work, parenting.
- Discover your strengths, with three books and online assessments: www.strengthsfinder.com.
  - Rath, T. *Strengths Finder 2.0*. New York: Gallup. Online assessment to discover top five talents. Thirty-four themes and many strategies for applying your strengths. Also *Strengths Explorer* to discover child's strengths.
  - Rath, T., & Conchie, B. *Strengths Based Leadership*. New York: Gallup. Explains why people follow leaders. Assessment and helps to lead with your top five strengths.
  - Rath, T., & Clifton, D. O. *How Full Is Your Bucket?* New York: Gallup. Describes how even the briefest interactions affect health, productivity, longevity, and relationships. Assessments reveal top five strengths. The other twenty-nine are identified for a fee.
- International Positive Psychology Association (IPPA) hosts world congresses on positive psychology of leading researchers and practitioners from around the world. (Mt. Royal, NJ, Tel: 856.423.2862; www.ippanetwork.org).
- The Random Acts of Kindness Foundation (www.randomactsofkindness.org) is a nonprofit organization dedicated to promoting kindness. Inspirational stories, newsletter, kindness ideas.
- Good News Network publishes good news around the world (http://www.goodnewsnetwork.org).
- Graduate programs. Among the few, but growing number of programs are:
  - Claremont Graduate University, Claremont, CA. Earn M.A. or Ph.D. (first doctoral program) in positive psychology. Dr. Mihaly Csikszentmihalyi (of "Flow" fame) serves on the faculty.
  - University of Pennsylvania offers the first master's degree program in positive psychology.
- Journals
  - *The Journal of Happiness Studies*
  - *Journal of Positive Psychology*
  - *Applied Psychology: Health and Well-Being*

Brain Resilience

- Posit Science (Tel: 866-599-6463; www.positscience.com). Neuroscientist Dr. Michael Merzenich's company has developed training software to sharpen brain function.

Happiness Books

- Brooks, A. C. *Gross National Happiness: Why Happiness Matters for America—and How We Can Get More of It*. New York: Basic. An accomplished researcher draws upon large and reputable data bases, mostly from recent studies, to draw conclusions on topics ranging from politics to family and religious values as they relate to happiness.
- Lyubomirsky, S. *The How of Happiness: A Scientific Approach to Getting the Life You Want*. New York: Penguin. A masterful combination of solid research and practical, tested methods to enhance happiness.
- Weiner, E. *The Geography of Bliss: One Grump's Search for the Happiest Places in the World*. New York: Twelve. A whimsical travelogue (ten countries) with rich concepts supporting the idea that happiness is found about anywhere. For those who don't want to be bothered with the research.

- Seligman, M. E. P., & Peterson, C. *Character Strengths and Virtues: A Handbook and Classification (CSV)*. Tenets of positive psychology. Defines twenty-four strengths of thriving, most of which correlate with happiness, and promote optimal functioning.
- Seligman, M.E.P. *Authentic Happiness: Using the New Positive Psychology to Realize Your Potential for Lasting Fulfillment*. New York: Free Press. Happiness and resilience share much overlap, including the signature strengths discussed here. Also, see Seligman's latest book, *Flourish*, for new insights on happiness and well-being.
- Anderson, M. *Laugher is an Instant Vacation*. Naperville, IL: Simple Truths (www.simpletruths.com). A compilation of humorous quotes.
- Dalai Lama, & Cutler, H. C. *The Art of Happiness: A Handbook for Living*. New York: Riverhead. Profound insights on self-esteem and compassion.
- Emmons, R. *Thanks! How the New Science of Gratitude Can Make You Happier*. New York: Houghton Mifflin. Scientific and religious underpinnings, plus practical guidelines for blessings counting in all circumstances.

Moral Strength

- O'Malley, W. J. *Building Your Own Conscience*. Allen, TX: Tabor. Principles, activities, and quotations that skillfully stimulate awareness and growth of a peaceful conscience.

Mindfulness

Mindfulness-Based Stress Reduction (MBSR)

- Search mindfulness or mindfulness-based stress reduction for local resources.
- University of Massachusetts Medical Center, Center for Mindfulness (www.umassmed.edu) hosts training and identifies places where MBSR classes are available.
- Mindfulness meditation CDs and tapes by Jon Kabat-Zinn, Ph.D. (www.stressreductiontapes.com).
- Goldstein, J., & Salzberg, S. *Insight Meditation: An In-Depth Correspondence Course*. A twelve-month mindfulness course by two respected meditation teachers includes twenty-four CDs and a workbook. From Sounds True, Louisville, CO (800-333-9185; www.soundstrue.com).

Mindfulness Books

- Schiraldi, G. R. *Ten Simple Solutions for Building Self-Esteem*. Oakland, CA: New Harbinger. Includes instructions for mindfulness meditation within the context of self-esteem enhancement.
- Kabat-Zinn, J. *Full Catastrophe Living*. New York: Bantam Dell. Still the classic work.
- Brach, T. *Radical Acceptance: Embracing your Life with the Heart of a Buddha*. New York: Bantam.
- Brantley, J. *Calming Your Anxious Mind: How Mindfulness and Compassion Can Free You From Anxiety, Fear, and Panic*. Oakland, CA: New Harbinger.
- McQuaid, J. R, & Carmona, P. E. *Peaceful Mind: Using Mindfulness & Cognitive Behavioral Psychology to Overcome Depression*. Oakland, CA: New Harbinger.

For Combatants

- Schiraldi, G. R. *The Resilient Warrior Before, During, and After War*. Ashburn, VA: Resilience Training International. The essential guide for anyone who is preparing to go to, serving in, or returned from a war zone—and their families. "A masterpiece!....'Required reading' for anyone in the military or law enforcement, for the families and loved ones of those who go in harm's way, and for those who treat or support [them]."

- Grossman, D. *On Combat: The Psychology and Physiology of Deadly Conflict in War and in Peace.* Millstadt, IL: PPCT Research Publications. A very thoughtful treatise on knowing what to expect and how to prepare to kill, when that is required. Lt. Col. Grossman's *On Killing* is also recommended.
- Tick, E. *War and the Soul: Healing Our Nation's Veterans from Post-Traumatic Stress Disorder.* Wheaton, IL: Quest. Tick argues that PTSD is best understood as an identity disorder and soul wound, and moral pain is a root cause. How the honorable warrior soul is healed and reclaimed.
- Gilmartin, K. M. *Emotional Survival for Law Enforcement: A Guide for Officers and Their Families.* Tucson, AZ: E-S Press. Down-to-earth, often humorous.
- Kirschman, E. *I Love a Cop.* New York: Guilford. A balanced treatment of the stresses no one talks about, as well as many practical tips. Useful for both cops and their families. Author also wrote *I Love a Fire Fighter.*

PTSD

- Schiraldi, G. R. *The Post-Traumatic Stress Disorder Source Book: A Guide to Healing, Recovery and Growth.* New York: McGraw-Hill. Clearly explains and normalizes the symptoms of PTSD, explains the range of treatment options (e.g., self-managed, professional, groups) and how to find them, and provides a comprehensive listing of resources. "The most valuable, user-friendly manual on PTSD I have ever seen. Must reading for victims, their families, and their therapists." (Dr. George Everly, founding executive editor, *International Journal of Emergency Mental Health*).

Finding a Trauma Specialist

- **SIDRAN Institute**, Baltimore, MD. (Tel: 410-825-8888; help@sidran.org; www.sidran.org). Helps locate psychotherapists specializing in PTSD. Readings, and other resources.
- **Intensive Trauma Therapy, Inc.**, Morgantown, WV (Tel. 304-291-2912; www.traumatherapy.us). Skillfully combines hypnosis, video technology, and art therapy into 1-2 week intensives with excellent results. Also trains providers.
- **Anxiety Disorders Association of America**, Silver Spring, MD (Tel: 240-485-1001; www.adaa.org). Provides members with a list of professionals who specialize in the treatment of anxiety disorders. Also provides information on self-help and support groups in your area. Has a catalog of available brochures, books, and audiocassettes. Newsletter. Annual national conference.
- **Mental Health America** (National Mental Health Association), Alexandria, VA (Tel: 703-684-7722; 800-969-NMHA; www.NMHA.org). Provides list of affiliate mental health organizations in your area that can provide resources and information about self-help groups, treatment professionals, and community clinics. Crisis line 1-800-273-TALK.
- **EMDR Institute**, Watsonville, CA (831-761-1040; inst@emdr.com; www.emdr.com). Finding clinicians trained in Eye Movement Densensitization and Reprocessing.
- **Association for Contextual Behavioral Science** (www.contextualpsychology.org). To find an Acceptance and Commitment Therapy (ACT) therapist.
- **Behavioral Tech**, Seattle, WA (Tel: 206-675-8588; www.behavioraltech.com). Dialectical behavior therapy, with link to clinical resource directory.
- **Seeking Safety**. To view research and locate Seeking Safety treatment for dual diagnosis of PTSD and substance abuse go to www.seekingsafety.org.
- **Traumatic Incident Reduction Association**, Ann Arbor, MI (Tel: 800-499-2751; info@tir.org; www.tir.org). TIR is a way of processing traumatic memories that some find helpful.

Organizations

- **International Critical Incident Stress Foundation**, Ellicott City, MD (Tel: 410-750-9600; www.icisf.org). Develops and disseminates crisis intervention, stress education, and recovery programs for all those affected by work related stress, disasters, and other traumatic events. Bi-annual conference, newsletter. Known for developing Critical Incident Stress Debriefing.
- **Outward Bound** (Tel: 888-837-5210; www.outwardboundwilderness.org/groups.html). A range of challenging wilderness environments coupled with emotional support to inspire self-respect and care for others, community, and environment. Since 1941. Groups customized for survivors of violence, war, sexual assault, incest, cancer, substance use disorders, mild traumatic brain injury, and grief.
- **American Psychological Association Help Center** at www.APA.org/helpcenter/. Help finding a psychologist, plus information on a wide range of topics. Brochures include resilience in war.

Military/Veterans Services

- **Military OneSource** (Tel: 800-342-9647, www.militaryonesource.com). For active duty, Guard, and Reserve members and families. Get a real voice, usually a licensed counselor, 24 hours a day. Initial assessment, then refers to private practice paid for by DOD, up to six sessions. Then referred to Tricare for additional sessions. Also resources for crisis, deployment, injury, and more.
- **Veterans Affairs Facilities.** The U.S. Department of Veterans Affairs (DVA) is the acknowledged expert in treating war-related trauma. DVA offers various treatment options. For compensation, educational, housing, medical, job training, or other benefits for PTSD, call or write your local DVA facility (e.g., vet center, regional office). If unable to locate one, call **Department of Veterans Affairs**, Washington, DC (Tel: 800-827-1000; www.va.gov —also check here for veterans service organizations, which can help you find needed help). Vet center readjustment counseling services are available to you if you have served in any combat zone or are a family member of a warrior. You need not be enrolled in the VA. Find a vet center at www.vetcenter.va.gov.
- **Outreach Center of the Defense Centers of Excellence for Psychological Health and TBI** (DCoE) (www.dcoe.health.mil/; Toll free line 866-966-1020) is staffed 24/7 to help anyone find psychological or brain injury resources in your area.
- **www.realwarriors.net.** Maintained by DCoE to build resilience, facilitate recovery, and support reintegration of returning service members, veterans, and their families. Much useful information and links to many resources. Inspiring stories of real service members.
- **The National Center for Telehealth and Technology** (T2) (www.t2health.org/). As the primary DOD office for cutting-edge approaches to the use of technology in the area of psychological health and traumatic brain injury, T2 promotes resilience, recovery, and reintegration of warriors and their families. Its site has a virtual PTSD experience to help service/family members learn about PTSD anonymously, as well as many other excellent resources that you can download or read/listen directly to on your computer. It is also developing free mobile technology apps for smart phones and other portable devices on PTSD, TBI, and/or relaxation/stress management. Search the website, Google *T2 mobile apps*, or search iPhone's AppStore or Android's market place to find out what's available.
- **www.afterdloyment.org.** Wellness resources for the military community include assessments, workshops, videos, and related resources on a broad range of relevant topics.

Appendix 10: The Best-kept Secrets of Resilience & Stress Management

At the University of Maryland, where I have taught resilience and stress management courses for over thirty years, we have taught as many as ten different graduate and undergraduate courses on these topics. I can think of several more I'd like to add. So when I'm asked to teach people about resilience and stress management—in less than an hour—I just smile. However, on a long recent road trip I had many hours of alone time. I put my pad beside me and thought, "Putting all the books aside, what have you learned in all your years of studying and teaching about stress and resilience?" I just began writing. What follows is what I call "The Best-kept Secrets of Resilience and Stress Management." It's a sometimes light-hearted summary of many of the points in this book.

1. *Always have a back-up plan.* "Plan A" won't always work.

2. *It's not enough to get stuff off the floor and beautify.* Have a retrieval system so you can find things when you need them. Use filing cabinets, shelves, labeled boxes, and the like.

3. *Correctly apportion the influence of the body on your performance and mood.* If you want to achieve more, be thinner, and feel better, do the following each day: Walk 30 minutes, get just over eight hours of sleep, follow the federal government's MyPlate eating guidelines, and drink six to eight cups of water each day.

4. *Take care of the externals, but especially mind your inner life.* When times get chaotic and unsafe this is particularly important. As WWII concentration camp survivor Viktor Frankl said, you can be happy in a prison camp if you have a mind to.

5. *Live within your means.* Interest on your debts never sleeps or vacations.

6. *Feelings are healthy. Listen to them.* There's a wisdom that will tell you what to do. Record the facts and your feelings in a journal for about twenty minutes each day. This has been found to lift the mood and improve immunity.

7. *Ask* why *like a scientist.* A scientist keeps her eyes open, with curious interest and calm detachment. She accepts what she sees. Depressed people don't, asking *why* a lot: "Why me? Why can't things be different? Why is the world as it is?" Here's the answer: "Because that's the way things are." Things are as they are because people and the world are imperfect. A friend told me about a foursome that was playing golf one day. A young golfer in the group kept saying, "Why did the ball have to go in the bunker?" "Why did I have to shank it?" "Why can't I play better?" Finally, a wizened golfer in the group said, "Son, I think I know your problem." The young golfer said with great anticipation, "What is it?" The older fellow said, "You're not that good." Once we accept the world as it is, we can get to work.

8. *Arrive ten minutes early.* If it's important, arrive earlier. A colleague who had played basketball at Duke University said he learned to hustle back on defense and be ready

for whatever comes. I noticed over the years that he would always be sitting calmly at meetings before the rest of us arrived at the last minute.

9. *Eat fish twice a week.* It helps to prevent depression, coronary heart disease, Alzheimer's, arthritis, migraines, asthma, and probably other diseases.

10. *A little salt on your French fries improves the taste.* Supple bends; rigid breaks. Steel is both strong *and* flexible.

11. *Respect all people.* Like them if you can.

12. *Release grudges and hatred.* These weigh you down.

13. *Don't let any of these define you:* salary, grades, the way people treat you, mistakes, your dating or marital status, or your weight. You are more than that. Viktor Frankl said that the prison camps gave many an inferiority complex, but worth is anchored in things spiritual, not externals.

14. *Try your honest best, speak from the heart, and don't get too attached to the outcome.* Most things don't matter as much as we think—and when they do, we can't always control them.

15. *Your family doesn't need a mansion.* They need a home. They need you.

16. *When you get down, look up.* There's beauty everywhere.

17. *Don't get so attached to your job or school that you lose sight of the big picture.* The Creator is in the big picture. Stay connected no matter how busy you get.

18. *Keep a spare car key in your wallet.* Keep a spare house key *well* hidden outside the house. A friend keeps his spare house key hidden in a fake black rock in his flowerbed. Only problem, there are no black rocks in his neck of the woods.

19. *Keep love in the details.* Otherwise, the final product isn't worth much.

20. *They lack peace who don't live up to their moral capacity.* (Norman Cousins)

21. *From time to time let yourself sit.* When agitated water is allowed to settle, it gets very clear.

22. *Keep change in the car for parking meters, air pumps for tires, and the like.*

23. *View life as a marathon, not a sprint.* Whether we're talking about conditioning, weight loss, careers, relationships, character growth, or child rearing, a steady pace and a good plan—not fits and starts—is generally best.

24. *Breathe low and slow.* Hyperventilation does bad things to us.

25. *Suffering ain't all bad.* Greet it cordially.

26. *Try as you might, you'll always be fallible, never perfect.* Fallible, but still infinitely worthwhile.

27. *Remember the Three-day Rule.* Don't get too concerned unless things haven't settled down by then.

28. *Heal your anger with compassion—first for yourself, then for the offender.* Hostile people are usually hurting people

29. *Don't watch too much violence and news.* These depress the mood and immune system.

30. *Oh yes, it's OK to laugh at your self.* We all do ridiculous things sometimes.

31. *Don't judge people.* You have to be omniscient to do that properly.

32. *Pray until anger leaves you so you can then work out your differences calmly.*

33. *Remember that we choose whom we let under our skin.* I'm grateful to Rex the painter for reminding me of this.

34. *Realize how little it takes to be happy:* A little food, shelter, time to think, sunshine, stuff like that.

35. *Storing additional supplies of food, water, money, and fuel for hard times gives one a secure feeling.*

36. *View yourself like a seed.* You don't stomp a seed and criticize it for being just a seed. Instead you fertilize it, water it, and place it in the sun, and then when it grows go, "Oh, boy!"

37. *Ascent is difficult.* Don't be surprised.

38. *Avoid thoughts that jangle up the nerves:* "This is awful." "I can't take it." "I'm losing my mind." "I should do better." "I'm a jerk." "Either I'm a hero or a heel; strong or a weakling; perfect or a loser." "Others (who might have more market or social worth than I) have more worth as a person."

39. *Plotting to do something kind elevates the spirits*—of others and yourself.

40. *Keep a written plan.* Make sure you plan to play, too

41. *Appreciate at every opportunity.* Dispense with criticism, sarcasm, and teasing.

42. *Save 5-10% of your income for a rainy day.*

43. *Be quietly self-assured.* Remember that you have as much right to sing as anyone.

44. *Scale back unreasonable expectations.*

45. *Keep lists in a loose leaf notebook or electronic planner of things you want to remember:* Goals; To Do's; birthdays; gifts and sizes; key addresses and phone numbers; favorite restaurants, movies, vacation places; things to buy (favorite books, vacuum cleaner bag models); and other things you are prone to forget, like lock combinations, passwords, PIN codes, and directions.

46. *Keep an even keel, steady as you go.* As a remarkable WWII survivor of Iwo Jima once told me, "Get too high and you fall. Get too low and you get depressed."

47. *"The real things haven't changed. It is still best to be honest and truthful."* (Laura Ingalls Wilder, American writer)

The last three come from the legendary, beloved sports figure, John Wooden, who, along with Mother Teresa, is one of my most admired and respected people.[1]

48. *"You're as good as anyone, but you're no better than anyone, and don't forget it."* Actually, Wooden's father told him this.

49. *"Courtesy is a small price to pay for the good will and affection of other people."*

50. *"True happiness comes from the things that cannot be taken away from you. All material things can be taken away."* Wooden also said, "Happiness begins where selfishness ends." Find ways to give back, uplift, beautify, and love in relation to your family, job, community, and nation.

Endnotes

Chapter 1

[1] All names have been changed, and/or represent composites.

[2] See, for example, the National Co-Morbidity Survey and its more recent replication (Kessler et al., 1994; Kessler et al., 2005).

[3] It's interesting that even very bright and informed people can miss the importance of prevention. A prominent general who led our troops into battle in the Middle East addressed an audience in our nation's capital concerning the large number of psychiatric casualties among these troops. Afterwards, I asked him privately what he thought about teaching skills in basic training to help troops cope with combat stress. He replied, "Our troops are strong. They don't need to be inoculated." In contrast, a Marine general said, "It's a simple matter of readiness. If any of my Marines are injured, whether physically or psychologically, I can't replace them so easily. So if you can tell me how to protect them, I'm listening." (Lt. Gen. Paul van Riper, then Deputy Commandant for Combat Development, roughly equivalent to Army G-3, quoted by Jonathan Shay, VA psychiatrist, visiting scholar at large for U.S. Naval War College and author of *Achilles in Vietnam,* in forward to Figley, C. R., & W. Nash, Eds., (2007), *Combat Stress Injury*, New York: Routledge, xvii. See Appendix 2 for quotations regarding the possibilities of primary prevention.)

[4] Positive psychology studies positive emotions, personal strengths, full and effective engagement in activities, and pathways to meaning and satisfaction in life. The psychologist Abraham Maslow coined the term *positive psychology* in 1957. However, the psychologist Martin Seligman is considered the Father of Positive Psychology, declaring it his main focus during his term as president of the American Psychological Association in 1998. Seligman stated that personal strengths such as courage, optimism, honesty, and perseverance are the most likely buffers against mental illness. Whereas Freud identified "ordinary human unhappiness" as psychotherapy's goal, positive psychology has a much more optimistic goal.

[5] Read more about Rescorla in *Heart of a Soldier,* a biography by James B. Stewart (Simon & Schuster, 2002) and Amanda Ripley's *The Unthinkable* (Three Rivers Press, 2009).

[6] If you are working in a group, it is very motivating to share with each other the responses to both the costs/benefits analysis and this sentence stem.

Chapter 2

[1] Quoted in Brooks & Goldstein (2001, p.xiii).

[2] VA researchers Friedman, Keane, and Resick (2007) note that at least eight meanings of resilience appear in the literature, including resistance, recovery, adapting, competent functioning, having key resources, the absence of pathology, and flexibility. Others have included as part of resilience optimal health and functioning across the lifespan, growth, and development.

[3] While environmental protections such as social support certainly influence one's adaptation, we will focus in this book on those strengths that are under the

individual's control. Individual strengths refer to strengths of mind and character, emotional intelligence, physical conditioning, and so on. While groups and communities can also be resilient, our focus is on first strengthening the individual.

4 Historically, people have typically resisted preventive efforts, or at least been slow to heed the call for them. Perhaps we overconfidently assume that disease will strike others, not ourselves. Perhaps we may not realize how effective and inexpensive prevention is, or we may not know how to do it. Perhaps we wrongly assume preventive skills are too difficult to learn.

5 Resilience is sometimes defined as the failure to develop PTSD following exposure to a traumatic event. Indeed some preventive efforts have been implemented with the express purpose of preventing PTSD and its co-morbid mental illnesses.

6 Two studies are provocative. Prostitutes in one study had a current PTSD prevalence of 42% (Valera, Sawyer, & Schiraldi, 2000). Their developmental profiles were comparable to those of 1832 female Navy recruits in terms of earlier sexual victimization, including childhood abuse and rape (Merrill et al., 1998), suggesting that the latter group would be at high risk for PTSD.

7 A study of 9/11 survivors reached similar conclusions. About one-third of those who were most highly exposed to traumatic events (e.g., being physically injured or having both seen the attack in person and lost a friend or relative) were resilient (defined as having one or no PTSD symptoms). Overall, about two-thirds of New York area residents were resilient in the months following 9/11 (Bonanno, 2006). It has been observed that the resilient survivors self-enhanced ("I know what I am doing and why I am doing it"), carried on despite sadness, expressed warm memories of the deceased, and appreciated community solidarity.

Chapter 3

1 The left PFC is associated with good moods, self-confidence, engagement with life, and the dampening of negative emotions—which will be important to remember when we discuss meditation later on.

2 Cortisol might spike with acute stressors, such as a traumatic event. Or cortisol might be chronically elevated at lower levels, say from persistent family discord, poor attachment to parents, or constant worry. Some experts suspect that cortisol levels that do not fluctuate according to normal daily rhythms might also disrupt brain function. The hippocampus signals the body to shut down cortisol production.

3 The brain rewires itself as learning causes neurons to connect through the growth of dendritic branches. Brain plasticity also means that unused regions of the brain can assume new tasks. Thus the visual region of the brain in a blind person can take on functions related to hearing and touch.

4 A very interesting study is reported by Ratey (2008). Students in Naperville, IL, were required to take aerobic training each day before classes started. Only 3% of the students were overweight, compared to the national average of 30%. They rose to number one nationally in science, and number six in math—a finding that was supported by other studies.

5 If you choose a low-carbohydrate diet, replacing animal proteins with vegetable proteins appears to boost heart health and longevity.

[6] Choose vegetable juices low in salt. Supplementing orange juice with plant sterols, an antioxidant, seems promising. In one study this kind of juice reduced cholesterol, C-reactive protein (a marker of inflammation), and LDL, while raising HDL.

[7] Reducing caloric intake also seems to help mitochondria be more efficient and reduce free radicals. Two baby aspirin (162 mg total) or half a regular aspirin daily also reduces inflammation.

[8] Mark Mattson at the National Institute on Aging found that 30% caloric restriction causes the release of four factors in the brain that promote brain plasticity, while increasing antioxidants. Other research links caloric restriction to less oxidative stress and inflammation.

[9] Supplements are generally useful for those with heart disease or high triglycerides. Check first with your doctor if you have diabetes or heart disease with angina, irregular heartbeats, and an implantable defibrillator. Avoid if you are using anticoagulants or have uncontrolled hypertension. Supplements are also useful for rheumatoid arthritis, psoriasis, and autoimmune disorders.

[10] Oxford researcher Bernard Gesch found that inmates taking vitamin and mineral supplements and omega oils showed marked reduction in aggressive behavior, suggesting how diet and supplements might beneficially work together. However, most people who eat a healthy diet will probably require minimal supplementation.

[11] The Mediterranean Diet, which helps to prevent cognitive decline, calls for six glasses of water daily.

[12] Fat cells generate inflammatory proteins, which impair hippocampal functioning. Exercise inhibits the production of inflammatory proteins.

[13] While the research is far from conclusive, insufficient calcium might favor weight gain. Calcium, especially from food, might curb hunger and promote fat excretion.

[14] In one study the Mediterranean and Atkins diets were equally effective at reducing weight. But the Mediterranean group maintained weight loss better and controlled blood sugar better.

[15] Stress hormones also decline as the night continues, perhaps further helping the hippocampus function.

[16] The reduction of deep sleep might also effect the hippocampus and impair memory formation.

[17] Both trauma and sleep shortage, which both raise cortisol levels, are thought to shrink the hippocampus, impairing its ability to down-tune the amygdala. An overactive amygdala is associated with disrupted REM sleep.

[18] Supplementing before bedtime with 600 mg of calcium, plus 300 mg of magnesium, is sometimes recommended.

[19] Benzodiazepines taken for anxiety can reduce deep sleep and lead to tolerance and rebound insomnia when you stop using.

Chapter 4

[1] Expanded and adapted from Slon & Gilbert (2008).

Chapter 6

[1] This is based on the Hook-Ups exercise from *Brain Gym* by Dennison, P. E., & Dennison, G. E., p.1289, Edu-Kinesthetics, Inc., Venura, CA.

[2] This section is adapted with permission, including the heart coherence diagram and the reprinting of The Quick Coherence® Technique respectively, from Childre, D., & Rozman, D., (2003), *Transforming Anger: The HeartMath Solution for Letting Go of Rage, Frustration, and Irritation*, Oakland, CA: New Harbinger (©2003, D. Childre & D. Rozman), and Childre, D., & Rozman, D., (2005), *Transforming Stress: The HeartMath Solution for Relieving Worry, Fatigue, and Tension*, Oakland, CA: New Harbinger (©2005, D. Childre & D. Rozman).

[3] Technically, this is called heart rate variability feedback. In general, heart coherence tends to increase heart rate variability, which is linked to numerous health benefits.

[4] In addition to the heart coherence skill, it appears that a number of other resilience strategies described in this book promote heart coherence, including cognitive restructuring, progressive muscle relaxation, slow breathing, and mindfulness (see, for example, Blumenthal et al., 2005, and Gervirtz & Lehrer, 2003).

[5] For example, one child learned to "go into my heart and talk to my kind friend" (or other caring individual).

Chapter 7

[1] Ellis originated the catastrophizing and shoulds distortions. Aaron Beck identified most of the distortions presently used in cognitive therapy, the idea of core beliefs, and the daily thought record.

[2] The nuclear attack submarine commanded by Navy Commander Scott Waddle inadvertently collided with a Japanese fishing boat, killing nine. After many tears and nightmares, he concluded, "When I die, I know I will be judged for all of my life, not just one event" (*Time*, April 23, 2001, p.36). In contrast, one who remained stuck on a distortion was a cop whose tactical team rushed an intruder who held a small boy at knifepoint. His team killed the intruder, but someone inadvertently also shot the boy. The cop said, "[Despite all the good I've done], it's this shooting I'll be remembered for" (Artwohl and Christensen, 1997, p.109).

[3] Suggested by Artwhohl and Christensen (1997).

[4] This and the next example suggested by Gilmartin (2002).

[5] The first five examples are adapted from Dicks' (1990) interviews with Vietnam vets.

[6] Duane A. Brudvig, quoted in Hansel et al. (1995, p.200).

[7] This example is adapted from Gilmartin (2002).

[8] Shame is feeling no good, dirty, or wrong to the core. Shame and negative self-appraisals predict PTSD symptoms, including dissociation. Shame is common to survivors of sexual assault, domestic violence, and discrimination. To protect against shame, people often become secretive. For example, Bob Kerrey led a squad of Navy SEALS, which returned fire on a mission in Vietnam. He later discovered that about fourteen women and children had been inadvertently killed. He said, "If you feel that shame it's very hard to talk about it" (*Time*, May 7, 2001, p.27). Yet talking about it is usually instrumental to the healing process.

⁹ This might surface as, "I should be able to save/protect everyone," to which one spouse replied, in effect, "What's with you guys that you think you're God and can control the universe?" (Smith, 2005). One Army general with PTSD, for example, thought that he should have done more to protect his people from a suicide bomber.

Chapter 8

¹ This section is adapted mainly from Hayes, S. C., with S. Smith, (2005), *Get Out of Your Mind and Into Your Life: The New Acceptance and Commitment Therapy*, Oakland, CA: New Harbinger Publications. Also, Hayes, S. C., & Strosahl, K. D., with K. G. Wilson, (1999), *ACT: An Experiential Approach to Behavior Change*. New York: Guilford Press.

Chapter 9

¹ As is the case with the other techniques in this part, if these do not provide sufficient relief seriously consider getting the help of a mental health professional who can treat PTSD, depression, etc. in a more thorough manner.
² The eye movements technique was developed by Dr. Larry D. Smyth, Sheppard and Enoch Pratt Hospital, as a useful adaptation of Dr. Francine Shapiro's eye movement desensitization and reprocessing. Detailed instructions are found in Smyth, L. D., (1996), *Treating Anxiety Disorders with a Cognitive-Behavioral Exposure Based Approach and the Eye-Movement Technique: Video and Viewer's Guide*, Havre de Grace, MD: RTR Publishing.
³ Moving the eyes back and forth for thirty seconds before trying to learn information has also been found to improve memory, perhaps by engaging both hemispheres of the brain.
⁴ Heart rate variability is related to heart coherence.
⁵ For example, in 2000 TFT was used to treat trauma in people from four to seventy-eight years of age in war-torn villages in Kosovo with complete relief reported in 98% of cases (Johnson et al., 2001). In an HMO setting, TFT led to significant improvements in a wide range of symptoms and, in reported cases, heart rate variability (Sakai et al., 2001). In Rwanda, a single session of TFT greatly reduced PTSD in orphaned children twelve years after they had witnessed genocide (Sakai, Connolly, & Oas, 2010). More controlled research is awaited.
⁶ Adapted with permission from modifications of Robert L. Bray, Ph.D., LCSW, Director, Thought Field Therapy Center of San Diego, www.rlbray.com .

Chapter 10

¹ Unresolved distressing events compete with attentional resources. Thus, for example, writing about negative events improved students' grades and memory, while reducing intrusive memories (Klein & Boals, 2001). Also, structured writing assignments worked as well as cognitive-behavioral therapy for PTSD, and reduced dissociation (van Emmerik, Kamphuis, & Emmelkamp, 2008).

2 We now know the likely mechanism: stress-induced secretion of cortisol impairs the hippocampus, allowing the amygdala to give excessive emotional charge to the memory and preventing the cool, integrated storage of the memory.

3 Adapted with permission from Dr. James Pennebaker's website: http://homepage.psy.utexas.edu/homepage/Faculty/Pennebaker/Home2000/Writin gandHealth.html

4 As a rule, younger men tend to favor action-oriented coping. When the situation can't be changed, we can actively express emotions. For example, the Navy SEAL Marcus Luttrell (2007) noted a common SEAL view that very few problems can't be solved with high explosives or a bullet. Such a view works well in certain tactical situations. It was not sufficient to deal with nightmares from being unable to help a wounded comrade when he was pinned down by overwhelming gunfire. Luttrell also observed that SEALs don't admit to fear. Again, this general rule often works, except when it doesn't. Sometimes it is good to acknowledge fear without judgment and then go on, lest your fears eat you up inside. As Lt. Col. Dave Grossman says, "There is no survival value in denial." Kirschman (2004, p.180) relates a story that demonstrates that actively expressing feelings can help us to get unstuck and then move on. Hours after a boat capsized in water rescue training, a seasoned firefighter got the shakes and feared returning to the water to resume training. Finally he worked up the nerve to disclose to his team, "I don't know about you guys but I thought I was going to die out there today and I doubt I'm the only one who felt that way." One by one the rest of the team acknowledged their fears of dying and never again seeing family, anger over dying so young, and sadness over an incomplete life. The discussion brought the team together as everyone realized there was no shame in experiencing those common feelings. Literally, they realized they were all in the same boat. The next day everyone was prepared to go out to train in the water again.

5 Adapted from Borkovec, T. D., (undated manuscript), *How to Reduce Worrying*, Pennsylvania State University, University Park, PA.

Chapter 11

1 These are adapted from Schiraldi (2009).

2 Compiled from Barrett (1996).

3 Recall that cortisol impairs the ability of the hippocampus to store memories in a "cool," functional way.

4 Recall the case of Navy SEAL Marcus Luttrell (2007). In his nightmares, he heard his best friend plead for Marcus to rescue him. Yet nothing could change the fact that this courageous warrior had been unable to rescue his dying friend because overwhelming enemy fire had his team pinned down.

5 Zadra, A. L., Recurrent Dreams: Their Relation to Life Events, in Barrett (1996, pp.232-247).

6 Modifying a dream, writing down the modified dream, and imaginally rehearsing the revised dreams has improved nightmares, sleep, and PTSD symptoms in sexual assault survivors with PTSD (Krakow, Hollifield, Johnston, et al., 2001).

7 King, J., & Sheehan, J. R., The Use of Dreams with Incest Survivors, in Barrett (1996, p.62).

Chapter 12

[1] Related in Herriott, J. (1982).

[2] This is consistent with the findings of other researchers, such as Emmy Werner, Emory Cowen, Michael Rutter, Norman Garmezy, and Rueven Bar-On, who have found that a positive sense of self characterizes resilient, competent children.

[3] Conversely, damaged self-esteem can result from traumatic exposure, such as when a rape victim who has been treated as an object concludes that she is worthless. Here self-esteem must be rebuilt as part of the healing process.

[4] See review, "The Use and Misuse of Self-esteem," in *Harvard Mental Health Letter*, (2007), *23*, 12, pp.1-3.

[5] Recall that cortisol impairs proper functioning of the hippocampus.

[6] The principles and skills that follow are adapted from Schiraldi (2001).

[7] Criminals are high in narcissism and only moderate in self-esteem.

[8] Kirschman (2004) notes that some people derive self-esteem from belonging to an elite culture, such as firefighters (we might add police, military, or any other group). She notes that those who derive self-esteem almost exclusively from success at the job are most at risk for problems.

[9] The instructions for the following skills are adapted from Schiraldi (2001).

[10] Reprinted with permission from Eyre, L., & Eyre, R., (1980), *Teaching Children Joy*, Salt Lake City, UT: Deseret. ©1980 Deseret Book Company.

[11] Gauthier, Pellerin, & Renaud (1983).

Chapter 13

[1] For example, an optimist who is fired might think, "My boss fired me because of the economic conditions."

[2] Notice that the pessimistic explanatory style is similar to the labeling distortion discussed in chapter 7. A label says, "I am _____(a loser, etc), and will always and in all ways be that way." Rather than remembering the three P's of pessimism (personal, pervasive, permanent), some prefer the words *me, everything, always*. Interestingly, optimists explain good outcomes using the three Ps. That is, they attribute success to inner strengths (acknowledging what they did in applying strengths and skills or marshaling resources) that generalize to other areas, and they expect good outcomes to continue. Attributing good outcomes to luck minimizes one's input or the input of others.

[3] Hendin & Haas (1984, p.219).

[4] Suggested by Amen (2008).

[5] In one study, writing about the best possible self actually increased mood more than writing about past traumas (King, 2001).

[6] This exercise combines elements described in: Austenfeld, Paolo, & Stanton (2006); King (2001); and Lyubomirsky (2008).

[7] Later you might break down goals into sub-goals and specific steps needed to accomplish these goals and sub-goals. Doing this in writing helps to clarify the process.

[8] Echterling, Presbury, & McKee (2005).

Chapter 14

[1] This table combines findings from a number of studies: Brown, Schiraldi, & Wrobleski (2003); Diener & Diener (1995); Fordyce (1985); and Fredrickson, Tugade, Waugh, & Larkin (2003). Jonathan Shay (1994) notes that Vietnam vets rate themselves as unhappy many times more often than their civilian counterparts, suggesting that happiness can be a casualty of war and that it is important to restore happiness in war veterans.

[2] In a 2008 review of 19 studies, the most satisfied people gained up to ten years of life, as much as giving up smoking by age thirty-five. Happy people have lower levels of cortisol and C-reactive protein, a marker for inflammation.

[3] Think of a time when you were intensely afraid. Perhaps your only thought was to get away from the situation immediately. Conversely, when we experience joy or relaxed pleasure we stop to think more broadly, considering more solutions. Think of how a good laugh provides comic relief or a vacation recharges the batteries—making us more open to solving problems.

[4] Reprinted with permission from Lyubomirsky, S., (2008), *The How of Happiness: A Scientific Approach to Getting the Life You Want,* New York: *Penguin.* ©2008 Sonja Lyubomirsky.

[5] The work of Michael Meaney, McGill University, is also instructive. Meaney found that parenting styles affected resilience in baby rats. Nurtured (i.e., licked) baby rats tolerated stress better than neglected baby rats. However, placing a neglected rat with a nurturing parent turned the baby rats into resilient adults. Nurturing parents also resulted in the development of hippocampi in the baby rats that were better at monitoring and regulating stress hormones. This research suggests that baseline temperament can be influenced by nurturing and the possibility that becoming a nurturing parent to oneself might help compensate for early negative experience.

[6] Although happy people tend to be more satisfied with their own appearance.

[7] In a study of two million people in eighty nations, happiness reaches a low point in the forties and fifties, but increases thereafter. As long as they are healthy, people in their sixties and seventies are as happy as young people.

[8] Although women are twice as likely to suffer from depression and anxiety.

[9] Those with graduate degrees tend to be less happy than those with college degrees, perhaps suggesting an issue of balance with the former group.

[10] The term *hedonic treadmill* was coined by Princeton University psychologist and winner of the Nobel Prize in economics Daniel Kahneman.

[11] I'm reminded of a song I used to sing as a child, "when you kiss your dollar bill, it doesn't kiss you back." In a 1998 Harvard study, faculty, staff, and students said they would prefer a lower-paying job where they would be earning more than their peers over a higher-paying job where they were out-earned by their peers. This reflects an insecurity and need to appear more successful than others; money is regarded as a status symbol, rather than a means to a satisfying living. It calls to mind a quote attributed to the actor Will Smith (and Will Rogers): "Too many people spend money they haven't earned, to buy things they don't want, to impress people they don't like."

[12] The data might seem surprising, since liberals tend to view government in a flexible, nurturing way. A 2008 Harris Poll also showed conservatives to be happier than

liberals. In the GSS surveys, conservatives also report better mental health and a greater sense of worth; they give more to charity, volunteer more, and give more blood. They are more religious and more likely to be married, but controlling for religion and other demographic variables, conservatives are still 10% happier. Philosophically, conservatives tend to emphasize individual action, while liberals tend to favor government solutions to social problems. Conservatives also are less likely to favor certain moral freedoms that have been associated with less happiness.

13 As happiness researcher David Myers has noted, "There are few stronger predictions of happiness than a close, nurturing, equitable, intimate, lifelong companionship with one's best friend" (quoted in Ben-Shahar, 2007, p.112).

Chapter 15

1 Medoff, M. (1986, November 9), In Praise of Teachers, *New York Times Magazine*, 72.

2 I'm grateful to Sonja Lyubomirsky, Ph.D., University of California, Riverside, for this idea.

3 This is not a suggestion to ignore troubling memories. Memories involving shame, guilt, or other intense emotions usually require processing. Once this has been accomplished, however, grateful reminiscing can shift the balance away from obsession with pain, and reinforce neural pathways related to happiness. Starve pain and feed joy, as the saying goes, and pain pathways tend to weaken.

4 You might make a mental note to go back and process the intrusion at a later time.

5 For this reason, Paul gloried in tribulation, knowing that suffering can help us develop endurance, experience/character, and sustaining hope (Rom 5:5).

6 Quoted in Klein (2002, p.195).

7 Luxemburg, Rosa, (2000), Briefe aus dem Gefangnis. Berlin. Quoted in Klein (2002, p.215).

8 Kung (2006, p.196).

9 I am thankful to Dr. Philip Watkins, Eastern Washington University, for suggesting these caveats in personal communication, February 23, 2009. See also a study on grateful processing of unpleasant memories in Watkins, Cruz, Holben, & Kolts (2008).

Chapter 16

1 Smith, T. W. (2007, April), "Job Satisfaction in America," National Opinion Research Center report. Seligman (2002) notes that lawyers are the richest and most depressed profession, and experience higher than average rates of alcoholism, illegal drugs, and divorce. Perhaps it is because they are trained to be aggressive, judgmental, adversarial, pessimistic, and emotionally detached. He recommends pro bono or mediation work to increase altruism.

2 Reported in American Psychological Association (2001, November), *Monitor on Psychology*, 32, (10), print version p.16 (www.apa.org/monitor/nov01/pentagon.aspx).

3 I think of a former student, an undercover narcotics agent for years, who somehow avoided becoming cynical. When he arrested people, he did so with good will and thought, "Something tells me not to judge. This is someone on the downward slope at

this time. He's not all bad. I remember many people helping me in my life. Perhaps helpful people could help turn him around, too."

Chapter 17

[1] LaRoche, L, "Fully Human, Fully Alive with Humor, Compassion, and Love," The Psychology of Health, Immunity, and Disease, vol. A, 326, in Proceedings of the Sixth International Conference of the National Institute for the Clinical Application of Behavioral Medicine" (quoted in Karren, Hafen, Smith, & Frandsen, (2002, p.619)).

[2] The renowned psychologist Albert Ellis observed that much of mental illness is over-seriousness. The ability to take problems with a lighter touch often signals recovery.

[3] When the comedian Martin Short was young, his brother and parents died. After his father died, he sized things up, concluding that he would be optimistic because the alternative was just too crushing to his soul.

[4] In the research, these four styles are measured by Martin's Humor Styles Questionnaire, comprised of four eight-item scales.

[5] Klein (1989, p.xxi) describes this kind of humor as "power in a powerless situation." Joke long enough about the most frightening word, such as *firing squad*, and often it becomes more like any other word.

[6] Reprinted with permission from Chesley, L., (1973), *Seven Years in Hanoi: A POW Tells His Story*, Salt Lake City, UT: Bookcraft. © 1973. Larry J. Chesley.

[7] Teasing *might* improve relationships when the teased person feels secure, accepted, and on a relatively equal footing with the teaser, and when humor is a habitual part of the relationship. The general rule applies: ensure that the teased person is enjoying the teasing. If in doubt, don't tease.

[8] An exception might be humor that disparages abusive, powerful people, such as POWs mocking their captors.

[9] From Anderson, N., (1984, out of print), *The Ha Ha Book*. Quoted in Klein (1989, p.112). This laughter exercise is similar to a Buddhist laughter mediation that has been practiced for centuries. See also the smile meditation in chapter 26 of this book.

Chapter 18

[1] Just as structural integrity means that something does not break or tear easily, so does moral integrity help one withstand adversity.

[2] Related words are moral intelligence, character, moral courage (doing what is right despite fear of ridicule, censure, disapproval or personal loss), integrity, value seeking life, and moral compass. The latter term suggests that morality is not imposed, but is pursued as an inner, personal choice.

[3] Most would also agree that morality includes avoiding behaviors that are not in the best interest of self and others, such as abuse, taking what is not freely given, and harmful addictions.

[4] Without honesty we are not trusted. When we compromise our honesty, we begin to distrust ourselves, and, eventually, others (after all, if I lie, cheat, or steal, I would expect others to do so, as well). Emotional honesty is a critically important type of honesty. Emotional honesty is being honest about what we truly feel, including what really hurts. Often we hide what we really feel with anger or blaming. The first step to

healing is to honestly acknowledge what hurts, so that the wounds can be healed. If avoided and unhealed, emotional hurts can lead to anxiety, abuse of painkillers and drugs, and other self-destructive addictions.

[5] In one poll 90% were self-reported serial liars, telling multiple lies each week. Lies can include misstating facts on a job application, bending the truth about one's whereabouts after work or what one paid for an item, giving an untruthful opinion about another's appearance, or calling in sick when one is not. Other reasons for stretching the truth are to protect a relationship, to protect one from harmful consequences, to save one's reputation, and to get a person off one's back.

[6] Another good question: "Short of defending your family from a murderer, what's worth compromising your integrity?"

[7] Angers (1999).

[8] In Siebert (1996, p.238), personal communication to author.

[9] Belief in abortion on demand is also associated with less happiness, correcting for age, income, education, race, and marital status. Consistent with the GSS data, an analysis of the 1996 National Longitudinal Survey of Adolescent Health data found that teenage girls and boys involved in premarital sex are much more depressed and more likely to attempt suicide than those who are not sexually active. The former were also more prone to regret, wishing they had waited longer before starting sexual activity.

Chapter 19

[1] See Marano, D. A., (2008, March/April), Food Chain, *Psychology Today*, 59-60.

[2] As Buddhist teachers refer to suffering.

[3] Rector, K., (2007, April 5), Survival and Success, *Diamondback*, 1.

[4] Reported by Hitti, M., (2006, August 28), Resilience Lets Katrina Survivors Cope, WebMD Medical News, retrieved March 13, 2007, from www.webmd.com/news/20060901/weeks-top-stories-090106

[5] Reported by Reilly, R., (posted 2007, May 7), Coaching the Grief Stricken, SI.com, retrieved from http://sportsillustrated.cnn.com/2007/writers/rick_reilly/05/07/dungy0430/1.html.

[6] Suggested by Williams, M. B., & Poijula, S., (2002), *The PTSD Workbook*, Oakland, CA: New Harbinger.

[7] Adapted from Barkely, P. S., Stress Reduction: Visual Imagery, Kentucky, http://slincs.coe.utk.edu/gtelab/learning_activities/25barp.html.

Chapter 20

[1] For example, spiritually-based programs have been developed to help with feelings of anger, abandonment, isolation, shame, and guilt; and to address negative images of God, appreciation of the body, and sexuality.

[2] Pargament (1999). A relationship with the sacred might be connection to God, a transcendent or universal power, nature, or others, according to the individual.

[3] For example, 40 of 41 WWII combat vets believed in God and felt that their faith helped them survive the stress of combat. See Schiraldi (2007).

[4] Peacock & Poloma (1999).

[5] Perhaps these themes can be collectively expressed by the word *shalom*, which suggests harmony and oneness with God and others, wholeness of self, and fulfilling individual functioning as God intended. See Ellison & Smith (1991).

[6] Religious dialogue, for example, can encourage people to confront difficult moral issues in advance, and settle in advance on a stance most likely to result in peace of conscience.

[7] For example, see Wiegand & Weiss (2006). In addition, regular churchgoers who feel "very close to God" are 27 percent more likely to be very happy than churchgoers who do not feel very close to God, according to 2004 GSS data.

[8] See review in Pargament, Desai, & McConnell (2006).

[9] Writes philosopher of religion John MacMurray (1999, p.171): "The maxim of illusory religion runs: 'Fear not; trust in God and He will see that none of the things you fear will happen to you': that of real religion, on the contrary, is 'Fear not: The things that you are afraid of are quite likely to happen to you, but they are nothing to be afraid of.'"

[10] Poloma & Gallup (1991).

[11] Pargament, Desai, & McConnell (2006).

[12] Reprinted with permission from Chesley, L., (1973), *Seven Years in Hanoi: A POW Tells His Story*, Salt Lake City, UT: Bookcraft. © 1973. Larry J. Chesley.

Chapter 21

[1] Another study of one thousand adolescents found that the adolescent happiness declined as parents were wealthier (Csikszentmihalyi & Schneider, 2000).

[2] See, for example, Sirgy (1998).

[3] In fact, a Harris Poll (Spring, 2008) found that those without credit cards were happier than those who had one or more credit cards.

[4] Wisely managed, wealth can provide financial security, some comfort in times of distress, and certain freedoms (e.g., to travel, be entertained, start a new business, escape a bad boss, give to others).

[5] Interestingly, three of the lower paying occupations show the greatest happiness and job satisfaction: clergy, firefighters, and educators—all professions with a strong altruism component, according to a National Opinion Research Center report (Smith, 2007).

[6] Flabella, E. R., (2007, November), *Ensign*, pp.14-15.

Chapter 22

[1] Adapted from Schiraldi (2009).

[2] Frankl (1963), p.166.

[3] Nakamura & Csikszentmihalyi (2003). The process need not be complicated. Mother Teresa taught potential helpers of the poorest of the poor to simply come and see what needs doing, and then do it.

[4] Adapted from Schiraldi (2009).

[5] Suggested by Yalom (1980).

⁶ Hecht (2007, p.50). As the humanitarian physician Albert Schweitzer said, "Success is not the key to happiness. Happiness is the key to success. If you love what you are doing, you will be successful."

⁷ Wrzesniewski, McCauley, Rozin, & Schwartz (1997).

⁸ Seligman (2002).

⁹ Frederickson, Tugade, Waugh, & Larken (2003).

¹⁰ Ten Boom (1971). Quotes pp.210, 215, & 217.

¹¹ This and the following quotation are from Hansel, Steidle, Zaczek, & Zaczek, Eds., (1995, pp.194 & 198).

Chapter 23

¹ Closely related to social intelligence, the term *sociability* implies liking, connecting with, and getting on well with others. It suggests a more active stance than social support.

² Fredrickson and Losada (2005) conclude that flourishing in business teams, marriage, and individual well-being is associated with ratios of positive to negative emotions above 2.9. Some genuine negative feelings are appropriate and useful (e.g., to resolve conflict or work through grief), but it is best to avoid corrosive contempt, disgust, and global and enduring shame (time limited guilt is useful). Genuine, but not feigned, positivity is useful. At a ratio of about 12, flourishing starts to deteriorate, perhaps because authentic negative feelings are avoided. But a ratio between approximately 3 and 12 is associated with innovation and flexibility.

³ A sociopath can read and manipulate another's emotions, but feel no compassion.

⁴ Goleman (2006) explains that the mind also mirrors the face. Thus, smiling tends to elicit happy emotions in the mind. This will be useful in the smile meditation that we'll learn in chapter 26.

⁵ For practice in reading facial expressions, you might wish to take Paul Ekman's online training (www.PaulEkman.com). The training, which takes less than an hour, has encouraging preliminary data. Ekman identified the seven basic emotions.

⁶ Simply naming emotions has been found to calm the amygdala.

⁷ The experience of Joshua Chamberlain is instructive. Chamberlain turned down a prestigious commission in the Union Army during the Civil War in order to first learn the trade of leading soldiers. His disciplined preparation later earned his troops' respect and enabled him to creatively lead them at Gettysburg, in the pivotal part of the pivotal battle of the war, with spectacular results.

⁸ A growing number of countries also have military units spend time together decompressing from combat before returning home.

⁹ Michelangelo would study a block of granite and try to see a form within it. He viewed his role as removing the superfluous marble and letting that form emerge. Similarly, leaders remove barriers and liberate the inner strengths of their followers.

¹⁰ The most successful coach in sports history was John Wooden. Wooden did not lead through fear, but taught that a pat on the back (a word, a smile, a nod) is a great motivator. Psychologists have long studied Wooden's methods. Although he was a taskmaster, he never demeaned his basketball players. Consequently, they were prepared physically, mentally, and emotionally to give their best.

[11] As DePree (1989, p.25) observes, "Having a say differs from having a vote."

[12] Schofield, J. M., "Address to the Corps of Cadets, August 11, 1879," in *Bugle Notes,* (West Point, NY: U.S. Military Academy, Vol. 90, 1998, p.258).

[13] www.srengthsfinder.com is one such site; there is a charge. See others in Appendix 9.

[14] Positive moods enhance left-brain functions, such as verbal functions.

[15] This section summarizes Carducci's research, adapted with author's permission. See an excellent synthesis in the following article, from which this section is mostly drawn: Carducci, B., (Jan/Feb 2000), Shyness: The New Solution, *Psychology Today*, pp.38-78. Dr. Carducci has written five excellent books on shyness. Also see Marano, H. E., The Eight Habits of Highly Popular People, in the same issue, pp.40-78.

[16] Many shy people have low self-esteem and fear rejection. In compensation, some affect an air of superiority, perhaps distrusting others.

[17] See also Schiraldi (2009) and Schiraldi & Kerr (2002), from which portions of this section are adapted.

[18] We are speaking here of the emotional debt. Sometimes it is best that the offender be brought to justice for the protection of himself and society. However, this can be done without hatred or vengeance.

[19] The very name suggests that we cancel the debt before someone deserves forgiveness or asks for it.

[20] It can be very healing to do this, even years after the offense (e.g., "I've been thinking about what happened. I wish it hadn't and I'm sorry."). If someone apprises you of an unintended offense, you might say, "I didn't see it that way or intend an offense, but since I hurt you I ask your forgiveness."

Chapter 24

[1] In Marano, H. E. (1992, January/February), Reinvention of Marriage, *Psychology Today*, pp.48-85.

[2] Deborah Tannen, Ph.D., (2001) is among the leaders in synthesizing this research. I am especially grateful to her contributions to this section.

[3] This section on validating is adapted with permission from Lundberg, G., & Lundberg, J., (1999), *I Don't Have to Make Everything All Better*, New York: Viking Penguin. © 1995 Gary B. Lundberg and Joy S. Lundberg.

[4] Avoidance of problems and unwillingness to discuss them is frequently cited as a problem among couples.

[5] Those who work out their issues, commit, and then marry fare better in a number of measures (including divorce, marital satisfaction, and arguing) compared to those who cohabitate.

[6] Suggested by Sherry Amatenstein, LMSW, author of *The Complete Marriage Counselor* (Avon, MA: Adams Media, 2010).

[7] See Jacob et al. (2008), and Bergin, M. S. (2009, Winter), Making Dinner Together Time, *BYU Magazine*, from which most of these ideas are adapted.

Chapter 25

1 It was not unusual to find these octogenarians still enthusiastically engaged in traveling, enjoying the arts, playing bridge, reading, being docents at museums, dancing, and even playing sports.

2 This means carving out a chunk of time with only a general plan, such as going to the zoo, and then just letting things happen spontaneously.

3 This and the remaining steps are adapted from the first edition of Schiraldi, G. R., (2000), *The Post-Traumatic Stress Disorder Sourcebook*, New York: McGraw-Hill.

Chapter 26

1 The practice of mindfulness meditation appears to increase the ratio of activity in the left prefrontal cortex to activity in the right prefrontal cortex. Left prefrontal cortex activity is associated with the positive emotions associated with happiness and resilience. It appears that compassion can be cultivated and that so doing calms the amygdala. As compassion is attended to, neural pathways associated with negative emotions simply degrade from disuse.

2 Hardiness is closely related to resilience.

3 For a more thorough and nuanced exploration of these attitudes, see Kabat-Zinn (1990).

4 Some PTSD practitioners teach, for example, that patients are not broken; they are simply stuck in the ordinary mind. Healing comes from reconnecting to the wisdom mind.

5 Or, as meditation teachers often say, "It is not time that heals, but love." Paradoxically, it takes more energy to avoid stressors than to turn toward them gently. Perhaps it is the struggle of avoidance that weakens us mentally and physically.

6 Think of the parallel with validating. Rather than trying to fix our mates' problems, it is usually best to bring full and kind awareness to the problem, and trust them to eventually solve it.

7 Carver (1997). Also, Cohn & Pakenham (2008).

8 Consider, for example, the combat veterans with PTSD who avoid memories, feelings, bodily sensations, and other reminders of the trauma. Perhaps they stay home or use alcohol to try to escape the reminders. Nothing changes as the pain is avoided. The antidote is acceptance of their symptoms and their selves.

9 The ensuing section on mindfulness training is adapted from Schiraldi (2007).

10 The very language sometimes used by cognitive therapists suggests the "thought struggle" in the ordinary mind: *fight back, talk back, rebut, punch back, control your thoughts*. Mindfulness instead greets distortions cordially ("This is just what the ordinary mind does") without trying to change them. Thus, mindfulness starves them by not feeding them emotionally.

11 According to respected neuroscience researcher and former Chief of the Section on Brain Biochemistry of the Clinical Neuroscience Branch of the National Institute of Mental Health, Candace Pert, Ph.D., (2000), people in the developed world have over ninety industrial chemicals in their bodies, and the body eliminates most of its wastes through breathing and the skin.

12 Some might prefer to use mantras such as *one* or *love*, which can work equally as effectively.

Chapter 27

1 Ben Sherwood, author of *The Survivors Club*, on The Diane Rehm Show (WAMU 88.5 radio), January 29, 2009.
2 Avoidant/passive coping is linked to PTSD and acute stress in various populations, including the military. See for example, Taylor et al. (2009).
3 As Army Ranger Nate Self, author of *Two Wars: One Hero's Fight on Two Fronts— Abroad and Within*, explained (2008), every emotional wound survived is a pathway to another's healing; everyone can help another from his experience in his own unique way. (Presentation to the Warrior Transition Brigade at Walter Reed Army Medical Center, Washington, DC, April 28, 2010.)
4 I'm grateful to Spencer G. Wood, Ph.D., (2005) for suggesting this activity.
5 The most successful coach in sports history, the legendary John Wooden, taught his players that success is not defined by the scoreboard. Sometimes the other players are simply better. However, success is the satisfaction of knowing that one has done his or her best. It was Wooden who taught his players to "be quick, but don't hurry."

Chapter 28

1 When I think of this model, I think of my rugby team captain at West Point. Learning from the British, he would encourage us during the games with, "Come on, lads," which I always found inspiring.
2 Adapted slightly and reprinted with permission from Wood, S. G., (2003), *Icebox: The Ultimate Mental Skills & Toughness Training System for Athletes,* Quakertown, PA: Ultimate Athlete LLC. [CD]. © 2003, Ultimate Athlete LLC.

Chapter 29

1 Occasionally creative insights come in a flash with little or no preparation. Usually, however, preparation precedes the insight, or as Pasteur said, "Chance favors the prepared mind."
2 Or as Naresh Kumar, M.D., Institute of Stress Medicine, in Canada, suggests, when you're caught in stressful situations, try the NICE strategy: Recast the upset as a New, Interesting, Challenging Experience.
3 This mental constriction is sometimes called perceptual narrowing or tunnel vision. See Amabile, Hadley, & Kramer (2002, August).
4 "My training is never complete" is part of the highly skilled U.S. Navy SEALs Creed.
5 For example, Biech (1996, p.141) notes that Harry M. Warner of Warner Brothers Pictures said around 1927, "Who the hell wants to hear actors talk?"
6 The messages acquired in the hero culture can work against getting needed help. Marcus Luttrell, the sole Navy SEAL survivor of an incredible battle in Afghanistan, gives exceptional insights into such messages. He writes that SEALS come to think that there are "very few problems that can't be solved with high explosives or a bullet"

370

(Luttrell, 2007, p. 9). Of course, nightmares and traumatic memories aren't fixed with explosives or bullets, He adds that "No SEAL would ever admit to being scared of anything" (p. 188). An alternative is to admit fear and then act despite it. As Lt. Col. Dave Grossman often says, "There is no survival value in denial." Tragically, some begin to think of themselves as invulnerable, and become too proud to ask for needed help. No one is invulnerable. The oak that survives bends in the wind, though it is firmly rooted.

7 Ideas and quotations are from Nixon (2008, May/June, p.57).

8 Adapted slightly and reprinted with permission from Wood, S. G., (2003), *Icebox: The Ultimate Mental Skills & Toughness Training System for Athletes,* Quakertown, PA: Ultimate Athlete LLC. [CD]. © 2003, Ultimate Athlete LLC.

Chapter 30

1 The teaching method of legendary coach John Wooden was frequently studied by psychologists. Wooden started the season by teaching his players how to properly put on socks in order to reduce blisters (i.e., starting with the most basic fundamentals). He was a kind, but strict taskmaster. When players improperly performed in practice, he paused the action. His three-step method was: (1) "I want you to do this" (then he'd demonstrate the right way). (2) "You are doing this" (this time demonstrating what he saw). (3) "I want you to do this" (demonstrating again and reinforcing the right way). All of this was done with respect and without belittling.

2 In a supporting study, a single hour of relaxation and mental rehearsal training resulted in lower anxiety and better performance in police recruits, as measured by assailant hits in live fire training. Subjects were trained to relax for ten minutes, and mentally rehearse skills acquired during training (such as not giving up if wounded) for twenty minutes, using energizing cue words and positive self-statements (e.g., "I can deal with this."). In most research with sports the combination of actual practice and mental rehearsal is best. See Shipley & Baranski (2002).

Chapter 31

1 Personal communication, circa April 21, 2007.

2 Recall that James Pennebaker instructed people to record facts and feelings about past events. This approach applies similar questions in an anticipatory manner, as does the emotional inoculation exercise that follows.

3 Personal communication, July 22, 2009.

4 Army psychiatrist Colonel Elspeth Ritchie calls killing "the dead elephant in the living room that nobody wants to talks about" (In Baum, 2004, p.47).

5 Perhaps we erroneously assume that avoiding the problem is helping combatants. Some wish to spare them the moral burden of contemplating killing. Some leaders assume that soldiers would never fire on another human if they truly understood the emotional risks. This denies combatants the chance to work through the moral dilemma of having to kill and to overcome the fear of killing when the cause is just. Most will do even this repugnant duty if they are clear about the reasons. Many therapists don't want to upset combat veterans by encouraging them to talk about

killing. It is curious that we generally don't use this thinking with regards to other traumas. We can't prepare for what we don't acknowledge.

[6]The points on killing, the five stages of killing, training considerations, and the discussion on being wounded are all adapted with permission from: Grossman, D., (1996), *On Killing: The Psychological Cost of Learning to Kill in War and Society*, New York: Back Bay, © 1996 David A. Grossman; Grossman, D., with Christensen, L. W., (2004), *On Combat*, Millstadt, IL: PPCT Research Publications, ©2004 David A. Grossman; and Grossman, D., (2009, February 26), *Bulletproof Mind*, training presented at International Critical Incident Stress Foundation 10th World Congress on Stress, Trauma & Coping, Baltimore, MD.

[7] In 2009, mental health disorders caused more hospitalizations among U.S. troops than any other reason (including injuries, battle wounds, or pregnancies), according to the Pentagon. The approximately 17,500 hospitalizations for mental health disorders far surpassed the 11,156 for injuries and battle wounds. Depression, anxiety, substance abuse, and adjustment problems such as PTSD cost the Pentagon 488 years of lost duty in 2009 (*USA Today*, May 14, 2010).

[8] However, as John Keegan, a graduate of the British Army Staff College, notes, once Americans commit to war, they go to battle in a workmanlike way (Grossman, 2004).

[9] Miller (2006) adds that freezing might lead to regrets, such as "My buddy might still be alive if I'd shot sooner." Freezing happens in times of uncertainty. The combatant accepts the fact that freezing can occur, and the fact that warriors accept the inevitable risk to their lives. At the same time, they train to act as decisively as humanly possible. Wise leaders and comrades will allow the officer who has killed time to sort through the complexities, and not encourage him to "get back to normal" too soon.

[10] For example, in the National Vietnam Veterans' Readjustment Study, atrocities were more causal of PTSD than combat. Sometimes atrocities are committed by one's own volition, as in the cases of one who goes berserk and kills civilians or one who kills enemy prisoners to avoid the inconvenience of having to guard them. Sometimes atrocities result from following immoral orders. I think for example, of U.S. Army lieutenant William Calley, who was convicted in the famous My Lai massacre of civilians in Vietnam. Although he was smiling when I met him shortly afterwards, he struck me as one who was troubled inside, perhaps uneasy from following what was likely an unlawful order. Conversely, Hugh Thompson, who saw the massacre unfolding, landed his chopper. He told the U.S. soldiers to stand down and evacuated ten civilians to safety. Though initially shunned by his peers, he had the peace of mind of knowing he'd done the right thing (Angers,1999).

[11] Shay (2002) argues that even war zone promiscuity cheapens the sexual experience and makes it more difficult to experience love and wholesome intimacy afterwards.

[12] Adapted with permission from Tick, E., (2005), *War and the Soul: Healing Our Nation's Veterans from Post-Traumatic Stress Disorder*, Wheaton, IL: Quest. © 2005 Edward Tick. Do not reproduce without written permission.

[13] The point here is only to indicate a different way to regard one's opponents.

Chapter 32

1 Social withdrawal and emotional numbing are common relationship problems. Cantrell and Dean (2005) sagely observe that stress can lead us to subconsciously build a firewall around us to prevent more suffering and pain, as if to say, "I've had enough." This is more likely among those who feel that stress shows weakness. Thus, social support, a vital recovery resource, is cut off.

2 It is interesting that many cops and firefighters moonlight or work overtime, allowing little down time to recover from stress.

3 Charles Morgan III, of Yale University and the National Center for PTSD, found that high dissociators, as measured by a short self-report scale, were significantly less likely to make it through the Military Survival School and the U.S. Army Special Forces course (as reported in Ripley, 2008).

4 This is less common, but is often seen in people who have experienced severe childhood trauma, such as sexual abuse. It is crucial to professionally treat this condition.

5 This model is consistent with the early formulations of pioneering trauma theorist Pierre Janet, who said that overwhelming fear leads to unspeakable terror and freezing. Unable to speak or physically expend the energy of distress, panic attacks logically follow.

6 Dissociation is not uncommon when people are tortured. This is undoubtedly merciful as the brain tries to protect the victim from pain. The victim can adapt a matter of fact attitude: "This is just my brain protecting me from pain. I'll flow with this until it's safe to focus on the present environment again."

7 Watchorn (2000).

Chapter 33

1 Those veterans with the most severe symptoms on average gained the least, probably suggesting the need for longer or more comprehensive treatment.

2 Quoted by Commander Thomas A. Gaskin, Ph.D., Marines Combat Operational Stress Control Program, in "Combat/Operational Stress Control Programs in the United States Navy and Marine Corps," The International Society for Traumatic Stress Studies, 23rd Annual Meeting, November 15-17, 2007, Baltimore, MD.

3 Vanden Brook, T., (2008, November 11), General's Story Puts Focus on Stress Stemming From Combat, *USA Today*. Also Shaughnessy, L., & Starr, B., (2009, March 6), Generals Share their Experience with PTSD, CNNhealth.com.

4 About pre-military trauma, VA counselor Jonathan Shay (2002, p.142) writes, "The most violent and intractable cases of combat trauma we have worked with in the VA Clinic have frequently experienced rapes or other severe abuse and neglect in childhood and/or adolescence prior to military service." Present PTSD symptoms can be a merciful signal to get these traumas from earlier life resolved.

5 Paradoxically, anger is often a way to avoid authentic, underlying feelings, such as sadness or fear.

Chapter 34

[1] For example, how might you help a buddy on a crisis intervention team? You might ask him privately: "How many missions have you been on recently? What have you been called out about?" (This is often not discussed. If one has been called out too frequently, especially for very difficult crises, coordinate with the team leader on how call-outs are made.); "Are you using anything that we've learned to cope?"; "Do you need a break?" (If necessary, you might say, "You need a breather so we don't lose you.") You might summarize the resilience skills, such as exercise, talking to someone, mindfulness, relaxation, or using a journal, and ask, "Would any of these help?" (Remind your buddy, "You must save yourself in order to be of use to others.") Team members must know when to back away from the table to recharge: they often feel like they can't give up their responsibility to help. You might also ask, "Would a talk with a mental health professional help?")

Appendix 10

[1] Johnson, N. L., (2003), *The John Wooden Pyramid of Success*, Los Angeles: Cool Titles, p.159, 125, 190, and 182, respectively.

Bibliography

Amabile, T., Hadley, C. N., & Kramer, S. J. (2002, August). Creativity Under the Gun. [Special Issue on the Innovative Enterprise: Turning Ideas into Profits]. *Harvard Business Review 80*, (8), 52-61.

Amen, D. G. (1998). *Change Your Brain, Change Your Life*. New York: Three Rivers Press.

Angers, T. (1999). *The Forgotten Hero of My Lai: The Hugh Thompson Story*. Lafayette, LA: Acadian House.

Artwohl, A., & Christensen, L. W. (1997). *Deadly Force Encounters: What Cops Need to Know to Mentally and Physically Prepare for and Survive a Gunfight*. Boulder, CO: Paladin.

Ashe, A., & Rampersad, A. (1993). *Days of Grace: A Memoir*. New York: Ballantine.

Austenfeld, J. L., Paolo, A. M., & Stanton, A. L. (2006). Effects of Writing About Emotions versus Goals on Psychological and Physical Health Among Third-Year Medical Students. *Journal of Personality, 74*, 1267-286.

Baker, D., & Greenberg, C., with Yalof, I. (2007). *What Happy Women Know: How New Findings in Positive Psychology Can Change Women's Lives for the Better*. New York: Rodale.

Baranowsky, A. B., Gentry, J. E., & Schultz, D. F. (2005). *Trauma Practice: Tools for Stabilization and Recovery*. Cambridge, MA: Hogrefe & Huber.

Barker, D. B. (2007). Antecedents of Stressful Experiences: Depressive Symptoms, Self-esteem, Gender, and Coping. *International Journal of Stress Management, 14*, (4), 333-349.

Barrett, D. (Ed.). (1996). *Trauma and Dreams*. Cambridge, MA: Harvard University Press.

Baylis, N. (2009). *The Rough Guide to Happiness*. London: Rough Guides.

Baum, D. (2004, July 12 & 19). The Price of War. *The New Yorker*, 44-52.

Ben-Shahar, T. (2007). *Happier: Learn the Secrets to Daily Joy and Lasting Fulfillment*. New York: McGraw-Hill.

Biech, E. (1996). *The ASTD Trainer's Sourcebook: Creativity & Innovation*. New York: McGraw-Hill.

Blumenthal, J. A., Sherwood, A., Babyak, M. A., Watkins, L. L., Waugh, R., Georgiades, A., Bacon, S. L., Hayano, J., Coleman, R. E., & Hinderliter, A. (2005). Effects of Exercise and Stress Management Training on Markers of Cardiovascular Risk in Patients with Ischemic Heart Disease: A Randomized Controlled Trial. *Journal of the American Medical Association, 293*, (13), 1626-1634.

Bonanno G. A., Galea, S., Bucciarelli, A., & Vlahov, D. (2006). Psychological Resilience After Disaster: New York City in the Aftermath of the September 11th Terrorist Attack. *Psychological Science, 17*, (3), 181-186.

Borkovec, T. D., Wilkinson, L., Folensbee, R., & Lerman, C. (1983). Stimulus Control Applications to the Treatment of Worry. *Behavior Research & Therapy, 21*, 247-251.

Boscarino, J. A., & Adams, R. E. (2008). Overview of Findings from the World Trade Center Disaster Outcome Study: Recommendations for Future Research after Exposure to Psychological Trauma. *International Journal of Emergency Mental Health, 10*, (4), 275-290.

Boscarino, J. A., Adams, R. E., & Figley, C. R. (2005). A Prospective Cohort Study of the Effectiveness of Employer-Sponsored Crisis Interventions after a Major Disaster. *International Journal of Emergency Mental Health, 7*, 9-22.

Broadfoot, B. (1974). *Six War Years 1939-1945.* New York: Doubleday.

Brooks, A. C. (2008). *Gross National Happiness: Why Happiness Matters for America—and How We Can Get More of It.* New York: Basic.

Brooks, R., & Goldstein, S. (2001). *Raising Resilient Children.* New York: McGraw-Hill.

Brosschot, J. F., & Van der Doef, M. (2006). Daily Worrying and Somatic Health Complaints: Testing the Effectiveness of a Simple Worry Reduction Intervention. *Psychology and Health, 21,* (1), 19-31.

Brown, J., & Dutton, K. (1995). The Thrill of Victory, the Complexity of Defeat: Self-esteem and People's Emotional Reaction to Success and Failure. *Journal of Personality and Social Psychology, 68,* 712.

Brown, S. L., Schiraldi, G. R., & Wrobleski, M. (2003, October). *Psychological Strengths as Correlates of Happiness and Health in College Students.* Paper presented at the Second International Positive Psychology Summit, Washington, DC.

Burns, G. (1984). *Dr. Burns' Prescription for Happiness.* New York: G. P. Putnam's Sons.

Cantrell, B. C., & Dean, C. (2005). *Down Range: From Iraq and Back.* Seattle: Wordsmith.

Carrier, C. (2000, May). From Darkness to Light. *Reader's Digest,* 100-106.

Carver, C. S. (1997). You Want to Measure Coping but Your Protocol's Too Long: Consider the Brief COPE. *International Journal of Behavioral Medicine, 4,* 92-100.

Casriel, E. (2007, March/April). Stepping Out. *Psychology Today,* 69-75.

Chaffee, J. (1998). *The Thinker's Way: 8 Steps to a Richer Life.* New York: Little, Brown & Co.

Chambers, O. (1963). *My Utmost for His Highest.* Uhrichsville, OH: Barbour.

Chesley, L. (1973). *Seven Years in Hanoi: A POW Tells His Story.* Salt Lake City, UT: Bookcraft.

Childre, D., & Rozman, D. (2003). *Transforming Anger: The HeartMath Solution for Letting Go of Rage, Frustration, and Irritation.* Oakland, CA: New Harbinger.

Childre, D., & Rozman, D. (2005). *Transforming Stress: The HeartMath Solution for Relieving Worry, Fatigue, and Tension.* Oakland, CA: New Harbinger.

Cicchetti, D., Rogosch, F. A., Lynch, M., & Hold, K. D. (1993). Resilience in Maltreated Children: Processes Leading to Adaptive Outcome. *Development and Psychopathology, 5,* 629-647.

Cohn, A., & Pakenham, K. (2008). Efficacy of a Cognitive-behavioral Program to Improve Psychological Adjustment among Soldiers in Recruit Training. *Military Medicine, 173,* (12), 1151-57.

Cohn, R., Culp, C., & Genser, S. (1987). *Human Problems in Major Disasters: A Training Curriculum for Emergency Medical Personnel.* Washington, DC: U.S. Government Printing Office, 1-23. DHH publication no (ADM) 88-1505.

Connor, K. M., & Davidson, J. R. T. (2003). Development of a New Resilience Scale: The Connor-Davidson Resilience Scale (CD-RISC). *Depression and Anxiety, 18,* 76-82.

Covey, S. R. (1990). *The Seven Habits of Highly Effective People.* New York: Fireside.

Creamer, M., Elliott, P., Forbes, D., Biddle, D., & Hawthorne, G. (2006). Treatment for Combat-Related Posttraumatic Stress Disorder: Two-Year Follow-Up. *Journal of Traumatic Stress, 19,* (5), 675-685.

Csikszentmihalyi, M. (1996). *Creativity: Flow and the Psychology of Discovery and Invention.* New York: Harper Perennial.

Csikszentmihalyi, M., & Schneider, B. (2000). *Becoming Adults: How Teenagers Prepare for the World of Work.* New York: Basic.

Dallaire, R., with Beardsley, B. (2003). *Shake Hands with the Devil: The Failure of Humanity in Rwanda*. Toronto: Vintage Canada.

Day, J. H., Vermilyea, E., Wilkerson, J., & Giller, E. (2005). *Risking Connection in Faith Communities*. Baltimore, MD: Sidran.

Department of the Army. (2003). *U.S. Army Combat Stress Control Handbook*. Guilford, CT: Lyons.

DePree, M. (1989). *Leadership is an Art*. New York: Dell.

Dicks, S. (1990). *From Vietnam to Hell: Interviews with Victims of Post-Traumatic Stress Disorder*. Jefferson, NC: McFarland & Co.

Diener, E., & Diener, M. (1995). Cross-cultural Correlates of Life Satisfaction and Self-Esteem. *Journal of Personality and Social Psychology, 68,* (4), 653-663.

Dumont, M., & Provost, M. A. (1999). Resilience in Adolescents: Protective Role of Social Support, Coping Strategies, Self-Esteem, and Social Activities on Experience of Stress and Depression. *Journal of Youth and Adolescence, 28,* (3), 343-363.

Echterling, L. G., Presbury, J. H., & McKee, J. E. (2005). *Crisis Intervention: Promoting Resilience and Resolution in Troubled Times*. Upper Saddle River, NJ: Pearson.

Edmunds, M. E. (1999). *Happiness: Finders, Keepers*. Salt Lake City, UT: Deseret.

Ellison, C. W., & Smith, J. (1991). Toward an Integrative Measure of Health and Well-being. *Journal of Psychology and Theology, 19,* (1), 35-48.

Emmons, R. A. (1986). Personal Strivings: An Approach to Personality and Subjective Well-being. *Journal of Personality and Social Psychology, 51,* 1058-1068.

Eyre, L., & Eyre, R. (1980). *Teaching Children Joy*. Salt Lake City, UT: Deseret.

Felitti, V. J. (2002). The Relation Between Adverse Childhood Experiences and Adult Health: Turning Gold into Lead. *The Permanente Journal, 6,* (1), 46-49.

Follette, V. M., & Pistorello, J. (2007). *Finding Life Beyond Trauma*. Oakland, CA: New Harbinger.

Fordyce, M. W. (1985). The Psychap Inventory: A Multi-scale Test to Measure Happiness and its Concomitants. *Social Indicators Research, 18,* 1-33.

Frankl, V. (1963). *Man's Search for Meaning*. New York: Pocket Books.

Franzini, L. R. (2002). *Kids Who Laugh*. Garden City, NY: Square One.

Fredrickson, B. L., & Losada, M F. (2005). Positive Affect and the Complex Dynamics of Human Flourishing, *American Psychologist, 60,* 678-686.

Fredrickson, B. L., Tugade, M. M., Waugh, C. E., & Larkin, G. R. (2003). What Good Are Positive Emotions in Crises? A Prospective Study of Resilience and Emotions Following the Terrorist Attacks on the United States on September 11th, 2001. *Journal of Personality and Social Psychology, 84,* (2), 365-376.

Friedman, M. J., Keane, T. M., & Resick, P. A. (2007). *Handbook of PTSD: Science and Practice*. New York: Guilford.

Gahm, G. A., Lucenko, B. A., Retzlaff, P., & Fukada, S. (2007). Relative Impact of Adverse Events and Screened Symptoms of Posttraumatic Stress Disorder and Depression Among Active Duty Soldiers Seeking Mental Health Care. *Journal of Clinical Psychology, 63,* 199-211.

Gauthier, J., Pellerin, D., & Renaud, P. (1983). The Enhancement of Self-esteem: A Comparison of Two Cognitive Strategies. *Cognitive Therapy and Research, 7,* (5), 389-398

Gevirtz, R. N., & Lehrer, P. (2003). Resonant Frequency Heart Rate Biofeedback. In M. S. Schwartz & F. Andrasik (Eds.), *Biofeedback: A Practitioner's Guide* (3rd ed.) (pp. 245-250). New York: Guilford.

Gilmartin, K. M. (2002). *Emotional Survival for Law Enforcement: A Guide for Officers and Their Families.* Tucson, AZ: E-S Press.

Goleman, D. (2006). *Social Intelligence: The New Science of Human Relationships.* New York: Bantam.

Gonzales, L. (2003). *Deep Survival: Who Lives, Who Dies, and Why.* New York: Norton.

Grossman, D. (1996). *On Killing: The Psychological Cost of Learning to Kill in War and Society.* New York: Back Bay.

Grossman, D., with Christensen, L. W. (2004). *On Combat.* Millstadt, IL: PPCT Research Publications.

Grossman, D. (2009, February 26). *Bulletproof Mind.* Training presented at International Critical Incident Stress Foundation 10th World Congress on Stress, Trauma & Coping, Baltimore, MD.

Hansel, S., Steidle, A., Zaczek, G., & Zaczek, R. (Eds.). (1995). *Soldier's Heart: Survivors' Views of Combat Trauma.* Lutherville, MD: Sidran.

Harter, S. (1986). Cognitive-developmental Processes in the Integration of Concepts about Emotions and the Self. *Social Cognition, 4,* 119-151.

Harter, S. (1999). *The Construction of the Self.* New York: Guilford.

Harvey, M.R. (1996). An Ecological View of Psychological Trauma and Trauma Recovery. *Journal of Traumatic Stress, 9,* 3-23.

Hayes, S. C., & Strosahl, K. D. (Eds.). (2004). *A Practical Guide to Therapy.* New York: Springer-Verlag.

Hayes, S. C., Strosahl, K. D., & Wilson, K.G. (1999). *Acceptance and Commitment Therapy: An Experiential Approach to Behavioral Change.* New York: Guilford.

Hayes, S. C., with Smith, S. (2005). *Get Out of Your Mind and Into Your Life: The New Acceptance and Commitment Therapy.* Oakland, CA: New Harbinger.

Hayes, S. C., & Strosahl, K. D., with Wilson, K. G. (1999). *ACT: An Experiential Approach to Behavior Change.* New York: Guilford Press.

Hecht, J. M. (2007). *The Happiness Myth. Why What We Think is Right is Wrong.* HarperSanFrancisco.

Hendin, H., & Haas, A. P. (1984). *Wounds of War: The Psychological Aftermath of Combat in Vietnam.* New York: Basic.

Herriott, J. (1982). *The Best of James Herriot: Favourite Memories of a Country Vet.* New York: St. Martin's Press.

Hobfoll, S., & London, P. (1986). The Relationship of Self-concept and Social Support to Emotional Distress among Women during War. *Journal of Social and Clinical Psychology, 4,* 189-203.

Hobfoll, S., & Walfisch, S. (1986). Coping with a Threat to Life: A Longitudinal Study of Self-Concept, Social Support, and Psychological Distress. *American Journal of Community Psychology, 12,* (1), 87-99.

Hughes, M., Patterson, L. B., & Terrell, J. B. (2005). *Emotional Intelligence in Action: Training and Coaching Activities for Leaders and Managers.* New York: Pfeiffer.

Jacob, J. I., Allen, S., Hill, E. J., Mead, N. L., & Ferris, M. (2008). Work Interference with Dinnertime as a Mediator and Moderator Between Work Hours and Work and Family Outcomes. *Family and Consumer Sciences Research Journal, 36,* (4), 310-327.

Janis, I. L. (1977). Adaptive Personality Changes. In A. Monat & R. S. Lazarus (Eds.), *Stress and Coping: An Anthology* (pp. 272-284). New York: Columbia Press.

Johnson, C., Shala, M., Sejdijaj, X., Odel, R., & Dabishevci, K. (2001). Thought Field Therapy: Soothing the Bad Moments of Kosovo. *Journal of Clinical Psychology, 57,* (10), 1237-1240.

Kabat-Zinn, J. (1990). *Full Catastrophe Living.* New York: Bantam Dell.

Karren, K. J., Hafen, B. Q., Smith, N. L., & Frandsen, K. J. (2002). *Mind/Body Health: The Effects of Attitudes, Emotions, and Relationships.* San Francisco: Benjamin Cummings.

Kasser, T., & Ahuvia, A. (2002). Materialistic Values and Well-Being in Business Students. *European Journal of Social Psychology, 32,* 137-146.

Kessler, R. C., Berglund, P., Demler, O., Jin, R., Merikangas, K. R., & Walters, E. E. (2005). Lifetime Prevalence and Age-of-onset Distributions of DSM-IV Disorders in the National Comorbidity Survey Replication. *Archives of General Psychiatry, 62,* (6), 593-602.

Kessler, R. C., McGonagle, K. A., Zhao, S., Nelson, C. B., Hughes, M., Eshleman, S., Wittchen, H. U., & Kender, K. S. (1994). Lifetime and 12-month Prevalence of DSM-III-R Psychiatric Disorders in the United States. *Archives of General Psychiatry, 51,* 8-19.

King, L. A. (2001). The Health Benefits of Writing About Life Goals. *Personality and Social Psychology Bulletin, 27,* 798-807.

Kirschbaum, C., Prussner, J. C., Stone, A. A., Federenko, I., Gaab, J., Lintz, D., Schommer, N., & Hellhammer, D. H. (1995). Persistent High Cortisol Responses to Repeated Psychological Stress in a Subpopulation of Healthy Men. *Psychosomatic Medicine, 57,* 468-474.

Kirschman, E. (2004). *I Love a Fire Fighter: What the Family Needs to Know.* New York: Guilford.

Klein, A. (1989) *The Healing Power of Humor.* New York: Jeremy P. Tarcher/Putnam.

Klein, K., & Boals, A. (2001). Expressive Writing Can Increase Working Memory Capacity. *Journal of Experimental Psychology: General, 130,* (2), 520-533.

Klein, S. (2002). *The Science of Happiness: How Our Brains Make Us Happy—and What We Can Do to Get Happier.* New York: Marlowe.

Krakow, B., Hollifield, M., Johnston, L., Koss, M., Schrader, R., et al. (2001). Imagery Rehearsal Therapy for Chronic Nightmares in Sexual Assault Survivors with Posttraumatic Stress Disorder: A Randomized Controlled Trail. *Journal of the American Medical Association, 286,* (5), 537-545.

Kung, C. (2006). *Buddhism: The Awakening of Compassion and Wisdom.* Taipei, Taiwan: The Corporate Body of the Buddha Educational Foundation.

Lee, H. J. (2002). Psychosocial Variables Associated with Resilience Among Mothers-Daughters Dyads. Unpublished doctoral dissertation, University of Maryland, College Park.

Levine, P. A., with Frederick, A. (1997). *Waking the Tiger, Healing Trauma.* Berkeley, CA: North Atlantic Books.

Lewinsohn, P., Munoz, R., Youngren, M., & Zeiss, A. (1986). *Control Your Depression.* New York: Prentice Hall.

Lundberg, G., & Lundberg, J. (1999). *I Don't Have to Make Everything All Better.* New York: Viking Penguin.

Luttrell, M., with Robinson, P. (2007). *Lone Survivor: The Eyewitness Account of Operation Redwing and the Lost Heroes of Seal Team 10.* New York: Little, Brown, & Co.

Lyubomirsky, S. (2008). *The How of Happiness: A Scientific Approach to Getting the Life You Want.* New York: Penguin.

MacMurray, J. (1999). *Persons in Relation.* Amherst, New York: Humanity Books.

Maguen, S., Metzler, T. J., Litz, B. T., Seal, K. H., Knight, S. J., & Marmar, C. R. (2009). The Impact of Killing in War on Mental Health Symptoms and Related Functioning. *Journal of Traumatic Stress, 22,* (5), 435-443.

Markman, H., Stanley, S., & Blumberg, S. L. (1994). *Fighting* for *Your Marriage: Positive Steps for Preventing Divorce and Preserving a Lasting Love.* San Francisco: Jossey-Bass.

Marra, T. (2005). *Dialectical Behavior Therapy in Private Practice.* Oakland, CA: New Harbinger.

Martins, A., Greenberg, J., & Allen, J. J. B. (2008). Self-esteem and Autonomic Physiology: Parallels Between Self-esteem and Cardiac Vagal Tone as Buffers of Threat. *Personality and Social Psychology Review, 12,* (4), 370-389.

Martin, R. A. (2007). *The Psychology of Humor: An Integrative Approach.* Boston: Elsevier Academic Press.

McCain, J, with Salter, M. (1999). *Faith of My Fathers: A Family Memoir.* New York: Random House.

McGhee, P. E. (1999). *Health, Healing and the Amuse System: Humor as Survival Training* (3rd ed.). Dubuque, Iowa: Kendall/Hunt.

Merrill, L. L., Newell, C. E., Thomsen, C. J., Gold, S. R., Milner, J. S., Koss, M. P., & Rosswork, S. G. (1999). Childhood Abuse and Sexual Revictimization in a Female Navy Recruit Sample. *Journal of Traumatic Stress, 12,* (2), 211-225.

Michael, R. T., Gagnon, J. H., Laumann, E. O., & Kolata, G. (1994). *Sex in America: A Definitive Survey.* Boston: Little, Brown, and Company.

Michalko, M. (2001). *Cracking Creativity: The Secrets of Creative Genius.* Berkeley, CA: Ten Speed Press.

Miller, L. (2006). Officer-involved Shooting: Reaction Patterns, Response Protocols, and Psychological Intervention Strategies. *International Journal of Emergency Mental Health, 8,* (4), 239-254.

Morgan, C. A., Hazlett, G., Wang, S., Richardson, E. G., Schnurr, P., & Southwick, S. M. (2001). Symptoms of Dissociation in Humans Experiencing Acute, Uncontrollable Stress: A Prospective Investigation. *American Journal of Psychiatry, 158,* 1239-1247.

Mother Teresa: A Film by Ann and Jeanette Petrie with a Narration by Richard Attenborough. (1986). Petrie Productions. [DVD]

Murray, K. R. (2006). *Training at the Speed of Life, Volume One.* Gotha, FL: Armiger.

Nakamura, J., & Csikszentmihalyi, M. (2003). The Construction of Meaning through Vital Engagement. In C. L. M. Keyes & J. Haidt (Eds.), *Flourishing: Positive Psychology and the Life Well-lived* (pp. 83-104). Washington, DC: American Psychological Association.

Nixon, R. (2008, May/June). Quit While You're Behind; Persistence Doesn't Always Pay: The Benefits of Plan B. *Psychology Today,* 57.

Pargament, K. I. (1999). The Psychology of Religion and Spirituality?: Yes and No. *International Journal for the Psychology of Religion, 9,* 3-16.

Pargament, K. I., Desai, K. M., & McConnell, K. M. (2006). Spirituality: A Pathway to Posttraumatic Growth or Decline? In L. G. Calhoun & R. G. Tedeschi (Eds.), *Handbook of Posttraumatic Growth: Research and Practice* (pp. 121-137). Mahway, NJ: Erlbaum.

Peacock, J. R., & Poloma, M. M. (1999). Religiosity and Life Satisfaction across the Life Course. *Social Indicators Research, 48,* 321-345.

Pennebaker, J. W. (1997). *Opening Up: The Healing Power of Expressing Emotion*. New York: Guilford.

Pert, C. (2000). *Your Body Is Your Subconscious Mind*. Boulder, CO: Sounds True.

Poloma, M. M., & Gallup, G. H., Jr. (1991). *Varieties of Prayer: A Survey Report*. Philadelphia: Trinity Press International.

Prigerson, H. G., Bierhals, A. J., Kasl, S. V., Reynolds, C. F., 3rd, Shear, M. K., Day, N., Beery, L. C., Newsom, J. T., & Jacobs, S. (1997). Traumatic Grief as a Risk Factor for Mental and Physical Morbidity. *American Journal of Psychiatry, 154*, 616-623.

Printz, A., & Wrangnert, R. (1999). *Inside the FBI: Surviving the Street*. Film produced by Printz Production AB. Distributed by Chevron Publishing Corporation, Ellicott City, MD.

Ratey, J. J., with Hagerman, E. (2008). *Spark: The Revolutionary New Science of Exercise and the Brain*. New York: Little, Brown, and Co.

Ripley, Amanda, (2008). *The Unthinkable: Who Survives When Disaster Strikes—and Why*. New York: Crown. Also see How to Survive a Disaster in *Time* (2008, June 9), pp. 40-45.

Sakai, C. E., Connolly, S. M., & Oas, P. (2010). Treatment of PTSD in Rwandan Child Genocide Survivors Using Thought Field Therapy. *International Journal of Emergency Mental Health, 12*, (1), 41-50.

Sakai, C., Paperny, D., Mathews, M., Tanida, G., Boyd, G., Simons, A., Yamamoto, C., Mau, C., & Nutter, L. (2001). Thought Field Therapy Clinical Applications: Utilization in an HMO in Behavioral Medicine and Behavioral Health Services. *Journal of Clinical Psychology, 57*, (10), 1215-1227

Sanders, T. (2005). *The Likeability Factor*. New York: Crown.

Schiraldi, G. R. (2001). *The Self-Esteem Workbook*. Oakland, CA: New Harbinger.

Schiraldi, G. R. (2007). *World War II Survivors: Lessons in Resilience*. Ellicott City, MD: Chevron.

Schiraldi, G. R. (2007). *Ten Simple Solutions for Building Self-Esteem*. Oakland, CA: New Harbinger.

Schiraldi, G. R. (2009). *The Post-Traumatic Stress Disorder Sourcebook* (2nd ed.). New York: McGraw-Hill.

Schiraldi, G. R., & Kerr, M. H. (2002). *The Anger Management Sourcebook*. New York: McGraw-Hill.

Scurfield, R. M. (1994). War-Related Trauma: An Integrative Experiential, Cognitive, and Spiritual Approach. In M. B. Williams & J. F. Sommer, Jr. (Eds), *Handbook of Post-traumatic Therapy* (pp. 179-204). Westport, CT: Greenwood Press,

Self, N. (2008). *Two Wars: One Hero's Fight on Two Fronts—Abroad and Within*. Carol Stream, IL: Tyndale House.

Seligman, M. E. P. (2002). *Authentic Happiness*. New York: Simon & Schuster.

Shay, J. (1994). *Achilles in Vietnam: Combat Trauma and the Undoing of Character*. New York: Touchstone.

Shay, J. (2002). *Odysseus in America: Combat Trauma and the Trials of Homecoming*. New York: Scribner.

Shipley, P., & Baranski, J. V. (2002). Police Officer Performance Under Stress: A Pilot Study on the Effects of Visuo-Motor Behavior Rehearsal. *International Journal of Stress Management, 9*, (20), 71-80.

Siebert, A. (1996). *The Survivor Personality*. New York: Perigee.

Sirgy, M. J. (1998). Materialism and Quality of Life. *Social Indicators Research 43*, 227-260.

Slon, S., & Gilbert, S. (2008). *Improving Memory: Understanding Age-related Memory Loss*. Boston, MA: Harvard Medical School.

Smith, J. (2005). *Our Brother's Keeper: My Family's Journey through Vietnam to Hell and Back*. New York: Wiley.

Smith, T. W. (2007, April). *Job Satisfaction in America*. Chicago: National Opinion Research Center Report.

Smith, W. P., Compton, W. C., & West, W. B. (1995). Meditation as an Adjunct to a Happiness Enhancement Program. *Journal of Clinical Psychology, 51*, (2), 269-273.

Smyth, J. M. (1998). Written Emotional Expression: Effect Sizes, Outcome Types, and Moderating Variables. *Journal of Consulting and Clinical Psychology, 66*, 174-184.

Snyder, C. R., & Lopez, S. J. (2007). *Positive Psychology: The Scientific and Practical Explorations of Human Strengths*. Thousand Oaks, CA: Sage.

Sprott, J. B.. & Doob, A. N. (2000). Bad, Sad, and Rejected: The Lives of Aggressive Children. *Canadian Journal of Criminology, 42*, (2), 123-133.

Talbot, J. A., Talbot, N. L., & Tu, X. (2004). Shame-proneness as a Diathesis for Dissociation in Women with Histories of Childhood Sexual Abuse. *Journal of Traumatic Stress, 17*, (5), 445-448.

Tannen, D. (2001). *I Only Say This Because I Love You*. New York: Random House.

Taylor, M, K., Mujica-Parodi, L. R., Padilla, G. A., Markham, A. E., Potterat, E. G., Momen, N., Sander, T. D., & Larson, G. E. (2009). Behavioral Predictors of Acute Stress Symptoms During Intense Military Training. *Journal of Traumatic Stress, 22*, (3), 212–217.

Ten Boom, C., with Sherrill, J., & Sherrill, E. (1971). *The Hiding Place*. New York: Bantam.

Tick, E. (2005). *War and the Soul: Healing Our Nation's Veterans from Post-Traumatic Stress Disorder*. Wheaton, IL: Quest.

Tick, E. (2008). *Forgiveness and Healing in Vietnam*. Troy, New York: Soldiers Heart [DVD].

Ursano, R. J., Fullerton, C. S., & Norwood, A. E. (1995). Psychiatric Dimensions of Disaster: Patient Care, Community Consultation, and Preventive Medicine. *Harvard Review of Psychiatry, 3*, 196-209.

Vaillant, G. E. (1977). *Adaptation to Life*. Boston: Little Brown & Co.

Valera, R. J., Sawyer, R. G., & Schiraldi, G. R. (2000). Violence and Post Traumatic Stress Disorder in a Sample of Inner City Street Prostitutes. *American Journal of Health Studies, 16*, (3), 149-155.

van Emmerik, A. A. P., Kamphuis, J. H., & Emmelkamp, P. M. G. (2008). Treating Acute Stress Disorder and Posttraumatic Stress Disorder with Cognitive Behavioral Therapy or Structured Writing Therapy: A Randomized Controlled Trial. *Psychotherapy and Psychosomatics, 77*, (2), 93-100.

Waite, L. J., Browning, D., Doherty, W. J., Gallagher, M., Luo, Y., & Stanley, S. M. (2002). *Does Divorce Make People Happy?: Findings from a Study of Unhappy Marriages*. New York: Institute for American Values.

Walter, J. L., & Peller, J. E. (1992). *Becoming Solution-focused in Brief Therapy*. New York: Brunner/Mazel.

Watchorn, J. (2000). *Role of Debriefing in the Prevention of PTSD*. Paper presented to the Inaugural Conference on Stress, Trauma, & Coping in the Emergency Services and Allied Professions, Melbourne, Australia.

Watkins, P. C., Cruz, L., Holben, H., & Kolts, R. L. (2008). Taking Care of Business? Grateful Processing of Unpleasant Memories. *Journal of Positive Psychology, 3*, 87-99.

Wiegand, K. E., & Weiss, H. M. (2006). Affective Reactions to the Thought of 'God': Moderating Effects of Image of God. *Journal of Happiness Studies 7*, (23,) 23-40.

Werner, E. E. (1992). The Children of Kauai: Resiliency and Recovery in Adolescence and Adulthood. *Journal of Adolescent Health, 13*, 262-268.

Wilburn, V. R., & Smith, D. E. (2005). Stress, Self-esteem, and Suicidal Ideation in Late Adolescents. *Adolescence, 40*, (157), 33-45.

Wood, S. G. (2003). *Icebox: The Ultimate Mental Skills & Toughness Training System for Athletes.* Quakertown, PA: Ultimate Athlete LLC [CD].

Wooden, J. R. (2003). *Values, Victory, and Peace of Mind.* Steve Jamison Productions [DVD].

Wrzesniewski, A., McCauley, C. R., Rozin, P., & Schwartz, B. (1997) Jobs, Careers, and Callings: People's Relations to their Work. *Journal of Research in Personality, 31*, 21-33.

Yalom, I. (1980). *Existential Psychotherapy.* New York: Basic Books.

Zach, S., Raviv, S., & Inbar, R. (2007). The Benefits of a Graduated Training Program for Security Officers on Physical Performance in Stressful Situations. *International Journal of Stress Management, 14*, (4), 350-369.

Zatzick, D. F., Marmar, C. R., Weiss, D. S., Browner, W. S., Metzler, T. J., Golding, J. M., Stewart, A., Schlenger, W. E., & Wells, K. B. (1997). Posttraumatic Stress Disorder and Functioning and Quality of Life Outcomes in a Nationally Representative Sample of Male Vietnam Veterans. *American Journal of Psychiatry, 154*, 1690-1695.

Zhang, L. (2005). Prediction of Chinese Life Satisfaction: Contribution of Collective Self-esteem. *International Journal of Psychology, 40*, (3), 189-200

Zimbardo, P., & Boyd, J. (2008). *The Time Paradox: The New Psychology of Time that will Change Your Life.* New York: Free Press.

About the Author

Glenn R. Schiraldi, Ph.D., LTC (ret.), has served on the stress management faculties at the Pentagon, the International Critical Incident Stress Foundation, and the University of Maryland, where he received the Outstanding Teacher Award in what is now the School of Public Health. He is the author of various articles and books on human mental and physical health, including: *The Post-Traumatic Stress Disorder Sourcebook; The Resilient Warrior Before, During, and After War; World War II Survivors: Lessons in Resilience; The Anger Management Sourcebook; The Self-Esteem Workbook; Ten Simple Solutions for Building Self-Esteem; Conquer Anxiety, Worry and Nervous Fatigue; Hope and Help for Depression;* and *Facts to Relax By: A Guide to Relaxation and Stress Reduction.* Glenn's writing has been recognized by various scholarly and popular sources, including the *Washington Post, American Journal of Health Promotion, the Mind/Body Health Review,* and *the International Stress and Tension Control Society Newsletter.* His books have been translated into nine foreign languages.

While serving at the Pentagon, he helped to design and implement a series of prototype courses in stress management for the Department of the Army—including hostility/anger management and communication skills. For the International Critical Incident Stress Foundation and Resilience Training International he designed and presents resilience training to prevent post-traumatic stress disorder and improve performance in high-risk groups (such as military, police, and firefighters). Serving at the University of Maryland since 1980, he has pioneered a number of mind/body courses, teaching coping skills to adults across a wide range of ages to prevent stress-related mental and physical illness, and demonstrating that such courses favorably impact multiple mental health indicators. One such course is "Beyond 9/11: Stress, Survival, and Coping." He has trained clinicians in the U.S. and Canada on various aspects of resilience.

He has served on the Board of Directors of the Depression and Related Affective Disorders Association, a Johns Hopkins Department of Psychiatry cooperative, the ABC News post-traumatic stress disorder working group, and the editorial board of the *International Journal of Emergency Mental Health.*

A Vietnam-era veteran and graduate of the U.S. Military Academy, West Point, he holds a doctorate from the University of Maryland and a master's degree from Brigham Young University. His research centers on personality and stress, including resilience, post-traumatic stress, anger/hostility, self-esteem, depression, and anxiety.

CPSIA information can be obtained at www.ICGtesting.com
Printed in the USA
LVOW09s2158200816

501209LV00006B/28/P